George Facer

EDEXCEL A LEVEL
CHEMISTRY

YEAR 1

Includes AS level

DYNAMIC LEARNING

HODDER EDUCATION
AN HACHETTE UK COMPANY

This book is dedicated to the memory of my father, John Facer, who inspired me, and many others, in the love of chemistry when he was a teacher at Epsom College.

Cover photo: science photo/Fotolia; p. 1 Corel, p. 2 ITAR-TASS Photo Agency/Alamy, p. 4 (top) Andrew Lambert Photography/Science Photo Library, p. 4 bottom Oleksiy Mark/Fotolia, p. 9 Pictorial Press Ltd/Alamy, p. 16 Robert Harding World Imagery/Alamy, p. 33 BrazilPhotos. com/Alamy, p. 34 Glasshouse Images/Alamy, p. 48 Nneirda/Fotolia, p. 50 logos2012/Fotolia, p. 53 megasquib/Fotolia, p. 54 (top) Julie S Woodhouse/Alamy, p. 54 (lower left) Carolina K Smith MD/Fotolia, p. 54 (lower right) Science Photo Library/Alamy, p. 58 sciencephotos/ Alamy), p. 68 AFP/Getty Images, p. 69 Mandrixta/Fotolia, p. 70 Tyler Boyes/Fotolia, p. 77 Tom Tarrant, p. 87 Andrew Lambert Photography/Science Photo Library, p. 100 John Olive, p. 104 John Olive, p. 113 Andrew Lambert Photography/Science Photo Library, p. 115 John Olive, p. 134 John Olive, p. 156 Leslie Garland Picture Library/Alamy, p. 205 Martyn F. Chillmaid/ Science Photo Library, p. 225 Andrew Brookes, National Physical Laboratory/Science Photo Library, p. 235 Phil Degginger/Alamy, p. 236 John Olive, p. 237 Phil Degginger/Alamy, p. 257 (left) kolvenbach/Alamy, p. 257 (right) macropixel/Fotolia, p. 263 R. Kowenicki, p. 271 Phil Degginger/Alamy, p. 277 Charles D. Winters/Science Photo Library

Although every effort has been made to ensure that website addresses are correct at time of going to press, Hodder Education cannot be held responsible for the content of any website mentioned in this book. It is sometimes possible to find a relocated web page by typing in the address of the home page for a website in the URL window of your browser.

Hachette UK's policy is to use papers that are natural, renewable and recyclable products and made from wood grown in sustainable forests. The logging and manufacturing processes are expected to conform to the environmental regulations of the country of origin.

Orders: please contact Bookpoint Ltd, 130 Milton Park, Abingdon, Oxon OX14 4SB. Telephone: +44 (0)1235 827720. Fax: +44 (0)1235 400454. Lines are open 9.00 a.m.–5.00 p.m., Monday to Saturday, with a 24-hour message answering service. Visit our website at www.hoddereducation. co.uk

© George Facer 2015

First published in 2015 by

Hodder Education,

Carmelite House,

50 Victoria Embankment,

London EC4Y 0DZ

Impression number   10 9 8 7 6

Year   2020

Typeset in Bembo 11/13 by Aptara, Inc.

Printed in Great Britain by Ashford Colour Press Ltd.

A catalogue record for this title is available from the British Library.

ISBN 978 1 4718 0740 4

Contents

Introduction

About this book

This textbook covers the first year of the Edexcel GCE Chemistry specification and all content for the AS GCE Chemistry specification. The order of topics follows that of the specification, but it need not be taught in this order.

All the organic chemistry is grouped together in Chapters 10 and 11. Chapter 16 is designed to help you prepare generally for the AS and A level papers and especially for answering practical-based questions.

Margin comments are provided throughout the book. These comprise valuable reminders and snippets of information, and include tips that clarify what you need to know and common sources of confusion.

This book is not a guide to the practical chemistry that all AS students will study. However, many of the reactions that will be met in the laboratory are detailed throughout the book.

At the back of the book (page 314), there is a periodic table that gives relative atomic masses to one decimal place. This should be referred to for atomic numbers, atomic masses and symbols of the elements. The table is similar to the one printed on the back of the examination papers.

● At the end of every chapter are a number of practice questions, including some typical exam-style questions. Questions marked with a purple bullet point are designed to challenge students in their thinking.

Online resources

Each chapter includes 'Test yourself' questions. The answers to these are available at https://www.hoddereducation.co.uk/FacerChemistry1. Answers to the end-of-chapter questions are available as part of George Facer's Edexcel A Level Chemistry Teaching and Learning Resources. Go to www.hoddereducation.co.uk/dynamiclearning to sign up for a free trial. A practice exam-style AS paper and multiple-choice tests to print off for students to complete are also available.

Required previous knowledge and skills

It is assumed that all AS chemistry students will have covered at least double award science to GCSE level. All students should be:

● familiar with the use of a calculator
● able to change the subject of an algebraic equation
● able to draw straight-line and curved graphs from supplied data and to extrapolate graphs
● confident in the use of scientific (standard) notation, e.g. that the number 1234 can be written as 1.234×10^3 and that 1.234×10^{-3} is the same as 0.001234

Scheme of assessment

Assessment objectives

There are three assessment objectives tested at AS and A level:

- **AO1** Knowledge and understanding of scientific ideas, processes, techniques and procedures — 32% of the AS mark.
- **AO2** Application of knowledge and understanding of scientific ideas, processes, techniques and procedures — 43% of the AS mark.
- **AO3** Analysis, interpretation and evaluation of evidence and information to reach conclusions or to develop practical designs and procedures — 25% of the AS mark.

The AS exam

The AS exam consists of two papers and a statement by the centre that the candidate has performed a number of practical experiments. Both papers are worth 80 marks each and must be completed in 1 hour 30 minutes. There will typically be 10 questions ranging from 4 to 15 marks each, including a few multiple-choice questions. In both papers between 20% and 25% of the marks will be awarded for the recall, evaluation and understanding of experimental methods. There is no internal assessment of practical skills that counts towards the candidate's final grade.

Paper 1 consists of questions on physical and inorganic chemistry, specifically:

- atomic structure and the periodic table
- formulae, equations and amounts of substances, including acid–base titrations
- bonding, structure and intermolecular forces
- redox
- groups 2 and 7
- practical aspects

Paper 2 consists of questions on physical and organic chemistry, specifically:

- formulae, equations and amounts of substances
- bonding, structure and intermolecular forces of organic molecules
- organic chemistry
- energetics
- kinetics
- equilibrium
- practical aspects

Hazard and risk

This book is not a laboratory manual. All experiments described in this book should be risk assessed by a qualified chemistry teacher before being performed either as a demonstration or as a class practical. Safety goggles and a laboratory coat or apron must be worn in all experiments. Certain hazards are described in some of the experiments described in the book.

1 Fundamental concepts

Chemistry is the study of matter and the changes that can be made to matter.

The term 'matter' means anything that has mass and takes up space. This includes metals, plastics and fertilisers, but not light or magnetism, or abstract ideas such as health or beauty.

Chemistry is concerned with the properties of matter — what happens when it is heated, when it is mixed with other substances, when electricity is passed through it — and the reasons for the changes that occur in the different circumstances.

Substances have two types of property:

- **Physical properties** are those that can be observed without changing the identity of the substance, for example by melting, compressing, magnetising or bending the substance. At the end of a physical change, the substance is still there, in a different shape or state. The physical states are solid, liquid and gas:
  - A solid has a fixed volume (at a given temperature) and shape.
  - A liquid flows and takes the shape of the part of the container that it fills. It has a fixed volume at a given temperature.
  - A gas completely fills the container in which it is placed. It can easily be compressed to fit in a container of a smaller volume.
- **Chemical properties** are those that are observed when the substance changes its identity, for example on the addition of acid or on burning in air. After a chemical change (chemical reaction) has taken place, one or more new substances are formed. Each substance has its own unique chemical properties.

Chemistry as a spectacle. (Inset) The Chinese characters for chemistry, which mean 'the study of change'

Elements

Key terms

An **element** is a substance that cannot be broken down into two or more different substances.

An **atom** is the smallest uncharged particle of an element.

A **compound** is made of two or more elements chemically joined together.

Elements are the building blocks from which all compounds are made.

The ancient Greeks thought that all matter was made from four elements — fire, earth, air and water. As scientists began to experiment and apply scientific method to analysing results, this idea was gradually abandoned. The big step forward came

Dmitri Mendeléev

in 1869 when Dmitri Mendeléev arranged the elements in order of atomic mass and produced a periodic table similar to that in use today.

One hundred and fourteen elements have been positively identified, although only 90 occur naturally on Earth. The others have either been made in nuclear reactors and particle accelerators, or have been found in the debris from a nuclear explosion. Livermorium and flerovium are the latest to have been made.

All the elements originally came from the stars. Inside a star, including our Sun, hydrogen atoms are converted into atoms of other elements by **nuclear fusion**. A small amount of mass is lost and this is turned into energy — the sunlight and starlight that we can see.

The creation of elements from hydrogen in the stars is taking place continually. However, as a star ages, its outer layer begins to collapse, which causes the temperature of the star to increase further. Some of the atoms of elements already created fuse together and form still heavier atoms, such as uranium, lead and gold. The temperature increase causes a huge explosion and the outer layers are thrown into space. This is what happens in a supernova. The debris from supernovae will eventually condense under the gravity of another star and form planets. Thus the elements formed in the stars form the rocks, the seas and even our own bodies (Table 1.1).

Table 1.1 The abundance by mass of the most common elements in the Earth's crust and in the human body

Earth's crust			Human body		
Rank	Element	% by mass	Rank	Element	% by mass
1st	Oxygen	49.5	1st	Oxygen	65
2nd	Silicon	25.7	2nd	Carbon	18
3rd	Aluminium	7.5	3rd	Hydrogen	10
4th	Iron	4.7	4th	Nitrogen	3
5th	Calcium	3.4	5th	Calcium	1.5
6th	Sodium	2.6	6th	Phosphorus	1.2
7th	Potassium	2.4	7th	Potassium	0.2
8th	Magnesium	1.9	8th	Sulfur	0.2
9th	Hydrogen	0.88	9th	Chlorine	0.2
10th	Titanium	0.58	10th	Sodium	0.1
11th	Chlorine	0.19	11th	Magnesium	0.05
12th	Phosphorus	0.12	12th	Iron	0.04

The periodic table

The modern form of the periodic table has the elements arranged in atomic number order (in order of the number of protons in the nucleus).

It is shown in Table 1.2 and also, in more detail, at the back of this book (page 314). It is printed on the back page of the question booklet in all AS and A-level examinations.

Table 1.2 The periodic table

	1	2											3	4	5	6	7	0
1	H																	He
2	Li	Be											B	C	N	O	F	Ne
3	Na	Mg											Al	Si	P	S	Cl	Ar
4	K	Ca	Sc	Ti	V	Cr	Mn	Fe	Ni	Cu	Zn		Ga	Ge	As	Se	Br	Kr
5	Rb	Sr	Y	Zr	Nb	Mo	Tc	Ru	Pd	Ag	Cd		In	Sn	Sb	Te	I	Xe
6	Cs	Ba	La*	Hf	Ta	W	Re	Os	Pt	Au	Hg		Tl	Pb	Bi	Po	At	Rn
7	Fr	Ra	Ac*	Rf	Db	Sg	Bh	Hs	Mt	Ds	Rg	Cp	Lv	Fl				

*There are 14 f-block lanthanide elements between lanthanum and hafnium, and 14 f-block actinide elements between actinium and rutherfordium.

- The vertical columns are called groups. Numbers in brown are the group numbers.
- The elements in a group, such as in groups 1, 2 or 7, show similar, but steadily changing, physical and chemical properties. In group 7, for example, fluorine and chlorine are gases, bromine is a liquid and iodine is a solid. All four react with hydrogen to form acids.
- The horizontal rows are called periods. Numbers in violet are the period numbers.
- The elements in a period change from metals on the left to non-metals on the right. The noble gases are in group 0 (sometimes called group 8).
  - The elements in red are metals.
  - The elements in green are metalloids (semi-metals).
  - The elements in blue are non-metals.

Tip

You need to know the names and symbols of at least the first 20 elements (hydrogen to calcium). You must also know to which group each belongs.

Test yourself

1 Identify the element in group 5 and period 3 of the periodic table.
2 Name two elements that are liquids at room temperature.

Important points about the periodic table

Metals

The metals are on the left and in the middle of the table.

The physical properties of metals are that:

- they conduct electricity when solid and when liquid
- they are malleable and ductile
- apart from mercury, they are all solids at room temperature

The chemical properties of metals are that:

- they form positive ions (**cations**) in their compounds; for example, sodium forms Na^+ ions and magnesium forms Mg^{2+} ions
- the more reactive metals react with an acid to give a salt and hydrogen; for example, magnesium reacts with dilute sulfuric acid to form magnesium sulfate and hydrogen gas
- the most reactive metals react with water to give a hydroxide and hydrogen; for example, sodium reacts with water to form sodium hydroxide and hydrogen gas

Three well-known metals: (a) copper, (b) mercury and (c) magnesium

- they react with cations of less reactive metals in displacement reactions; for example, zinc reacts with a solution of copper sulfate to form zinc sulfate and a residue of copper metal
- they become more reactive *down* a group in the periodic table; for example, potassium is more reactive than sodium
- their oxides and hydroxides are bases; for example, magnesium oxide is a base and reacts with nitric acid to form magnesium nitrate and water

Test yourself

3 Identify the most reactive metal in group 2 of the periodic table.

Non-metals

Non-metals are on the right of the table.

The chemical properties of non-metals are that:

- they form negatively charged ions (**anions**) in many compounds with metals; for example, chlorine forms Cl^- ions and oxygen forms O^{2-} ions
- they form covalent bonds with other non-metals
- apart from in group 0, they become more reactive *up* a group in the periodic table; for example, chlorine is more reactive than bromine, which is more reactive than iodine
- their oxides are acidic, reacting with water to form a solution of an acid; for example, sulfur dioxide reacts with water to form sulfurous acid, H_2SO_3, which ionises to form $H^+(aq)$ ions, making the solution acidic

Organic chemistry is about compounds in which carbon is covalently bonded to other carbon atoms, and to other elements such as hydrogen, oxygen and nitrogen.

Metalloids

Between the metals and non-metals there are some elements that do not fit easily into either category. These elements are called semi-metals or metalloids. The properties of metalloids are that:

- they do not form ions
- they are semiconductors of electricity, particularly when a small amount of impurity is added
- their oxides are weakly acidic; for example, silicon dioxide reacts with the strong alkali sodium hydroxide to form sodium silicate

Silicon is used as a semiconductor in computers

Force and energy

Force

There are four types of force:

- strong nuclear
- weak nuclear
- gravitational
- electromagnetic

Strong and weak nuclear forces are only important inside the nucleus of an atom. Gravitational forces are so weak that they are only effective if at least one of the objects is astronomically large, such as the Sun or the Earth. The only forces that affect chemistry are the electromagnetic forces.

A positively charged object attracts a negatively charged object; there is a force of repulsion between two objects that have the same charge.

Tip

Remember this as 'unlike charges attract; like charges repel'.

The strength of the force depends on:

- the size of the charges — the *bigger* the charges, the stronger is the force acting between them
- the distance between the centres of the two objects — the smaller the distance between the centres, the stronger is the force between them

In chemistry, the most common charged particles are ions.

- A **cation** is an atom or group of atoms that has lost one or more electrons and so is *positively* charged. Metals form cations. Na^+ and Mg^{2+} are examples.
- An **anion** is an atom or group of atoms that has gained one or more electrons and so is *negatively* charged. Non-metals form anions. Cl^-, OH^- and O^{2-} are examples.

Key term

An **Ion** is a charged atom or group of atoms.

Energy

If there is a force of attraction between two particles, energy has to be supplied to separate them. The amount of energy required depends on the strength of the force between the particles, which in turn depends on the size of the charges and how close the two centres are. This means that more energy is required to separate small, highly charged ions than less highly charged or bigger ions.

Conversely, if two oppositely charged particles are brought closer together, energy is released.

Energy can neither be created nor destroyed. However, one type of energy can be converted into other types.

The unit of energy is the joule, J. However, this is so small that chemists normally use the kilojoule, kJ.

In an **exothermic** reaction, chemical energy is converted to heat energy. This means that the temperature increases as heat is produced. The combustion of petrol is an example of an exothermic reaction.

If heat is absorbed, the chemical reaction is **endothermic**, and the temperature falls as heat energy is converted into chemical energy.

Chemical energy is measured as a quantity called **enthalpy**, H. In an exothermic reaction, chemical energy is lost as it is changed into heat energy. Therefore, the value for the *change* in enthalpy, ΔH, is negative. In an endothermic reaction, the value of ΔH is positive.

The Greek letter Δ means a change, so ΔH means a change in the quantity H (enthalpy or chemical energy available as heat).

Amount of substance

When we go shopping we buy cheese by weight, drinks by volume and cans of baked beans by number. Scientists measure substances by mass or volume.

Mass

The unit of mass normally used is the gram. However, other mass units, such as the kilogram, kg, milligram, mg, nanogram, ng, or tonne are sometimes used.

$$1\,g = 1000\,mg \text{ or } 1\,mg = 10^{-3}\,g$$

$$1\,g = 1\,000\,000\,000\,ng \text{ or } 1\,ng = 10^{-9}\,g$$

$$1\,kg = 1000\,g$$

$$1\,tonne = 1000\,kg$$

Volume

The common units of volume are the cm^3 and the bigger unit dm^3 (also called the litre, l).

$$1\,000\,000\,cm^3 = 1\,m^3$$

$$1\,cm^3 = 0.001\,dm^3$$

$$1\,dm^3 = 1000\,cm^3$$

Worked example 1

A liquid has a volume of $23.75\,cm^3$. Convert this to a volume in dm^3.

Answer
$$\text{volume} = \frac{23.75}{1000} = 0.02375\,dm^3$$

Worked example 2

A gas has a volume of $24\,dm^3$. Convert this into a volume in cm^3.

Answer
$$\text{volume} = 24 \times 1000 = 24\,000\,cm^3$$

Test yourself

4 a) Convert $12\,kg$ into grams.

   b) Convert $0.0234\,g$ into milligrams (mg).

The mole

Although substances are measured out according to their mass or volume, chemicals react by numbers of particles.

The equation for the formation of water from hydrogen and oxygen is:

$$2H_2 + O_2 \rightarrow 2H_2O$$

This means that hydrogen and oxygen react in the ratio of two molecules of hydrogen to one molecule of oxygen.

Atoms and molecules are so small that when two chemicals are mixed and react, billions and billions of molecules are involved.

The number of carbon-12 atoms in exactly $12\,g$ of carbon-12 can be calculated as 6.02×10^{23}. It is called the Avogadro constant and has the symbol, L or N_A.

The mass of one molecule of water is 2.99×10^{-23} g and in 1 g of water there are 3.34×10^{22} molecules, or 33 400 000 000 000 000 000 000 molecules. Counting in such large numbers is almost impossible. To get round this problem the concept of the mole was introduced. The mole is a very large number of particles. For example:

- 1 mol of sodium, Na, contains 6.02×10^{23} sodium atoms.
- 1 mol of water, H_2O, contains 6.02×10^{23} water molecules and therefore 1.204×10^{24} hydrogen atoms.
- 1 mol of sodium chloride, Na^+Cl^-, contains 6.02×10^{23} pairs of Na^+ and Cl^- ions.

Chemicals react in a ratio by moles. The energy released in an exothermic reaction depends on the number of moles that react. Therefore, ΔH has units of $kJ\,mol^{-1}$. An understanding of the mole is essential to AS and A-level chemistry.

Test yourself

5 Calculate:

a) the number of atoms in 1 mol of CO_2

b) the number of chloride ions in 1 mol of calcium chloride, $CaCl_2$

(The Avogadro constant, $N_A = 6.02 \times 10^{23}\,mol^{-1}$.)

Mole ratios

Consider the equation:

$$H_2SO_4 + 2NaOH \rightarrow Na_2SO_4 + 2H_2O$$

Sulfuric acid and sodium hydroxide react in the **molar ratio** of 1:2. This means that 0.111 mol of sulfuric acid reacts with 0.222 mol of sodium hydroxide. The equation also shows that 0.111 mol of sodium sulfate and 0.222 mol of water are formed.

The mole concept is further developed in Chapter 8.

Worked example 1

Calculate the number of moles of silver nitrate that react with 1.23 mol of sodium chloride, according to the equation:

$$AgNO_3 + NaCl \rightarrow AgCl + NaNO_3$$

Answer

moles of $AgNO_3$:moles of NaCl = 1:1

moles of silver nitrate = moles of sodium chloride

= 1.23 mol

Tip

Remember that the number of moles is a measure of the number of particles, and that mole ratios are found from the balanced chemical equation for the reaction.

Questions

1 Identify the most reactive metal in group 2 of the periodic table.

2 An element X loses three electrons. What is the charge on the ion formed?

3 Convert $1.2 \times 10^6\,g$ into tonnes.

4 Convert $22.4\,dm^3$ into a volume in cm^3.

5 Convert a volume of $23.7\,cm^3$ into a volume in dm^3.

6 Nitrogen reacts with hydrogen to form ammonia, according to the equation:

$$N_2 + 3H_2 \rightarrow 2NH_3$$

Calculate:
a) the number of moles of nitrogen, N_2, that react with 0.246 mol of hydrogen, H_2
b) the number of moles of ammonia produced

7 Nitric acid reacts with calcium hydroxide according to the equation:

$$Ca(OH)_2 + 2HNO_3 \rightarrow Ca(NO_3)_2 + 2H_2O$$

Calculate the number of moles of calcium hydroxide that react with 0.0642 mol of nitric acid.

2 Atomic structure and the periodic table (Topic 1)

Atomic theory

The father of modern atomic theory was John Dalton, a schoolteacher who was born in 1776.

He used measurements of the masses in which elements combine to propose his hypothesis, which was that:

- all matter is made of atoms
- all atoms of a given element are identical, with the same mass, but have different masses from the atoms of other elements
- a compound is a combination of the atoms of two or more elements in a specific ratio
- atoms can neither be created nor destroyed
- in a chemical reaction, atoms in the reactants are rearranged to give the products of the reaction

Dalton thought of an atom as a spherical hard object, rather like a marble. The word atom is derived from Greek and means 'uncuttable'. Dalton's theory formed the basis for understanding chemical reactions, formulae and chemical equations and allowed huge advances to be made in the nineteenth century.

John Dalton

The nuclear atom

Doubts about the accuracy of Dalton's atomic theory began to form around the beginning of the twentieth century. J. J. Thomson discovered that all metals, when heated, give off identical, tiny, negatively charged particles and he was able to measure their mass-to-charge ratio ($\frac{m}{z}$). Millikan measured the charge on these particles and hence the mass. He found that they had a mass nearly two thousand times smaller than that of a hydrogen atom. These particles are called **electrons**.

If atoms contain negatively charged electrons, they must also contain positively charged particles. The discovery of radioactivity by Becquerel and the separation of radium from the uranium ore pitchblende by Marie Curie led to the knowledge that alpha particles are helium atoms that have lost two electrons. Geiger and Marsden, working on suggestions by Rutherford, bombarded gold foil with alpha particles. Their results led Rutherford to propose the nuclear theory of the atom:

- An atom contains a small, central, positively charged nucleus.
- The diameter of the nucleus is about $\frac{1}{10000}$ that of the atom. This means that if an atom were the size of a football, the nucleus would be smaller than a full stop on this page. Alternatively, if the nucleus were the size of a golf ball, the atom would have a diameter of about 400 metres.
- Almost all the mass of the atom is concentrated in the nucleus.
- The electrons orbit the nucleus.

Aston invented the **mass spectrometer** to measure the masses of atoms precisely. He made the startling discovery that not all the atoms of an element have the same mass. In a sample of neon, 91% of the atoms have a mass of 3.32×10^{-23} g, which is 20 times heavier than a hydrogen atom. However, there are atoms of neon with masses 21 and 22 times heavier than hydrogen atoms. Other elements were also found to have atoms of different mass but identical chemical properties. These different atoms of the same element are called **isotopes**.

This immediately caused a problem with the simple nuclear theory. How could the positive centre of one atom of an element differ from that of another atom of the same element?

There was a further long-standing problem associated with the periodic table. This is an arrangement of the elements in increasing atomic mass devised by Mendeléev. Argon has a relative atomic mass of 40, which is one greater than that of potassium. This means that potassium, on the basis of mass only, should be placed in group 0 with the noble gases, and argon in group 1 with the alkali metals. This is clearly absurd. No-one could solve this riddle, until Moseley devised an experiment that measured the positive charge in the nucleus. This positive charge is called the atomic number. A simultaneous discovery of the proton led to the theory that the atomic number is the number of protons in the nucleus. This value is the same for all isotopes of an element. Thus the elements in the periodic table used today are arranged in order of *increasing atomic number* and not according to their atomic mass.

A third subatomic particle was then suggested — this is the **neutron**.

Tip

The development of the understanding of the atom, from Dalton to Rutherford and beyond, is an example of How Science Works. A theory is suggested, based on experimental evidence, and that theory is modified steadily as more experimental evidence is obtained.

Rutherford suggested that an atom consisted of a tiny nucleus surrounded by orbiting electrons and his colleagues, Geiger and Marsden, tested this theory with the gold foil experiment (Figure 2.1).

Most of the positively charged α particles passed straight through but a few (about 1 in 8000) were deflected through 90° by the positive nucleus.

The final Rutherford atomic theory is as follows:

- The nucleus of an atom of a particular element contains a fixed number of positively charged protons. This number is called the **atomic number**.
- The nucleus also contains a number of neutrons. The number varies from one isotope to another. Neutrons are not charged (neutral).
- The **mass number** of an isotope is the sum of the number of protons and neutrons in the nucleus of an atom of that isotope.
- The number of electrons in a neutral atom of an element is equal to the number of protons in the nucleus.
- The electrons orbit the nucleus.

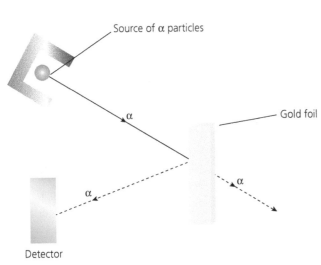

Detector

Figure 2.1 The gold foil experiment

The masses and charges of these three subatomic particles are shown in Table 2.1.

During the last 50 years, many more subatomic particles, such as mesons and neutrinos, have been discovered. However, this is beyond the scope of A-level chemistry.

Table 2.1 Masses and charges of subatomic particles

Particle	Symbol	Charge/C	Relative charge	Mass/g	Relative mass
Proton	p	$+1.60 \times 10^{-19}$	+1	1.67×10^{-24}	1
Neutron	n	0	0	1.67×10^{-24}	1
Electron	e^-	-1.60×10^{-19}	−1	9.11×10^{-28}	0.00055 (which is usually ignored)

Never state that the mass of an electron is zero. You do not need to know the charges on subatomic particles in coulombs or their masses in grams. It is the *relative* values that you must know.

Definitions

> ## Key terms
>
> The **atomic number** (Z) of an element is the number of protons in the nucleus of an atom of that element.
>
> The **relative atomic mass** (r.a.m.) of an element is the weighted average mass of an atom of that element divided by $\frac{1}{12}$ the mass of a carbon-12 atom.
>
> The **relative molecular mass** of an element (such as O_2) or a compound (such as H_2O) is the average mass of a molecule of that element or compound divided by $\frac{1}{12}$ the mass of a carbon-12 atom.
>
> The **mass number** of an isotope of an element is the sum of the number of protons and neutrons in the nucleus of an atom of that isotope.
>
> The **relative isotopic mass** is the mass of an atom of that isotope divided by $\frac{1}{12}$ the mass of a carbon-12 atom.
>
> **Isotopes** are atoms of the same element that have the same number of protons but different numbers of neutrons.

Mass numbers apply only to *isotopes* and are always whole numbers.

All atoms and ions of a given element have the same atomic number, which is different from the atomic numbers of other elements.

Relative atomic mass values used by Edexcel are given to one decimal place. The mass of an atom of the carbon-12 isotope is defined as being exactly 12 atomic mass units and is the reference used for all relative atomic and isotopic masses.

Isotopes apply to a single element. They have the same number of protons in the nucleus, so they have the same atomic number. However, they have different numbers of neutrons in the nucleus, so the mass numbers are different. Isotopes of the same element have identical chemical properties because they have identical electron configurations.

Most elements have more than one stable and naturally occurring isotope. Some of these are shown in Table 2.2.

Tip

Do not confuse relative atomic mass, which is an *average*, with relative isotopic mass, which refers to a single type of atom.

Relative isotopic masses
are not whole numbers
because some mass is
converted to energy when
nuclei are formed. ^{12}C is
exactly 12 by definition —
it is the reference point.

Table 2.2 Some naturally occurring isotopes

Element	Name of isotope	Symbol	Atomic number	Number of neutrons	Mass number	Relative isotopic mass	%
Hydrogen	Protium	^1H	1	0	1	1.008	99.99
	Deuterium	^2H	1	1	2	2.014	0.01
Lithium	Lithium-6	^6Li	3	3	6	6.015	7.42
	Lithium-7	^7Li	3	4	7	7.016	92.58
Carbon	Carbon-12	^{12}C	6	6	12	12 exactly	98.89
	Carbon-13	^{13}C	6	7	13	13.003	1.11
	Carbon-14	^{14}C	6	8	14	14.003	<0.01

Test yourself

1 Explain the difference between the terms 'relative isotopic mass' and 'relative atomic mass'.

Mass spectrometry

The masses of atoms, molecules and fragments of molecules can be measured using a mass spectrometer. Standard mass spectrometry consists of four stages:

- ionisation
- acceleration
- deflection
- detection

1 All the air in the spectrometer is first pumped out.

2 A sample of the element or compound in gaseous form is injected into the mass spectrometer (Figure 2.2, compartment A) and is bombarded with high-energy electrons from an electron gun. If the substance is a solid, it has to be heated to produce a sufficient number of gaseous particles.

The energy from the bombarding electrons strips electrons from the atoms or molecules, forming positive ions:

$$A(g) + energy \rightarrow A^+(g) + e^-$$

where A represents an atom

$$M(g) + energy \rightarrow M^+(g) + e^-$$

where M represents a molecule

The positive ions formed from molecules can then fragment into two or more particles, one positive and the other neutral. For instance, from chlorine:

$$Cl_2(g) \rightarrow Cl_2^+(g) \rightarrow Cl^+(g) + Cl(g)$$

and from ethanol:

$$C_2H_5OH(g) \rightarrow C_2H_5OH^+(g) \rightarrow C_2H_5^+(g) + OH(g)$$
$$C_2H_5OH(g) \rightarrow C_2H_5OH^+(g) \rightarrow C_2H_5(g) + OH^+(g)$$

3 The positive ions are accelerated by the high electric potential (Figure 2.2, compartment A), pass through slits and emerge as a parallel beam of ions. All the ions have the same energy, so those of a particular mass have the same speed.

4 The ions are then deflected by a powerful magnetic field (Figure 2.2, compartment B). Ions with the same charge but with a greater mass are deflected less than those of a smaller mass. The angle deflected depends on the strength of the magnetic field and the mass-to-charge ratio ($\frac{m}{e}$ or $\frac{m}{z}$) of the ion.

5 The ions of lowest mass are detected first (Figure 2.2, compartment C). The magnetic field is gradually increased and the ions of greater mass are then detected. The detector is coupled to a computer that calculates the $\frac{m}{z}$ ratio of each positive ion and its relative abundance compared with the most abundant particle. This is then converted into a percentage for each positive ion.

Tip

Some atoms or molecules lose two electrons and so form 2+ ions. These are deflected more than those with a 1+ charge and the same mass.

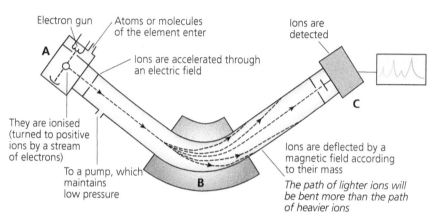

Figure 2.2 A representation of a mass spectrometer

Tip

Remember that these positive ions could be positively charged atoms, positively charged molecules or positively charged fragments of molecules.

To summarise, the stages in standard mass spectrometry are:

- **bombardment** by high-energy electrons to create positive ions
- **acceleration** of positive ions by an electric potential
- **deflection** of positive ions by a magnetic field
- **detection** of positive ions followed by amplification of the signal

Mass spectrum of diatomic molecules

Many elements have isotopes and so their mass spectra will have lines for each possible combination.

Chlorine consists of two isotopes — ^{35}Cl with an abundance of 75% and ^{37}Cl with an abundance of 25%. The mass spectrum will therefore consist of three lines in the region around $\frac{m}{z} = 70$ caused by the molecular ion Cl_2^+ (Figure 2.3).

^{35}Cl–^{35}Cl with $\frac{m}{z} = 70$ with a probability of $\frac{3}{4} \times \frac{3}{4} = \frac{9}{16}$

^{35}Cl–^{37}Cl with $\frac{m}{z} = 72$ with a probability of $\frac{3}{4} \times \frac{1}{4} \times 2 = \frac{6}{16}$

^{37}Cl–^{37}Cl with $\frac{m}{z} = 74$ with a probability of $\frac{1}{4} \times \frac{1}{4} = \frac{1}{16}$

The spectrum will also have two peaks at $\frac{m}{z} = 35$ and $\frac{m}{z} = 37$ due to $^{35}Cl^+$ and $^{37}Cl^+$.

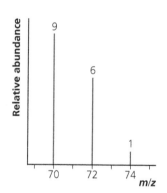

Figure 2.3 Mass spectrum of chlorine in the $\frac{m}{z} = 70$ region

There are two ways of getting 72: ^{35}Cl–^{37}Cl and ^{37}Cl–^{35}Cl.

Molecular mass from mass spectra

When a volatile (usually organic) molecule is investigated in a mass spectrometer, the peak with the largest $\frac{m}{z}$ ratio could be due to the molecular ion, M^+. Its value can then be used to determine the molecular formula from an empirical formula (see page 121).

The mass spectrum of ethanol, C_2H_5OH, is shown in Figure 2.4.

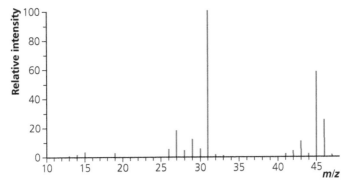

The peak at $\frac{m}{z} = 31$ is due to CH_2OH^+, caused by loss of the CH_3 group from the molecular ion:

$$C_2H_5OH^+ \rightarrow CH_3\cdot + CH_2OH^+$$

Figure 2.4 Mass spectrum of ethanol

The peak with the largest $\frac{m}{z}$ value of 46 is due to the molecular ion, so the relative molecular mass of ethanol is 46.

Modern mass spectrometers

Time of flight (TOF)

The sample is ionised and accelerated by an electric potential. All the ions will have the same kinetic energy ($\frac{1}{2}mv^2$), but the heavier ones will move more slowly and so reach the detector later than the lighter ones. The time between ionisation and detection is measured.

Electrospray ionisation (ESI)

The sample is dissolved in a volatile solvent containing a little ethanoic acid. Some of the sample's molecules, M, become protonated, forming $[MH]^+$ and $[MH_n]^{n+}$ ions. The solution is rapidly evaporated as it enters the evacuated chamber of the mass spectrometer and gaseous $[MH]^+$ and $[MH_n]^{n+}$ ions are released. This is known as 'soft' ionisation because the energy is so low that little or no fragmentation occurs. It is therefore useful for identifying complex molecules, such as biologically active molecules, but not for elucidating their structure.

This method is especially powerful when coupled with liquid chromatography and so is also used in forensic chemistry to prove the presence of drugs, poisons and their metabolites.

Uses of mass spectrometers

Determination of relative atomic mass of an element

Data that have been obtained from a mass spectrometer, such as those in Figure 2.5, can be used to calculate the relative atomic mass of an element.

m/z	%
6.015	7.42
7.016	92.58

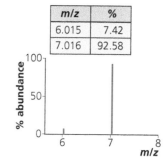

Figure 2.5 The signal and data from a mass spectrum of lithium

---

Worked example

Lithium has two isotopes, ^{6}Li and ^{7}Li. Use the data in Figure 2.5 to calculate the relative atomic mass of lithium.

Answer

$$\text{r.a.m.} = \frac{(m/z\,^6\text{Li} \times \%\,^6\text{Li}) + (m/z\,^7\text{Li} \times \%\,^7\text{Li})}{100}$$

$$= \frac{(6.015 \times 7.42) + (7.016 \times 92.58)}{100}$$

$$= 6.94$$

Test yourself

3 The relative atomic mass of copper is 63.5. Calculate the relative abundance of the two copper isotopes with relative isotopic masses of 63.0 and 65.0.

Tip

Don't forget that the species detected are positively charged.

Detection of drugs and their metabolites in urine and blood samples

Most drugs, for example the anabolic steroid nandrolone, have a unique molar mass. A urine sample is taken from an athlete, placed in a low-energy mass spectrometer and ionised using the technique of electrospray ionisation (ESI). The spectrum is then analysed. If there is an $\frac{m}{z}$ peak equivalent to that of the molecular ion of nandrolone, then the athlete is shown to have used that steroid.

In the pharmaceutical industry

The identity of a new compound can be determined by measuring the $\frac{m}{z}$ value of the peak caused by the molecular ion. First a pure sample has to be obtained, usually by chromatography. A solution of the substance is sprayed through a needle at high electric potential and is analysed in the mass spectrometer for its $\frac{m}{z}$ value.

Carbon-14 dating suggests that the Turin shroud is only around 500 years old

Carbon-14 dating

The relative amounts of the isotopes carbon-12 and carbon-14 in a sample can be found using a mass spectrometer. Carbon-14 is radioactive and its activity halves every 5730 years as it changes to nitrogen-14.

When cosmic rays collide with nuclei in the Earth's upper atmosphere, neutrons are produced. If a neutron collides with a nitrogen nucleus, an atom of carbon-14 and a proton are formed. The ratio of carbon-14 to carbon-12 remained fairly constant until the Industrial Revolution, when 'old' carbon in coal was burnt, releasing carbon dioxide with a very low carbon-14 content. The difference between the historical ratio and that measured in the mass spectrum of a carbon-containing object is the basis of carbon-14 dating.

Some rocks can be dated by a similar method. Uranium-238 decays eventually to lead-206. If the ratio of these two isotopes is 1:1, it means that half the uranium has decayed. As its half-life is about 4×10^9 years, this would mean that the rock was formed 4×10^9 years ago.

Ionisation energy

Ionisation energy is the energy needed to remove an electron from an atom or ion. The units are $kJ\,mol^{-1}$.

The first ionisation energy is always a positive number (denoting an endothermic process, which requires energy). It can be represented by the equation:

$$A(g) \rightarrow A^+(g) + e^-$$

This means that a mole of gaseous positive ions is formed, regardless of whether the element is a metal or a non-metal.

For chlorine, it is the energy change *per mole* for

$$Cl(g) \rightarrow Cl^+(g) + e^-$$

The value of the first ionisation energy depends on:

- the number of protons in the nucleus — the more that there are, the larger the value
- the extent to which the positive charge of the nucleus is shielded by inner electrons — the more the shielding the less the value
- the distance that the outermost electron is from the nucleus — the greater the distance the less the value

> **Tip**
>
> Remember that all ionisation energies are quoted per mole.

> **Key term**
>
> The **first ionisation energy** of an element is the energy required to remove one electron from a mole of **gaseous** atoms of that element.

> **Test yourself**
>
> 4 Write equations to represent the first ionisation of:
>
> a) potassium   b) argon   c) bromine

More energy is required to remove the second electron than to remove the first electron. This is because the second electron is being removed from a positive ion, which is also smaller than the original atom and experiences a greater force of attraction to the nucleus. Even more energy would be required to remove the third electron, and so on.

The second ionisation energy can be represented by the equation:

$$A^+(g) \rightarrow A^{2+}(g) + e^-$$

> **Key term**
>
> The **second ionisation energy** is the energy required to remove one electron from each ion of a mole of gaseous singly charged positive ions of that element.

For the element calcium, the second ionisation energy is the energy change *per mole* for:

$$Ca^+(g) \rightarrow Ca^{2+}(g) + e^-$$

The energy required for the process $Ca(g) \rightarrow Ca^{2+}(g) + 2e^-$ is the sum of the first and second ionisation energies.

Test yourself

5 Write an equation to show the fifth ionisation energy of fluorine.

First ionisation energies of hydrogen to rubidium

The first ionisation energies of the elements show periodicity. The pattern from lithium to neon is repeated exactly with the elements sodium to argon. Apart from the insertion of the *d*-block elements, this pattern is seen again from potassium to rubidium.

The trend down a **group** is for the first ionisation energy to decrease. Although the number of protons increases, so does the number of shielding electrons. The main factor is the increase in the atomic radius, making the outermost electron further from the nucleus and so easier to remove.

The general trend across a **period** is for the first ionisation energy to increase. However, there are a number of slight variations from this trend.

Figure 2.6 shows that there are maxima at each noble gas and minima at each group 1 metal. There are dips after the second and fifth elements in both periods 2 and 3.

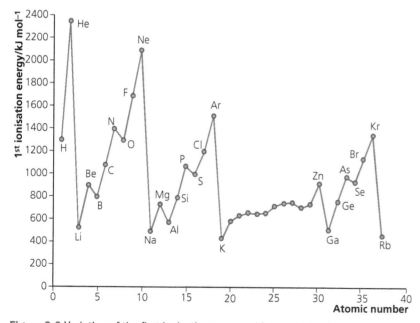

Figure 2.6 Variation of the first ionisation energy with atomic number

These factors can be explained as follows:

- The atomic radius decreases across a period. This is because the number of protons increases but the number of shielding electrons remains the same. This causes a general increase in the effective nuclear charge, which reaches a maximum at the noble gas in group 0 at the end of the period. The result is an increasing attraction for the highest-energy electron and so a general increase in the first ionisation energy.
- The group 1 element immediately after a noble gas has its outer electron in the next shell of higher energy. This electron is well shielded from the nucleus by the inner electrons. The effective nuclear charge is close to +1 and the atomic radius is greater than that of any atom in the preceding period. Therefore, the first ionisation energy of the group 1 element is lower than that of any of the previous elements.
- In period 2, the energy level of the $2p$-electron is significantly higher than that of the $2s$-electron, because it is partially shielded by the $2s$-electrons (page 28). This means that less energy is required to remove the $2p$-electron from a boron atom than is required to remove the $2s$-electron from a beryllium atom.
- The electron configurations of nitrogen and oxygen are shown in Figure 2.7.

Figure 2.7 The electron configurations of nitrogen and oxygen

- When an oxygen atom is ionised, it loses one of the two electrons in the $2p_x$-orbital. As there is more repulsion between the two electrons in this orbital than between electrons in different orbitals, it is easier to remove one of the paired $2p$-electrons of oxygen than to remove one of the unpaired $2p$-electrons of nitrogen.
- The same arguments explain the discrepancies in period 3, where the first ionisation energy of aluminium is lower than that of magnesium and the first ionisation energy of sulfur is lower than that of phosphorus.

In period 4, there are dips after zinc and after arsenic. The electron configuration of zinc is [Ar] $3d^{10} 4s^2$ and that of the next element, gallium, is [Ar] $3d^{10} 4s^2 4p^1$. As the $4p$-orbital is at a higher energy level than either the $4s$- or the $3d$-orbital, less energy is required to remove the $4p$-electron in gallium than is required to remove one of the $4s$-electrons in zinc.

The reason why the first ionisation energy of selenium (group 6) is lower than that of arsenic (group 5) is similar to the reason for the dip after nitrogen in period 2.

Successive ionisation energies

If the successive ionisation energies of an element are listed, it can be seen that there are steady increases and that big jumps occur at defined places. This is a major piece of evidence for the existence of orbits or quantum shells.

Aluminium has 13 electrons. Its successive ionisation energies are shown in Table 2.3. The places where the ionisation energy has jumped to a proportionately much higher value are shown in red.

Table 2.3 The successive ionisation energies of aluminium/kJ mol^{-1}

1st	2nd	3rd						
580	1820	2750						

4th	5th	6th	7th	8th	9th	10th	11th
11 600	14 800	18 400	23 300	27 500	31 900	38 500	42 700

12th	13th							
200 000	222 000							

- The data in Table 2.3 show that the first three electrons are considerably easier to remove than the fourth, as there is a big jump from the third to the fourth ionisation energies. These first three electrons come from the outer shell.
- The last two electrons are very much harder to remove than the preceding eight, as there is a huge jump between the eleventh and twelfth ionisation energies. These electrons come from the inner shell.
- As the shells or orbits of the electrons get further from the nucleus, the energy level rises, so less energy is required to remove an electron from that shell. The values in Table 2.3, with the jumps after the third and eleventh ionisation energies, mean that an aluminium atom has three electrons in its outer orbit, eight nearer to the nucleus in an inner orbit and two electrons very close to the nucleus.

For Al, the first big jump occurs between the third and fourth ionisation energies, so Al has three outer electrons and is in group 3.

The big jumps provide evidence for quantum shells. Aluminium has two electrons in the first quantum shell, eight in the second and three in the third.

The group in which an element is found can be worked out by looking at where the first big jump in the successive ionisation energy occurs. If it occurs between the fourth and fifth ionisation energies, then the element has four outer electrons and is in group 4.

Another way of presenting the data is in graphical form. As the variation between the first and last ionisation energies is so great, it is usual to plot the values as the logarithm of the ionisation energy. This is shown in Figure 2.8 for the element sodium ($Z = 11$).

This method of identifying the group to which an element belongs does not apply to the d-block elements because they all have two electrons in their outer orbit, apart from chromium and copper, which have only one outer electron.

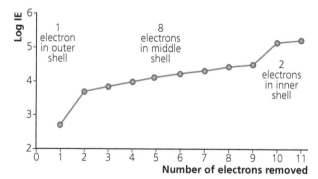

Figure 2.8 Successive ionisations of sodium

It can be seen that there is a big jump between the first and second ionisation energies and another big jump between the ninth and tenth. This means that sodium has one electron in its outer orbit, eight in the next inner orbit and two in the orbit nearest to the nucleus. Thus, the electronic structure of sodium is 2,8,1.

Tip

Remember that the first electron to be removed comes from the outer orbit.

The successive ionisation energies/kJ mol^{-1} of element X are listed below. Identify the group in the periodic table in which X occurs.

Ionisation energies of X:

1st 950; 2nd 1800; 3rd 2700; 4th 4800; 5th 6000; 6th 12 300; 7th 15 000

Answer

There is a big jump between the fifth and sixth ionisation energies. Therefore, the element has five electrons in its outer orbit and is in group 5.

Electron configuration

Rutherford tried to explain the arrangements of electrons around the nucleus in terms of classical physics — Newton's laws of motion — but this did not work. An orbiting electron should spiral towards the nucleus and become absorbed by it and it was calculated that an atom would exist for less than a nanosecond! This problem was solved by quantum theory.

When it was proposed by Max Planck in 1900, quantum theory shook the foundations of the scientific world. However, it became gradually accepted over the next few years. Planck suggested that energy was not continuous, but came in tiny packets called 'quanta'. In terms of electron configuration, this means that an electron can only have certain discrete levels of energy. For instance, in a hydrogen atom, an electron can have specific energies, such as 5.45×10^{-19}J or 2.43×10^{-19}J, but not any value in between.

Niels Bohr understood the importance of quantum theory and used it to explain the electromagnetic radiation emitted when elements are excited when heated to high temperatures or by being placed in discharge tubes.

When hydrogen is energised in a discharge tube, spectral lines of different frequencies are emitted (Figure 2.9). One series, the Lyman series, is found in the ultraviolet region and another, the Balmer series, in the visible part of the electromagnetic spectrum. Each series has lines with frequencies that converge on a single value.

The spectra of other elements and their compounds are more complex. The visible spectrum of energised lithium or sodium vapour contains many lines; that of sodium also includes a pair of lines very close together (a doublet).

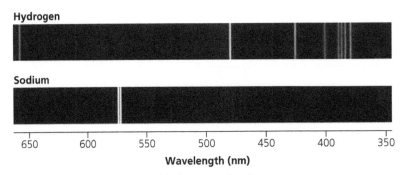

Figure 2.9 Emission spectra of hydrogen and sodium

Bohr suggested that the electron in hydrogen can exist in definite circular **orbits** around the nucleus. The first orbit is the closest to the nucleus, the second is further away and so on. The first orbit has the lowest energy. The electron can only have the energy associated with a particular orbit, which means that an electron can be in a certain orbit or in a different orbit but not in between the two. These orbits are sometimes called **quantum shells**.

A quantum shell defines the energy level of the electrons. All electrons in a given quantum shell have similar, but not identical, energies and electrons in the first quantum shell are in the lowest energy level for that element. A simplified view of a quantum shell is that it is the region around the nucleus in which an electron is found. The first quantum shell or orbit is in the region closest to the nucleus.

When hydrogen atoms are heated, electrons are promoted from the '**ground state**' (their most stable or lowest energy state) to a higher, excited state. In terms of electron orbits, this means that the electron is promoted from the first orbit to an outer orbit. This is not a stable state and the electron drops back, giving out energy in the form of light. The energy given out is the difference between the energy of the electron in its outer orbit and the energy of the orbit into which it drops.

- The Lyman series is obtained when an electron in a hydrogen atom drops from an excited state back to the ground state, which is when it is in the first orbit.
- The Balmer series is caused by the electron dropping back to the second orbit.

The energy levels in a hydrogen atom and the transitions that cause the spectral lines are shown in Figure 2.10. The orbit number (principal quantum number) is represented by n.

Unfortunately, this simple picture did not explain the complex spectra of other elements. The next step was to suggest that the orbits could be divided into sub-orbits consisting of different orbitals.

Spectra together with ionisation energies provide the evidence for orbits (or quantum shells) and for orbitals.

Summary of evidence of electronic configuration

1 The emission spectra provide evidence of discrete quantum shells (orbits)

2 Successive ionisation energies provide evidence for the number of electrons in the outer orbit

3 The discontinuities in the first ionisation energies show the existence of sub-shells or orbitals.

The **first orbit** is not divided. Its orbital is spherical and is designated 1s, where 1 means the first orbit and the s means that it is an s-type orbital.

The **second orbit** is divided into two types of orbital, s and p. The 2s-orbital is the same shape as the 1s-orbital but has a larger radius (Figure 2.11).

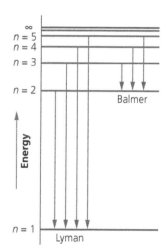

Figure 2.10 Energy transitions in a hydrogen atom

Key term

An **orbital** is a region in space occupied by one or two electrons.

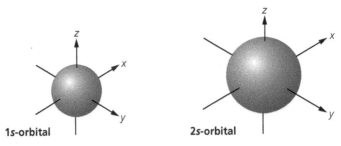

Figure 2.11 The shape of 1s- and 2s-orbitals

There are three 2p-orbitals which lie along the *x*, *y* and *z* axes (Figure 2.12). A common error is to think that the shape of each can be considered to be like two pears stuck together.

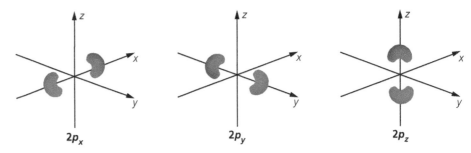

Figure 2.12 The shape of the 2p-orbitals

The size and shape of an orbital is drawn so that there is a 90% probability of finding the electron within its boundary. This fits with the modern theory that describes electrons in atoms as having the properties of standing waves. The standing wave for any *s*-electron is such that it can be found much closer to the nucleus than a *p*-electron in the same shell. This is called **penetrating** towards the nucleus. Because of this, the energy level of the 2s-orbital is slightly lower than that of the 2p-orbital. However, the energies of the three 2p-orbitals are the same.

The **third orbit** consists of three subshells with different types of orbital.

- One subshell consists of a 3s-orbital, which is a spherical orbital with a slightly bigger radius than that of the 2s-orbital.
- The second subshell has three 3p-orbitals, which are the same shape as 2p-orbitals but bigger. Electrons in these 3p-orbitals penetrate less towards the nucleus than do the 3s-electrons.
- The third subshell has five 3d-orbitals, the shapes of which are shown in Figure 2.13. Electrons in the 3d-orbitals penetrate towards the nucleus even less than electrons in the 3p-orbitals.

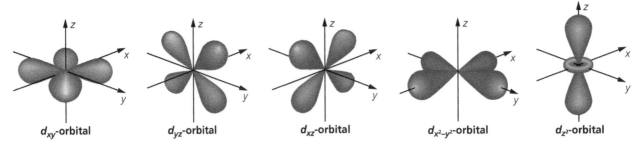

Figure 2.13 The shapes of d-orbitals

The energies of the subshells (s-, p- and d-orbitals) differ from each other because of the effect of penetrating towards the nucleus. The energy level of the 2s-orbital is lower than that of the 2p-orbitals. The energy level of the 3s-orbital is lower than that of the 3p-orbitals, which is lower than that of the 3d-orbitals. In a particular element, all 3p-orbitals have the same energy as each other and all 3d-orbitals have the same energy as each other, which is higher than that of the 3p-orbitals.

The **fourth orbit** contains one 4s-, three 4p-, five 4d- and seven 4f-orbitals.

The extent to which the energies of the subshells are split from each other depends upon the number of protons in the nucleus. In hydrogen (one proton) there is no splitting. If there are more than 18 protons, the splitting is so great that the energy level of the 4s-orbital becomes lower than that of the 3d-orbital. This has a significant effect on the electronic structure of elements beyond argon.

Detailed electron configuration

The exact electronic structure of an isolated atom in the ground state can be predicted using the energy level diagram (Figure 2.14) and the following rules:

- An orbital can hold a maximum of two electrons, one with a spin in the clockwise direction and one in the counter-clockwise direction. Electrons with opposite spins are represented by ↑ and ↓, or ↑ and ↓
- The aufbau (building up) principle states that electrons go into an atom starting in the lowest energy orbital, then to the next lowest and so on until the correct number of electrons has been added.
- Hund's rule states that if there is more than one orbital in a subshell, electrons are initially added to the orbitals so that the electrons have parallel spins and not two electrons in one orbital and none in the other of the same energy level.
- Pauli's exclusion principle states that all electrons in an atom must be in different orbitals or have different spins.

Overall, this means that:

- A single orbital can hold a maximum of two electrons, with opposite spins.
- The first orbit can hold a maximum of two electrons — both in the 1s-orbital, but with opposite spins.
- The second orbit can hold a maximum of eight electrons — two in the 2s- and two in each of the three 2p-orbitals, i.e. $(1 \times 2) + (3 \times 2) = 8$.
- An element with three electrons in p-orbitals in a given orbit will have one electron in each of the p_x, p_y and p_z orbitals.
- The third orbit can hold a maximum of 18 electrons — two in the 3s-, two in each of the three 3p- and two in each of the five 3d-orbitals, i.e. $2 + 6 + 10 = 18$.
- The fourth orbit can hold a maximum of 32 electrons, i.e. $2 + 6 + 10 + 14 = 32$.

> The ground state of an atom is where the electrons occupy the lowest possible energy levels.

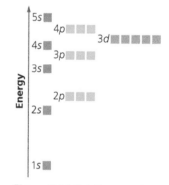

Figure 2.14 Relative energy levels of orbitals in an atom with atomic number greater than 18

Test yourself

6 State the number of orbitals in the third shell of an atom.

Worked example

Sulfur has an atomic number of 16. Complete its detailed electronic configuration, $1s^2$, $2s^2 \, 2p_x^2 \, 2p_y^2 2p_z^2$, $3s^2$ ...

Answer

$(1s^2, 2s^2 \, 2p_x^2 \, 2p_y^2 2p_z^2, 3s^2) \, 3p_x^2 \, 3p_y^1 \, 3p_z^1$

The electron configurations of magnesium and vanadium are shown in Figure 2.15.

The electron configuration of magnesium can be written as $1s^2 \, 2s^2 \, 2p^6 \, 3s^2$.

The electron configuration of vanadium can be written as $1s^2 \, 2s^2 \, 2p^6 \, 3s^2 \, 3p^6 \, 3d^3 \, 4s^2$. Note that the three $3d$ electrons are in different orbitals and have parallel spins.

> **Tip**
>
> Vanadium's electronic configuration is sometimes written $1s^2 \, 2s^2 \, 2p^6 \, 3s^2$ $3p^6 \, 4s^2 \, 3d^3$, which is in order of increasing energy.

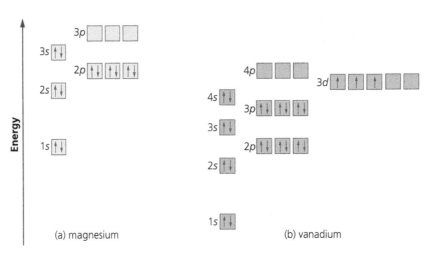

(a) magnesium   (b) vanadium

Figure 2.15 The electron configuration of (a) a magnesium atom and (b) a vanadium atom

A full list of the electron configurations of the first 36 elements is given in Table 2.4.

A short way of writing an electron configuration is to give the symbol of the preceding noble gas followed by the detail of the electrons added subsequently. For example, the electron configuration of manganese is $[Ar] \, 3d^5 \, 4s^2$ and that of bromine is $[Ar] \, 3d^{10} \, 4s^2 \, 4p^5$, where $[Ar]$ means $1s^2$ $2s^2 \, 2p^6 \, 3s^2 \, 3p^6$.

The order of filling orbitals is $1s$, $2s$, $2p$, $3s$, $3p$, $4s$, $3d$, $4p$, $5s$, $4d$, $5p$, $6s$... This is shown diagrammatically in Figure 2.16.

Note that the d-orbitals fill 'late', after the s-orbital of the next orbit (or shell) has received electrons. However, there are two slight variations in the order of filling:

- chromium is $[Ar] \, 3d^5 \, 4s^1$ *not* $[Ar] \, 3d^4 \, 4s^2$
- copper is $[Ar] \, 3d^{10} \, 4s^1$ *not* $[Ar] \, 3d^9 \, 4s^2$

This is because an atom is more stable if it has a half-filled or filled set of $3d$-orbitals and a single electron in the $4s$-orbital, rather than four or nine $3d$-electrons and two in the $4s$-orbital.

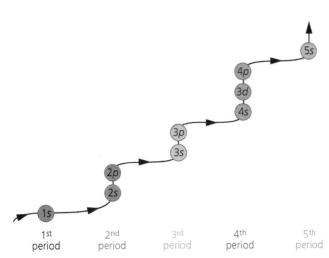

| 1st period | 2nd period | 3rd period | 4th period | 5th period |

Figure 2.16 The order in which orbitals are filled

Table 2.4 Electron configuration of the first 36 elements

Atomic number	Symbol	Electron configuration							
1	H	$1s^1$							
2	He	$1s^2$							
3	Li	$1s^2$	$2s^1$						s-block elements
4	Be	$1s^2$	$2s^2$						
5	B	$1s^2$	$2s^2$	$2p^1$					p-block elements
6	C	$1s^2$	$2s^2$	$2p^2$					
7	N	$1s^2$	$2s^2$	$2p^3$					
8	O	$1s^2$	$2s^2$	$2p^4$					
9	F	$1s^2$	$2s^2$	$2p^5$					
10	Ne	$1s^2$	$2s^2$	$2p^6$					
11	Na	$1s^2$	$2s^2$	$2p^6$	$3s^1$				s-block elements
12	Mg	$1s^2$	$2s^2$	$2p^6$	$3s^2$				
13	Al	$1s^2$	$2s^2$	$2p^6$	$3s^2$	$3p^1$			p-block elements
14	Si	$1s^2$	$2s^2$	$2p^6$	$3s^2$	$3p^2$			
15	P	$1s^2$	$2s^2$	$2p^6$	$3s^2$	$3p^3$			
16	S	$1s^2$	$2s^2$	$2p^6$	$3s^2$	$3p^4$			
17	Cl	$1s^2$	$2s^2$	$2p^6$	$3s^2$	$3p^5$			
18	Ar	$1s^2$	$2s^2$	$2p^6$	$3s^2$	$3p^6$			
19	K	$1s^2$	$2s^2$	$2p^6$	$3s^2$	$3p^6$	$3d^0$	$4s^1$	s-block elements
20	Ca	$1s^2$	$2s^2$	$2p^6$	$3s^2$	$3p^6$	$3d^0$	$4s^2$	
21	Sc	$1s^2$	$2s^2$	$2p^6$	$3s^2$	$3p^6$	$3d^1$	$4s^2$	d-block elements
22	Ti	$1s^2$	$2s^2$	$2p^6$	$3s^2$	$3p^6$	$3d^2$	$4s^2$	
23	V	$1s^2$	$2s^2$	$2p^6$	$3s^2$	$3p^6$	$3d^3$	$4s^2$	
24	Cr	$1s^2$	$2s^2$	$2p^6$	$3s^2$	$3p^6$	$3d^5$	$4s^1$	
25	Mn	$1s^2$	$2s^2$	$2p^6$	$3s^2$	$3p^6$	$3d^5$	$4s^2$	
26	Fe	$1s^2$	$2s^2$	$2p^6$	$3s^2$	$3p^6$	$3d^6$	$4s^2$	
27	Co	$1s^2$	$2s^2$	$2p^6$	$3s^2$	$3p^6$	$3d^7$	$4s^2$	
28	Ni	$1s^2$	$2s^2$	$2p^6$	$3s^2$	$3p^6$	$3d^8$	$4s^2$	
29	Cu	$1s^2$	$2s^2$	$2p^6$	$3s^2$	$3p^6$	$3d^{10}$	$4s^1$	
30	Zn	$1s^2$	$2s^2$	$2p^6$	$3s^2$	$3p^6$	$3d^{10}$	$4s^2$	
31	Ga	$1s^2$	$2s^2$	$2p^6$	$3s^2$	$3p^6$	$3d^{10}$	$4s^2$ $4p^1$	p-block elements
32	Ge	$1s^2$	$2s^2$	$2p^6$	$3s^2$	$3p^6$	$3d^{10}$	$4s^2$ $4p^2$	
33	As	$1s^2$	$2s^2$	$2p^6$	$3s^2$	$3p^6$	$3d^{10}$	$4s^2$ $4p^3$	
34	Se	$1s^2$	$2s^2$	$2p^6$	$3s^2$	$3p^6$	$3d^{10}$	$4s^2$ $4p^4$	
35	Br	$1s^2$	$2s^2$	$2p^6$	$3s^2$	$3p^6$	$3d^{10}$	$4s^2$ $4p^5$	
36	Kr	$1s^2$	$2s^2$	$2p^6$	$3s^2$	$3p^6$	$3d^{10}$	$4s^2$ $4p^6$	

Test yourself

7 Place the orbitals $4s$, $4p$, $4d$, $5s$, $5p$, $5d$, $6s$ in order of increasing energy levels.

The periodic table

Since the time of Dalton, chemists have tried to bring order out of the chaos of the chemical and physical properties of the elements. A number of attempts were made. For example, Newland suggested that there was a repeating pattern of properties every eight elements — his 'Law of Octaves'. Newland's contribution to modern understanding was the idea of **periodicity**. This is that there is a pattern of regularly repeating physical and chemical properties.

It was Mendeléev who put this on a sound basis and produced the periodic table, the understanding of which is fundamental to chemistry. He arranged the elements in ascending atomic mass, grouping those with similar chemical properties in vertical columns. He left two gaps between zinc and arsenic as he was sure that arsenic is in group 5. He predicted that elements numbered 32 and 33 would be discovered later and was vindicated within a few years with the discovery of gallium and germanium.

Mendeléev's original table has subsequently been modified and the modern form is provided at the back of this book (page 314). You should use it whenever you need relative atomic mass values, as well as when you are studying the chemistry of the elements and their compounds.

> **Tip**
>
> Mendeléev's prediction is an example of How Science Works.

Groups, periods and blocks

The periodic table is divided into groups, periods and blocks.

The vertical columns are called **groups**. All the elements in a group contain the same number of electrons in their outer shell. For example, all the elements in group 1 have one electron in their outer shell, which is in an s-orbital. All the elements in group 7 have seven electrons in their outer orbit, arranged $s^2 p^5$.

The horizontal rows are called **periods**. All elements in the same period have the same number of shells containing electrons. For example, all the elements in the third period, Na to Ar, have electrons in the first, second and third shells.

The table is also divided into **blocks**:

- The s-block consists of the elements in groups 1 and 2. An s-block element has its highest-energy electron in an s-orbital, i.e. the last electron added goes into an s-orbital.
- The p-block contains the elements in groups 3 to 7 and group 0 (the noble gases). A p-block element has its highest-energy electron in a p-orbital, i.e. the last electron added goes into a p-orbital.
- The d-block contains the elements scandium to zinc in period 4 and those elements below them. A d-block element cannot be defined in terms of energy because the energy level of the d-orbitals is altered by the presence of electrons in the outer s-orbital. It can only be defined in aufbau terms, i.e. the last electron added to a d-block element goes into a d-orbital.
- The f-block contains the 14 rare-earth elements (cerium to lutetium), which fit in the periodic table between lanthanum ($Z = 57$) and hafnium ($Z = 72$), and the 14 actinide elements (thorium to lawrencium), which come after actinium ($Z = 89$). The last electron added to an f-block element goes into an f-orbital.

Z is the atomic number of an element. It is the number of protons in the nucleus and so equals the charge on the nucleus.

The periodic table can be used to predict the electron configuration of an element because it indicates the order in which orbitals are filled (Figure 2.17).

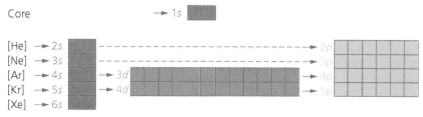

Figure 2.17 The periodic table and the order of filling orbitals

Forces that act on electrons in an atom

The forces that act on electrons in an atom are electromagnetic. They obey Coulomb's law, which states that the magnitude of the force between two charged objects is directly proportional to the product of their charges and inversely proportional to the square of the distance between their centres. This is expressed mathematically as:

$$\text{force} \propto \frac{q_+ q_-}{r^2}$$

where q_+ and q_- are the charges on the two objects and r is the distance between their centres.

The rules are:

- opposite charges attract; like charges repel
- the bigger the charges, the stronger is the force
- the further apart the particles, the weaker is the force

This means that electrons are attracted towards the nucleus (Figure 2.18). The greater the atomic number, the stronger is the force of attraction. Electrons that are further away from the nucleus are attracted less than those closer to the nucleus.

In addition, because they have the same charge, electrons repel each other. Because they are more densely packed, the inner electrons repel outer electrons much more than the other outer electrons repel each other.

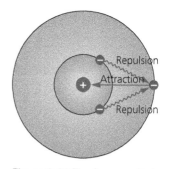

Figure 2.18 The forces acting on an electron in an atom

Shielding and the effective nuclear charge

Effective nuclear charge across period 1

In a hydrogen atom, the nucleus has a charge of +1 and there is one electron in a 1s-orbital. There are no forces of repulsion, so the electron feels the full force of attraction of a +1 charge.

In a helium atom, the nucleus has a charge of +2 and there are two electrons in the 1s-orbital. These electrons repel each other slightly. The result is that the net force of attraction between the nucleus and each electron is slightly less than that between a +2 charge and one electron. Therefore, the helium nucleus is said to have an effective nuclear charge of slightly less than 2.

Effective nuclear charge across period 2

The situation becomes more complicated for lithium and the remaining elements. In lithium, the nucleus has a charge of +3 and the outer 2s electron is strongly repelled

> **Key term**
>
> The **effective nuclear charge** is the net charge on the nucleus, after allowing for the electrons in orbit around the nucleus shielding its full charge.

by the two inner 1*s* electrons. The nucleus is **shielded** by the inner electrons and the effective nuclear charge is approximately +1. This is the +3 nuclear charge, minus the effect of two negatively charged screening electrons.

The next element is beryllium. The nucleus has a charge of +4, there are two 1*s* electrons shielding the nucleus and two 2*s* electrons that also repel each other slightly. Therefore, the effective nuclear charge is not exactly +2 (+4 nuclear charge minus the effect of the two negative inner electrons) — it is slightly less than +2 because of the extra repulsion by the two electrons in the outer orbit.

The situation is slightly more complicated with the next element, boron. The atomic number of boron is five (a nuclear charge of +5). There are two 1*s* electrons that shield the outer electrons from the nucleus. The two 2*s* electrons are closer to the nucleus than the single 2*p* electron and they repel it. Therefore, the effective nuclear charge is significantly less than the +3 value predicted by the simplified idea that effective nuclear charge is equal to the atomic number of the element minus the number of inner-shell electrons.

Similar arguments apply to other periods — the effective nuclear charge increases across a period, but does not increase by as much as +1 between successive elements.

Effective nuclear charge in a group

The nuclear charge and the number of inner shielding electrons increase by the same amount in a group. This leads to an assumption that the effective nuclear charge acting on the outer electrons of the elements in the same group of the periodic table hardly varies, but this is a simplification of a more complex situation.

For instance, sodium has 11 protons and, therefore, a nuclear charge of +11. It has two electrons in the first shell and eight in the second shell. These ten electrons shield the outer, third-shell electron very efficiently and the effective nuclear charge is close to +1 (+11 − 2 − 8 = +1).

Potassium has 19 protons and, therefore, a nuclear charge of +19. The outer, fourth-shell electron is shielded from the nucleus by two electrons in the first shell, eight electrons in the second shell and eight electrons in the third shell, making a total of 18 inner shielding electrons. From sodium to potassium, the number of protons has increased by eight and the number of shielding electrons has also increased by eight. Therefore, potassium also has a similar effective nuclear charge close to +1.

Shielding in the *d*-block elements

The increase in atomic number and hence in the nuclear charge is matched by the increase in the number of inner shielding electrons. Therefore, the effective nuclear charge of the *d*-block elements in the same period hardly alters.

- Scandium has 21 protons. Its electron configuration is $1s^2\ 2s^2\ 2p^6\ 3s^2\ 3p^6\ 3d^1\ 4s^2$. Therefore, it has 19 inner electrons shielding the 21 protons and has an effective nuclear charge of approximately +2.
- *d* electrons are less effective at shielding the nucleus than are *p* electrons in the same shell which, in turn, are less effective than *s* electrons.
- Titanium has 22 protons. Its electron configuration is $1s^2\ 2s^2\ 2p^6\ 3s^2\ 3p^6\ 3d^2\ 4s^2$. Therefore, it has 20 inner electrons shielding the 22 protons and has an effective nuclear charge of approximately +2.

Tip

Do not state that there is more shielding in potassium than in sodium. This fails to make the important point that there is more to shield because of the increase in nuclear charge.

- Vanadium has 23 protons. Its electron configuration is $1s^2\ 2s^2\ 2p^6\ 3s^2\ 3p^6\ 3d^3\ 4s^2$. Therefore, it has 21 inner electrons shielding the 23 protons and has an effective nuclear charge of approximately +2.

Periodicity

Periodicity refers to the recurring trends that are seen in the properties of an element with increasing atomic number.

Melting temperatures

The melting temperatures of the elements lithium to neon increase steadily for the first four elements and then fall dramatically at the fifth. This pattern is repeated with the elements sodium to argon (Table 2.5). This is an example of periodicity.

Element	Melting temperature/ °C	Boiling temperature/ °C	Element	Melting temperature/ °C	Boiling temperature/ °C
Lithium	180		Sodium	98	
Beryllium	1278		Magnesium	639	
Boron	2300		Aluminium	650	
Carbon	3500		Silicon	1414	
Nitrogen	−210	−196	Phosphorus	44	277
Oxygen	−218	−183	Sulfur	115	445
Fluorine	−220	−188	Chlorine	−101	−34
Neon	−249	−246	Argon	−189	−186

Table 2.5 Melting temperatures of the elements in period 2 and period 3

The melting temperatures of the metals increase across a group as more electrons are involved in bonding (see page 37). They decrease down a group as they get bigger and so are further apart, making separation easier.

Carbon, silicon and boron have very high melting temperatures as they exist as giant structures involving a network of covalently bonded atoms.

The other non-metals in the 2nd period are all diatomic except for neon, which is monatomic, and have weak forces between their molecules. Thus their melting and boiling temperatures are very low.

The other non-metals in the 3rd period are more complex. Phosphorus is P_4, sulfur S_6 and chlorine Cl_2, while argon is monatomic. These melting and boiling temperatures depend on the number of electrons in the molecule. This is explained further in Chapter 4.

Valency

The **valency** of an element can be defined as the number of electrons that it uses in bonding. Thus sodium (electron configuration 2,8,1) loses one electron when it forms a Na^+ ion and so has a valency of 1. Likewise chlorine (2,8,7) gains an electron to form the Cl^- ion, so it also has a valency of 1. The valencies of the elements in the period lithium to fluorine are in the order 1, 2, 3, 4, 3, 2, 1. This pattern is repeated exactly for the lowest valencies of the elements sodium to chlorine in the next period.

Atomic radius

The radius of an atom is found by measuring the distance between the nuclei of two touching atoms, and then halving that distance.

Trends across a period

Even though extra electrons are being added, the atoms get smaller going across a period from left to right. From lithium to fluorine, the outer electrons are all in the 2nd shell, being screened by the $1s^2$ electrons. The increasing number of protons in the nucleus as you go across the period pulls the electrons in more tightly. This is slightly offset by the increased repulsion of the electrons from each other. However, the net effect is a decrease in radius (Figure 2.19). This pattern is repeated in the 3rd period.

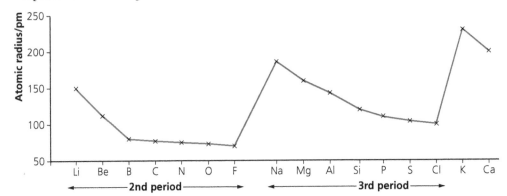

Figure 2.19 Trends in atomic radius

Trends in a group

Down a group, the trend is for atomic radii to increase steadily because of the increase in the number of occupied shells:

- Lithium: electron structure 2,1 — two occupied shells.
- Sodium: electron structure 2,8,1 — three occupied shells.
- Potassium: electron structure 2,8,8,1 — four occupied shells.

Size of positive ions

A positive ion is always *smaller* than its neutral atom. If an atom loses all its outer electrons, the radius of the resulting ion is much smaller than the atomic radius. This is because:

- there is one fewer shell of electrons
- there are fewer electrons in the positive ion than in the atom, so the electron–electron repulsion is less, causing a further reduction in the radius

For ions with the same electron configuration (e.g. Na^+, Mg^{2+} and Al^{3+}), the ion with the greatest charge will have the smallest radius.

The three positive ions in Table 2.6 have the same number of electrons (ten) arranged in the same way ($1s^2\ 2s^2\ 2p^6$). Therefore, the electron–electron repulsion is the same.

Table 2.6 Atomic and ionic radii

	Group 1	Group 2	Group 3	Group 4	Group 5	Group 6	Group 7
Atomic	Na	Mg	Al	C	N	O	F
Radius/pm	186	160	143	70	65	60	50
Ionic	Na^+	Mg^{2+}	Al^{3+}		N^{3-}	O^{2-}	F^-
Radius/pm	95	65	50		171	140	136

The nuclear charge increases from 11 to 12 to 13. The force of attraction between the nucleus of the aluminium ion (13 protons) and its ten electrons is, therefore, greater than that between the nucleus of the other ions and their ten electrons. This causes the Al^{3+} ion to have the smallest radius.

> Ions with the same electron structure are called isoelectronic.

Size of negative ions

A negative ion is always *larger* than its neutral atom (Figure 2.20). To form a negative ion, an atom must gain one or more electrons. The atom and the ion have the same atomic number, so forces of attraction remain the same. However, there is extra repulsion due to the increased number of electrons in the same shell. This causes the ion to expand, moving the electrons further from the nucleus until, once again, there is a balance between the forces of attraction and the forces of repulsion.

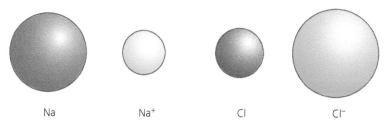

Na Na⁺ Cl Cl⁻

Figure 2.20 Relative sizes of atoms and ions

> **Key term**
>
> The **first electron affinity** is the energy change when one electron is added to each atom in a mole of neutral gaseous atoms.

Electron affinity (EA)

Electron affinity can be represented by the equation:

$$A(g) + e^- \rightarrow A^-(g)$$

The negatively charged electron being added is brought towards the positively charged nucleus. There is a force of attraction between the two and, therefore, energy is released when the two are brought closer together.

> The values of first electron affinities are negative (exothermic).

The first electron affinity of oxygen is $-142 \, \text{kJ} \, \text{mol}^{-1}$. This is the energy change, per mole, for the process:

$$O(g) + e^- \rightarrow O^-(g)$$

The second electron affinity can be represented by the equation:

$$A^-(g) + e^- \rightarrow A^{2-}(g)$$

The second electron affinity of an element is always positive (endothermic) because energy is required to add an electron to an already negative ion. The incoming electron is repelled by the negative ion. Therefore, energy has to be supplied to bring the ion and the electron together.

> **Key term**
>
> The **second electron affinity** is the energy change when one electron is added to each ion in a mole of singly charged gaseous negative ions.

> The second (and third) electron affinities are always positive numbers. They are endothermic reactions.

The second electron affinity of oxygen is $+844\,\text{kJ}\,\text{mol}^{-1}$. This is the energy change, per mole, for the process:

$$O^-(g) + e^- \rightarrow O^{2-}(g)$$

Test yourself

8 Write an equation to show the first electron affinity of:

  a) magnesium   b) nitrogen

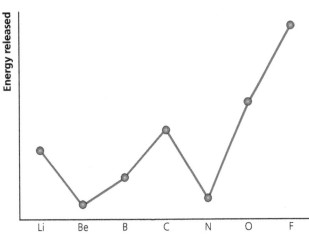

Figure 2.21 Energy released in the process $A(g) + e^- \rightarrow A^-(g)$

The variation of the first electron affinities of the elements in the second period is shown in Figure 2.21.

The electron is added to the outer orbit of the atom. As an electron is negatively charged and is being brought towards a positive nucleus, energy is released. The general trend is upwards because atomic radii decrease from lithium to fluorine, which causes the force of attraction to increase.

The dip at beryllium occurs because the added electron goes into a higher-energy $2p$ orbital and so less energy is released. The dip at nitrogen is caused by the extra repulsion of putting a second electron into the singly occupied $2p_x$-orbital.

The forces inside the nucleus

Inside an atom, there are forces that act inside the nucleus and forces that act on the electrons. Inside the nucleus there are so-called strong and weak nuclear forces, which are responsible for holding the nucleus together. Whenever there is a change in nuclear structure, very large amounts of energy are involved.

Radioactivity

The nuclei of some isotopes, such as carbon-14 and all the isotopes of radium and uranium, are unstable and spontaneously emit radiation. The level of radioactivity given off by a radioisotope is determined by its half-life. A short half-life means that the isotope is very radioactive but the radioactivity decreases rapidly over a short time. Some radioisotopes have long half-lives, such as the 4 billion years of the uranium-238 isotope. A long half-life means that exposure to the radioisotope for a short period is not as dangerous as exposure to those with half-lives from several seconds to a few years.

The radiation is of three main types:

- **α-rays** — alpha-rays are fast-moving helium nuclei. A helium nucleus consists of two protons and two neutrons. Alpha-rays are stopped by a few centimetres of air or by a sheet of paper.
- **β-rays** — beta-rays are very fast-moving electrons. They are stopped by a thin sheet of metal.
- **γ-rays** — gamma-rays are similar to X-rays but have an even higher frequency and hence energy. They need a thick layer of lead or concrete to absorb them.

It is dangerous to breathe in or eat any material containing α- or β-emitters (e.g. polonium-210, which is an α-emitter). This is because the radiation will destroy cells that absorb the chemical containing the isotope. However, use can be made of this. Iodine is concentrated in the thyroid gland. Cancers of the thyroid are treated with minute doses of the radioactive isotope, iodine-131. Its half-life is 8 days, so the radioactivity rapidly decreases to a negligible level.

Beta and gamma rays can be absorbed by human tissue, causing changes to the cells. High doses will kill cells and lower doses may cause mutations. Cancer cells are more likely to be destroyed than healthy cells. Radiotherapy, with controlled doses from cobalt-60, is used to treat many forms of cancer. It has a half-life of 5.27 years and decays into nickel-60, giving off an electron (β-ray) and two gamma photons.

Nuclear fission

Some heavy nuclei, such as uranium-235 and plutonium-239, are **fissile**. This means that when the nucleus absorbs a neutron, it becomes so unstable that it breaks into several smaller pieces.

Huge amounts of energy are released. A typical fission of uranium-235 produces strontium-90, xenon-143 and three neutrons. Uranium-235 absorbs slow (thermal) neutrons more efficiently than it absorbs fast neutrons. Therefore, if the neutrons produced in the fission of one nucleus are slowed down (by a moderator such as graphite), another fission reaction will occur. This is known as a **chain reaction**, and is the principle behind a nuclear reactor.

A nuclear reactor

Nuclear fission can be regarded as an environmentally friendly way of generating electricity. It does not produce any greenhouse gases and, as so little is used to produce a year's supply of electricity, there is a virtually unlimited source of uranium. One gram of uranium-235 produces as much energy by fission as burning over 2 tonnes of coal.

All developed and developing countries require vast amounts of electrical energy. Traditionally, this has been provided by power stations fired by fossil fuels. However, these produce huge amounts of carbon dioxide, a gas that contributes to global warming. In the medium term, nuclear fission is a possible answer to the threat of climate change. The disadvantage of nuclear power is that the fission products and the materials with which the reactor is built become dangerously radioactive, and have to be safely stored for thousands of years. Also, the technology of nuclear power can be adapted to make nuclear weapons.

Accidents, such as that at the nuclear power plant at Fukushima in Japan, can cause many deaths. However, so can accidents in coalmines and death can result from

First test explosion of an atomic bomb in Alamogordo, New Mexico, USA, 1945

breathing the pollution from fossil-fuel power stations and from wars over limited oil resources. If the sea levels rise significantly as a result of global warming caused by burning fossil fuels, people in low-lying countries could be displaced as a result of extensive flooding.

Nuclear fusion

When the nuclei of light isotopes such as hydrogen-1 or hydrogen-2 (deuterium) fuse together to make isotopes such as helium-4, enormous amounts of energy are released. This is the source of the energy that drives the universe. All stars were originally made of hydrogen. Under the enormous pressures and temperatures of these massive astronomical bodies, fusion takes place. Energy is released as electromagnetic radiation, in the form of radio waves, visible light and X-rays.

In a hydrogen bomb, a fusion reaction is triggered by the extreme conditions created by the explosion of a uranium fission device. If this reaction is harnessed, it will be possible to generate power without the problems associated with nuclear fission reactors.

Summary tasks

Write in your own words:

- the difference between atomic number and relative atomic mass
- the difference in shape and energy of the orbitals in the 1st, 2nd and 3rd shells
- why the first ionisation energy of potassium is less than that of sodium even though a potassium atom has eight more protons than a sodium atom
- why the 1st electron affinity of oxygen is exothermic whereas the 2nd is endothermic

Make sure you can define:

- relative atomic mass and relative isotopic mass
- first and successive ionisation energies
- electron affinity

Check that you can explain:

- the principles of a mass spectrometer and calculate relative atomic mass from mass spectra
- the number of peaks and their relative heights in the mass spectrum of a diatomic molecule
- the variation of first ionisation energies from hydrogen to calcium
- the trends in melting and boiling temperatures of the elements from hydrogen to calcium

Questions

1 Study the table below.

Species	Number of protons	Number of neutrons	Number of electrons
A	19	20	18
B	17	18	17
C	12	12	10
D	17	20	16
E	35	44	36
F	18	22	18

a) Identify the two species from A–F that are isotopes of the same element.
b) Identify which of A–F are neutral atoms.
c) Identify which of A–F are cations.
d) Identify which of A–F are anions.
e) Identify which of A–F have the same electron configuration.

2 a) Explain why the relative atomic mass of copper is not an exact whole number.
b) The relative atomic mass of copper is 63.5. Calculate the relative abundance of the two copper isotopes with relative isotopic masses of 63.0 and 65.0.

3 The data about silicon in the table below were obtained from a mass spectrometer.

m/z	% abundance
28	92.2
29	4.7
30	3.1

Calculate the relative atomic mass of silicon to one decimal place.

4 Bromine has two isotopes of mass numbers 79 and 81. The mass spectrum of a sample of bromine is shown below.

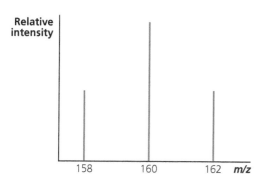

a) Identify the particles responsible for the peaks.

b) Deduce the relative abundance of the two isotopes.
c) Small peaks are also seen at $\frac{m}{z}$ values of 79 and 81. Write a chemical equation to show the formation of the particle that gives the peak at $\frac{m}{z} = 79$.

5 Complete the electron configurations of atoms of the following elements:
a) Phosphorus: [Ne]…
b) Cobalt: [Ar]…

6 Write the full electron configuration of an excited sodium atom.

7 Fill in the outer electrons of a phosphorus atom in the boxes below.

3s   3p

8 Explain, with an example, the meaning of the term periodicity.

9 Consider atoms of boron, magnesium and bromine. In which is the effective nuclear charge the largest and in which is it the smallest?

10 List the particles Cl, Cl$^-$ and K$^+$ in order of increasing radius.

11 Explain why the first ionisation energies of the noble gases decrease from helium to krypton.

12 The successive ionisation energies of an element, X, are given in the table. To which group of the periodic table does element X belong?

Ionisation	Ionisation energy/kJ mol^{-1}
1st	1000
2nd	2260
3rd	3390
4th	4540
5th	6990
6th	8490
7th	27100
8th	31700
9th	36600
10th	43100

13 Discuss the relative advantages and disadvantages of ESI and TOF mass spectrometers.

14 By considering the relative effectiveness of s, p and d electrons in shielding the nucleus, suggest why the difference between the atomic radii of fluorine and chlorine is 50 pm whereas that between chlorine and bromine is only 15 pm.

Exam practice questions

1 a) Define the term **first ionisation energy**. (2)

b) This part is about four sets of ionisation energies:

   i) Which are the values of the successive ionisation energies for an element in group 4 of the periodic table?

     A 496, 738, 578, 789, 1012, 1000
     B 578, 1817, 2745, 11 578, 14 831, 18 378
     C 1086, 2353, 4621, 6223, 37 832, 47 278
     D 1314, 1000, 941, 869, 812 (1)

   ii) Which are the values for the first ionisation energies of consecutive elements in the same period?

     A 496, 738, 578, 789, 1012, 1000
     B 578, 1817, 2745, 11 578, 14 831, 18 378
     C 1086, 2353, 4621, 6223, 37 832, 47 278
     D 1314, 1000, 941, 869, 812 (1)

c) i) Define the term **electron affinity**. (2)

   ii) Which is the equation that relates to the first electron affinity of chlorine?

     A $\frac{1}{2}Cl_2(g) + e^- \rightarrow Cl^-(g)$
     B $Cl(g) + e^- \rightarrow Cl^-(g)$
     C $Cl(g) - e^- \rightarrow Cl^-(g)$
     D $Cl_2(g) + 2e^- \rightarrow 2Cl^-(g)$ (1)

(Total 7 marks)

2 This question is about mass spectrometry.

a) A mass spectrometer can be used to find the percentage composition of the isotopes of an element. Explain how the following are achieved in a mass spectrometer:

   i) ionisation (1)
   ii) acceleration (1)
   iii) deflection (1)

b) Analysis of a sample of iron in a mass spectrometer gave the following results:

Isotope	Relative isotopic mass	%
^{54}Fe	53.94	5.94
^{56}Fe	55.93	91.78
^{57}Fe	56.94	2.28

Calculate the relative atomic mass of iron to two decimal places. (2)

c) The mass spectrum of bromine has lines at $\frac{m}{z}$ values of 158, 160 and 162, but none at 159 or 161. What causes the line at 160?

   A $(^{80}Br - ^{80}Br)^+$
   B $(^{80}Br - ^{80}Br)^-$
   C $(^{79}Br - ^{81}Br)^-$
   D $(^{79}Br - ^{81}Br)^+$ (1)

d) State and outline one modern use of mass spectrometry. (3)

(Total 9 marks)

3 The first ionisation of elements sodium to argon is shown below.

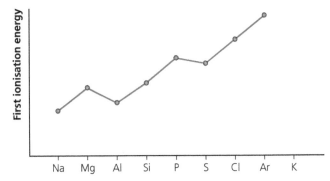

a) Explain why the general trend from sodium to argon is upwards but why the value for sulfur is less than that for phosphorus. (5)

b) Mark on the graph where the value for potassium would be. (1)

c) Explain why the value for the second ionisation of sodium is very much larger than that of its first ionisation. (2)

(Total 8 marks)

3

Bonding and structure I (Topic 2)

Bonding

There are three ways in which atoms can be chemically bonded to other atoms:

- **Metallic** bonding occurs between the atoms of metallic elements.
- **Ionic** bonding in compounds is usually between a metal and a non-metal.
- **Covalent** bonding occurs between two atoms of a non-metallic element (e.g. between two oxygen atoms in O_2) or between two atoms of different elements (e.g. between a hydrogen and a chlorine atom in HCl). Most covalent bonds exist between two non-metallic elements. However, some do occur between a metal and a non-metal, for example in beryllium chloride, $BeCl_2$.

▌ Metallic bonding

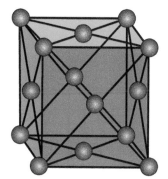

Face-centred cubic

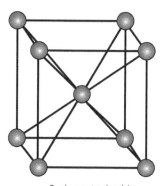

Body-centred cubic

Figure 3.1 The structure of a metal is a regular arrangement of cations held together by a sea of electrons

The simplest theory for metallic bonding is that the metal atoms lose their valence (outer shell) electrons and form cations. These cations are arranged in a regular lattice, with one layer of ions above another layer, and are surrounded by a 'sea' of electrons that can move through the lattice (Figure 3.1). The electrons are not localised in-between the metal ions; they are **delocalised** through the structure. The bonding is the attraction between the positive ions, which are fixed in position, and the negative electrons, which are constantly moving between the ions. There are slight spaces between the metal ions, which are occupied by the delocalised electrons. Therefore, the metallic radius is slightly larger than the ionic radius.

The strength of the metallic bond depends upon:

- the charge on the metal ion (which is equal to the number of delocalised electrons)
- the metallic radius (Table 3.1)
- the structure of the metallic lattice, for example body-centred cubic for the group 1 metals and face-centred cubic for calcium, magnesium and aluminium

Physical properties of metals

Density and melting temperature

The group 1 metals have low densities and low melting temperatures (Table 3.1). The electron configuration of their atoms is ns^1, where n is the orbit number of the outer s orbital, and they lose the outer s-electron.

The group 2 metals lose both the ns^2 electrons. This causes the ion to be smaller than the group 1 ion in the same period. Therefore, because of the smaller radius and the higher charge, there is a greater attraction between the metal's cation and the delocalised electrons. Thus the group 2 metals are denser and have higher melting temperatures.

A stronger force of attraction means that more energy has to be supplied to overcome that force and melt the solid. Therefore, a higher temperature is needed than in metals with weaker metallic bonds.

The d-block metals use their $(n-1)d$ electrons as well as their ns^2 electrons in bonding. The result is that they are much harder, denser and have significantly higher melting temperatures.

Table 3.1 Physical properties of metals

	Electron configuration	Metallic radius/nm	Ionic radius/nm	Melting temperature/°C	Density/ g cm⁻³
Sodium	[Ne] $3s^1$	0.19	0.095	98	0.97
Magnesium	[Ne] $3s^2$	0.16	0.065	649	1.74
Aluminium	[Ne] $3s^2\ 3p^1$	0.14	0.050	660	2.70
Potassium	[Ar] $4s^1$	0.23	0.13	63	0.86
Calcium	[Ar] $4s^2$	0.20	0.099	839	1.54
Titanium	[Ar] $3d^2\ 4s^2$	0.15	(+2) 0.090	1675	4.54
Iron	[Ar] $3d^6\ 4s^2$	0.13	(+2) 0.076	1535	7.86
Copper	[Ar] $3d^{10}\ 4s^1$	0.13	(+2) 0.069	1083	8.92

The melting temperature of metals increases across a period because the metallic radius decreases and more electrons are released for bonding. It decreases down a group because the metallic radius increases and the force of attraction between the metal ions and the delocalised electrons becomes less.

Electrical conductivity

Electricity is a flow of charge. All metals conduct electricity when solid and when molten. The sea of electrons is mobile and moves through the lattice of metal ions. Therefore, the electric current in a metal is a flow of electrons.

Thermal conductivity

Metals are good conductors of heat. This is also because of the free-moving electrons, which pass kinetic energy along a piece of metal.

Metals and graphite conduct electricity by the movement of electrons through the solid. Ionic substances conduct electricity by the movement of ions. This only happens when the ionic compound is molten or dissolved, *not* when it is a solid.

Malleability

Metals can be hammered or pressed into different shapes. One layer of metal ions can slide over another layer. This is because there are always electrons between the layers, preventing strong forces of repulsion between the positive ions in one layer and the positive ions in another layer. Some metals, such as lead and gold, are extremely soft. The d-block metals are much harder because there are more electrons that bind the layers together.

Chemical properties of metals

Ionisation energy

Metals are on the left-hand side of the periodic table. Metal atoms have one, two or three electrons in their outer orbits (apart from lead and tin, which have four). Therefore, the effective nuclear charge is smaller than for the elements that occur later in the same period. This means that the outer electron is held less firmly than in non-metals and the first ionisation energies are smaller than for non-metals in the same period.

Electronegativity

Metals have the lowest electronegativity values in the periodic table. Electronegativity decreases down a group and increases across a period. Therefore, caesium has the lowest electronegativity of all the elements.

> **Key term**
>
> **Electronegativity** of an element is defined as the extent to which it attracts a pair of bonding electrons in a covalent bond.

Formation of positive ions

The low values of the first ionisation energies and electronegativities make it energetically feasible for metals to lose electrons in bonding and to form positive ions that are then either bonded in an ionic lattice or hydrated.

Reaction with acids

The more reactive metals react with dilute acids to form hydrogen gas and a solution of a salt. For example, the ionic equation for the reaction of zinc with a strong acid such as sulfuric acid is:

$$Zn(s) + 2H^+(aq) \rightarrow Zn^{2+}(aq) + H_2(g)$$

Reaction with water

The most reactive metals react with cold water to form hydrogen gas and an alkaline solution of the metal hydroxide. For example, the ionic equation for calcium reacting with water is:

$$Ca(s) + 2H_2O(l) \rightarrow Ca^{2+}(aq) + 2OH^-(aq) + H_2(g)$$

Reaction with ions of a less reactive metal

A more reactive metal will reduce the ions of a less reactive metal. For example, when a piece of iron is placed in a solution of copper sulfate, the blue solution fades as a red-brown deposit of copper metal is formed:

$$Fe(s) + Cu^{2+}(aq) \rightarrow Fe^{2+}(aq) + Cu(s)$$

> **Test yourself**
>
> 1 Write equations for the reaction of magnesium with:
>   a) dilute hydrochloric acid
>   b) copper sulfate solution

Ionic bonding

Ionic bonds form between atoms with significantly different electronegativities. For example, sodium (electronegativity 0.9) and chlorine (electronegativity 3.0) form an ionic compound.

If the difference in electronegativity exceeds 1.5 the bonding will be predominately ionic.

Ionic compounds are electrically neutral. They consist of positive ions (cations) and negative ions (anions) held together by the attraction between opposite charges.

An ionic bond is the attraction between the opposite charges of cations and anions.

A **cation** is formed from a metal atom by the loss of one or more electrons. The ion has more protons than electrons and, therefore, is positively charged.

Polyatomic cations, such as NH_4^+, also exist.

There are many polyatomic anions, usually containing oxygen. Examples are SO_4^{2-} and NO_3^-.

An **anion** is formed from a non-metal atom by the gain of one or more electrons. The ion has more electrons than protons and, therefore, is negatively charged.

In simple terms, ion formation can be thought of as one atom (the metal) giving one or more electrons to another atom (a non-metal). For example, sodium (11 protons and 11 electrons) gives one electron to a chlorine atom (17 protons and 17 electrons), forming a Na^+ ion (11 protons and 10 electrons) and a Cl^- ion (17 protons and 18 electrons). However, sodium chloride can be made in a number of ways and it is impossible to tell which electron comes from which atom.

The electron configurations of a sodium ion and a chloride ion, showing all the electrons, are given in Figure 3.2.

Sodium ion
2,8

Chloride ion
2,8,8

Figure 3.2

> **Tip**
>
> The electron configuration of sodium changes from 2,8,1 to 2,8 – it has eight electrons in its outer orbit. These must be included in any electron configuration diagram, even if you are asked to show the outer electrons only.

Figure 3.3

The dot-and-cross diagram for sodium chloride, showing the outer electrons only, indicates where the electrons come from if sodium chloride were made by the reaction of sodium with chlorine (Figure 3.3).

In the solid, each sodium ion is surrounded by six chloride ions and each chloride ion is surrounded by six sodium ions in a giant structure called a lattice. The ratio of Na^+ ions to Cl^- ions is 1:1.

The arrangement is shown in Figure 3.4. Each red sphere represents the centre of a sodium ion and each green sphere the centre of a chloride ion.

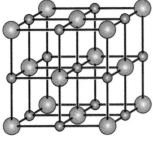

Figure 3.4 Sodium chloride ionic lattice

> **Test yourself**
>
> 2 a) Define ionic bond.
>
> b) Explain, in terms of electrons, how an ionic bond forms between atoms of calcium and atoms of fluorine.
>
> c) Draw electron configuration diagrams for a calcium ion and for a fluoride ion, showing their charges and outer electrons.

Strength of ionic bonds

The strength of an ionic bond depends on the forces of attraction between neighbouring ions of opposite charge and the forces of repulsion between near-neighbouring ions of the same charge. It is mainly determined by:

- the charges on the ions. The force of attraction depends on the product of the charges. Therefore, the attraction between a 2+ ion and a 1− ion is twice that between a 1+ and a 1− ion.
- the radii of the ions. The force of attraction varies *inversely* with the sum of the ionic radii. This means that smaller ions form stronger ionic bonds.
- the geometry. For example, caesium chloride has an 8:8 structure whereas sodium chloride has a 6:6 structure (see Figure 3.4).

The melting temperature is determined by the ionic bond strength. Strong bonds give rise to a high melting temperature.

Thus, magnesium chloride is more strongly ionically bonded than sodium chloride. The magnesium ion is 2+ and has a smaller radius than the 1+ sodium ion.

Ionic radius

The position of the centres of ions in an ionic crystal can be identified by electron diffraction patterns. The distance between a sodium ion and one of the adjacent chloride ions is the sum of the ionic radii, r (of Na^+) + r (of Cl^-). Positive ions are *smaller* than their parent atoms; negative ions are *bigger* than their parent atoms (Table 3.2).

Table 3.2 Atomic and ionic radii

	Ion	Electron configuration of ion	Atomic radius/nm	Ionic radius/nm
Sodium	Na^+	2,8	0.19	0.095
Magnesium	Mg^{2+}	2,8	0.16	0.065
Calcium	Ca^{2+}	2,8,8	0.20	0.10
Barium	Ba^{2+}	2,8,18,8	0.22	0.14
Chlorine	Cl^-	2,8,8	0.10	0.18
Bromine	Br^-	2,8,18,8	0.11	0.20
Iodine	I^-	2,8,18,18,8	0.13	0.22
Oxygen	O^{2-}	2,8	0.073	0.14
Hydroxide	OH^-			≈ 0.12

Note that the best ionic size match in the group 2 oxides and hydroxides is with the biggest cation, Ba^{2+}.

Trend in ionic radius down a group

As a group is descended, the ions have more electron shells. Therefore, down the group, the ions get larger. For example, the chloride ion has electrons in three shells and is smaller than the bromide ion, which has electrons in four shells. So, the radii of the group 7 ions increase in the order $F^- < Cl^- < Br^- < I^-$.

Trend in ionic radius from group 5 in one period to group 3 in the next period

The ions N^{3-}, O^{2-}, F^-, Na^+, Mg^{2+} and Al^{3+} all have the electron configuration 2,8. These six ions are said to be **isoelectronic**, as they have identical electron configurations. Their radii decrease from N^{3-}, which is the largest, to Al^{3+}, which is the smallest. This is because the charge on the nucleus increases from 7 in N^{3-} to 13 in Al^{3+}. The greater nuclear charge is experienced by the same number of electrons, so the attraction between the nucleus and the orbiting electrons goes up, making the ions progressively smaller.

An atom and the ion formed from it have the same number of protons in the nucleus. It is only the number of electrons that changes.

> **Test yourself**
>
> 3 Arrange the following in order of size of radius, with the largest first and the smallest last: Na, Na^+, Mg, Mg^{2+}, Cl, Cl^-

Evidence for the existence of ions

Conduction of electricity

An electric current is a flow of charged particles. When a metal, either a solid (e.g. copper) or a liquid (mercury), conducts electricity, the delocalised electrons move across the applied electric potential. The current is a flow of electrons.

Ionic *solids*, such as sodium chloride, do not conduct electricity because:

- they do not have delocalised electrons
- the ions are fixed in the lattice

However, when the solid is melted or dissolved, the lattice breaks down and the ions are free to move across an applied potential. The current is a flow of ions.

The positive ions move towards the negatively charged cathode, where they are reduced to atoms. The negative ions move towards the positively charged anode, where they are oxidised to atoms. If an electric current is passed through molten sodium chloride, the following reactions take place at the electrodes.

At the cathode (−), reduction occurs as each Na^+ ion gains an electron:

$$Na^+ + e^- \rightarrow Na$$

At the anode (+), oxidation occurs as each Cl^- ion loses an electron:

$$Cl^- \rightarrow \tfrac{1}{2}Cl_2 + e^-$$

The clearest evidence for ionic bonding is when the molten substance, or a solution of it, conducts electricity and new substances are produced at the electrodes. This process is called **electrolysis**.

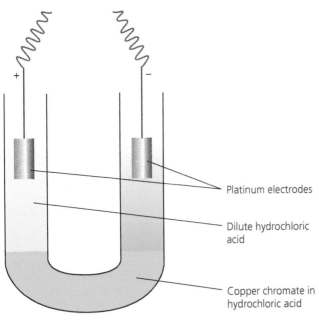

Platinum electrodes

Dilute hydrochloric acid

Copper chromate in hydrochloric acid

Figure 3.5 Electrolysis of copper(II) chromate solution
(Hazard: chlorine gas evolved and chromate ions are toxic)

The movement of ions can be demonstrated by the following experiment.

Some copper(II) chromate, $CuCrO_4$, is dissolved in the minimum of dilute hydrochloric acid. This solution is then saturated with urea, a water-soluble covalent substance. This increases the density of the solution. A U-tube is half-filled with dilute hydrochloric acid and the copper(II) chromate solution is poured carefully down a long-stemmed funnel so that it forms a separate layer beneath the dilute hydrochloric acid (Figure 3.5).

Graphite or platinum electrodes are then placed in the dilute hydrochloric acid layer just above the copper(II) chromate layer and an electric current is passed through the solution for at least 30 minutes. The Cu^{2+} ions move towards the negative terminal and the solution around this terminal becomes blue-green because of the copper ions. The solution around the positive terminal becomes yellow because of the migration of the CrO_4^{2-} ions towards it.

Melting temperature and solubility

Ionic compounds have very high melting temperatures. Only a few, for example potassium nitrate, can be melted in a test tube in the laboratory. This is because of the strong forces of attraction between the ions, so a large amount of energy has to be supplied to separate the ions when the solid is melted.

Many ionic compounds are soluble in water. Oxygen is more electronegative than hydrogen, so in water the oxygen atoms become negatively charged. These are then attracted to the positive cations and the positively charged hydrogen atoms of water are attracted to the negative anions (Figure 3.6).

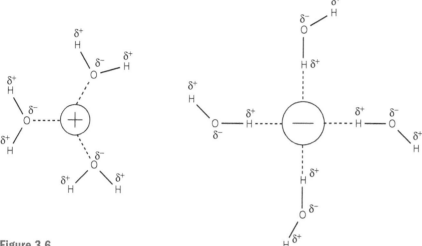

Figure 3.6

When the ions become hydrated, the energy released compensates for that required to break the bonds between positive and negative ions in the lattice. Positive ions are surrounded by the δ^- oxygen atoms of water molecules; the negative ions are surrounded by the δ^+ hydrogen atoms.

These properties are not proof of ionic bonding. Some covalent substances also have very high melting temperatures — for example, diamond, graphite and silicon dioxide, which have giant covalent structures (see Figure 3.18 on page 47). In diamond, each carbon atom is covalently bonded to four other carbon atoms, which are covalently bonded to other carbon atoms. In silicon dioxide, each silicon atom is covalently bonded to four oxygen atoms, each of which is bonded to two silicon atoms. These covalent bonds are strong and have to be broken to melt the solid. Therefore, the melting temperature is high. This type of covalent compound is insoluble in water. However, some other covalent substances, such as ethanol, are water-soluble.

This means that a high melting temperature, combined with solubility in water, is strong evidence for ionic bonding.

Electron-density maps

When X-rays are passed through a crystal, the radiation is scattered and a diffraction pattern is obtained. The extent of the scattering of the X-rays depends on the electron density. In this way, the position of atoms and ions in a solid can be determined. This analysis can be extended to measure the electron density in the atoms or ions. The result is a contour map, where the lines join places with the same electron density — just like the contour lines on a geographical map that join places of equal height above sea level.

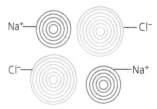

Figure 3.7 Electron-density map of sodium chloride

The electron-density map of sodium chloride is shown in Figure 3.7. It can be seen clearly that the electron density drops to zero between the ions, showing them to be discrete entities that are not joined to specific atoms or ions.

Covalent bonding

A covalent bond is the strong electrostatic attraction between the nuclei of two atoms and the shared pair of electrons between the two atoms. The electrons that are, or could be, involved in bonding are called **valence** electrons. Covalent bonds form between atoms with an electronegativity difference of less than approximately 1.5 units.

In a covalent bond, each atom supplies one electron that is then shared by both atoms.

In 1916, G. N. Lewis proposed that atoms share pairs of electrons in order to reach the electron configuration of a noble gas:

- The halogens are all one electron short of a noble gas configuration. They can gain one electron by sharing and go from $ns^2\ np^5$ to $ns^2\ np^6$ to form one covalent bond, as in H–Cl.
- Oxygen has the electron configuration [He] $2s^2\ 2p^4$. Therefore, it is two electrons short of the noble gas structure. It forms two covalent bonds, thereby gaining two electrons to have the configuration of neon. An example is in water, H–O–H.
- Nitrogen is [He] $2s^2\ 2p^3$. It requires three electrons to reach the electron configuration of neon. Thus, it forms three covalent bonds.
- Carbon is [He] $2s^2\ 2p^2$. It needs four more electrons and so forms four covalent bonds.

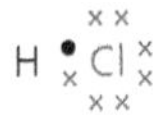

Covalent bonding can be shown by dot-and-cross diagrams. The dot-and-cross diagram for hydrogen chloride is shown in Figure 3.8. The electron of hydrogen is shown as a dot and the outer chlorine electrons by crosses.

Figure 3.8

Some people prefer to draw circles around each atom. In this method, the shared electrons are in the overlap of the two circles, as in a Venn diagram where the species in the overlap are common to both sets.

The electrons are not really different, but it is easier to count them if they are differentiated in this way.

Examples of both types of dot-and-cross diagram are shown in Figure 3.9.

These examples obey the octet rule. This states that atoms proceed, as far as possible, towards having eight electrons in their outer orbit.

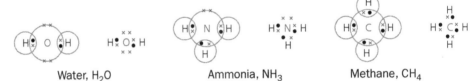

Water, H$_2$O   Ammonia, NH$_3$ Methane, CH$_4$

Figure 3.9 Dot-and-cross diagrams for water, ammonia and methane

Lewis's theory works well for all the period 2 non-metals except boron and for many period 3 and period 4 non-metal compounds. However, it breaks down with such compounds as PCl_5 and SF_6, and particularly with compounds of the noble gases, such as XeF_4.

A more modern theory is that a covalent bond is caused by the overlap of two atomic orbitals, each containing a single unpaired electron. This overlap can happen in several ways:

- The simplest is an overlap of two s-orbitals (Figure 3.10a). An example is hydrogen.
- Another possibility is the overlap of one s-orbital with a p-orbital (Figure 3.10b). An example is hydrogen chloride.
- Two p-orbitals can overlap to form a covalent bond (Figure 3.10c). An example is chlorine.

These are examples of 'head-on' overlap between two atomic orbitals, in which the overlap lies on the line between the centres of the atoms. This is called a **sigma-bond** (σ-bond).

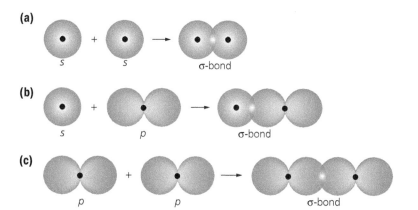

Figure 3.10

(a)

σ-bond

(b)

σ-bond

(c)

σ-bond

There is a slight problem with carbon. The electron configuration of carbon is [He] $2s^2\ 2p_x^{\ 1}\ 2p_y^{\ 1}\ 2p_z^{\ 0}$. There are only two unpaired electrons and so carbon might be expected to form only two covalent bonds. However, one of the $2s$-electrons is promoted into the empty $2p_z$-orbital, giving it a temporary configuration of [He] $2s^1\ 2p_x^{\ 1}\ 2p_y^{\ 1}\ 2p_z^{\ 1}$, with four unpaired electrons. It can now form four covalent bonds. The energy released in forming four, rather than two, bonds more than compensates for the small amount of energy required to promote an electron from the $2s$- into the empty $2p_z$-orbital (Figure 3.11).

Figure 3.11

The electrons marked in blue are outer electrons of carbon; those marked in red come from the atoms to which the carbon is bonded.

Expansion of the octet

This concept of promotion explains why phosphorus can form five covalent bonds. Its electron configuration is [Ne] $3s^2\ 3p_x^{\ 1}\ 3p_y^{\ 1}\ 3p_z^{\ 1}$. Therefore, it has three unpaired electrons. When PCl_3 is formed, the three unpaired electrons are used to form three covalent bonds and the configuration of a noble gas is reached. However, phosphorus has five empty $3d$-orbitals, with energy close to that of the $3s$-orbital. Therefore, one of the $3s$-electrons can be promoted into an empty $3d$-orbital (Figure 3.12). The electron configuration becomes [Ne] $3s^1\ 3p_x^{\ 1}\ 3p_y^{\ 1}\ 3p_z^{\ 1}\ 3d^1$ with five unpaired electrons. It can now form five covalent bonds.

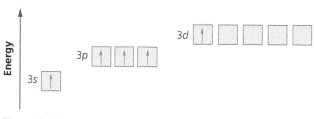

Figure 3.12

The extra energy released in forming the two extra bonds is much greater than that required to promote one electron from the $3s$- to the $3d$-orbital. In PCl_5, the phosphorus atom has ten electrons in its outer orbit (Figure 3.13), rather than the octet predicted by the Lewis theory.

Phosphorus does not form PI_5 because the P–I bond is not strong enough to compensate for the energy required to promote the $3s$-electron of phosphorus into the $3d$-orbital.

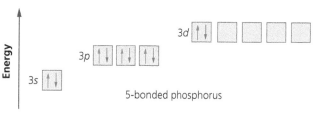

Figure 3.13

Figure 3.14

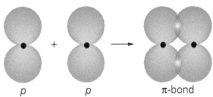

Nitrogen   Ethyne

Figure 3.15

Single and double bonds

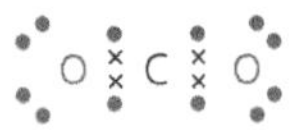

A single bond is a σ-bond between two atoms and is the sharing of one pair of electrons. In carbon dioxide, two double bonds exist between the carbon and the oxygen atoms. The dot-and-cross diagram for carbon dioxide is shown in Figure 3.14.

Here four electrons are shared between the central carbon atom and each oxygen atom. This sharing of two electron pairs is called a **double bond**.

A **triple bond** occurs when three pairs of electrons are shared by two atoms. The dot and cross diagram for nitrogen, N_2, and ethyne, C_2H_2, are shown in Figure 3.15

The orbital overlap theory easily explains a double bond. An orbital in one atom overlaps head-on with an orbital in the other atom, forming a σ-bond. However, a p-orbital, which is at right angles to the σ-bond, overlaps sideways with a p-orbital in the second atom to form a **pi-bond** (π-bond). A π-bond is shown in Figure 3.16.

> A double bond is the sharing of two pairs of electrons between two atoms.

p   p   π-bond

Figure 3.16 A π-bond

A π-bond is formed by two p-orbitals overlapping, so that the overlap lies above and below the line joining the centres of the two atoms. A double bond consists of a σ-bond and a π-bond between two atoms.

It is not possible to rotate the atoms around a double bond without breaking the π-bond. At room temperature the molecules do not possess enough energy for this to occur. This is why geometric isomers (pages 174–75) are distinct compounds. The rotation is possible if the substance is strongly heated.

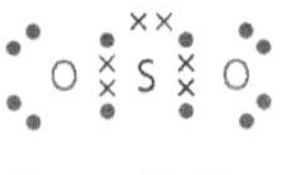

In sulfur dioxide, the sulfur atom forms two double bonds. The electron configuration of sulfur is [Ne] $3s^2\ 3p_x^2\ 3p_y^1\ 3p_z^1$. To form two double bonds, one electron must be promoted from the $3p_x$ orbital into an empty $3d$-orbital. There are now four unpaired electrons and it can form two σ-bonds and two π-bonds (Figure 3.17).

The sulfur atom has one unused pair of valence electrons. This is called a **lone pair** of electrons.

Figure 3.17

> A lone pair of electrons is a pair of valence electrons that is not used in bonding.

Covalent bond strength

The strength of a covalent bond is measured by the amount of energy needed to break the bond in a gaseous molecule. This energy arises from the attraction between the two nuclei and the shared electrons.

Diamond consists of a regular three-dimensional lattice of carbon atoms each covalently bonded to four other carbon atoms (Figure 3.18). In order to melt diamond, all these covalent bonds have to be broken. The extremely high melting temperature of nearly 4000K shows the strength of these covalent bonds. Silicon dioxide, SiO_2, is a giant lattice in which each silicon atom is covalently bonded to four oxygen atoms and each oxygen atom to two silicon atoms. On melting, these covalent bonds have to be broken and, as they are slightly weaker than those in diamond, the melting temperature is around 2000K. This is still higher than the melting temperatures of most ionic compounds.

(a)

(b)

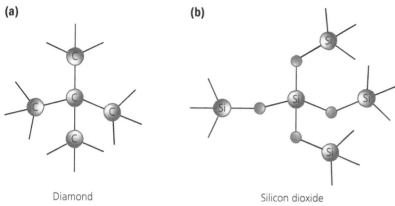

Diamond

Silicon dioxide

Figure 3.18 The basic structure of (a) diamond and (b) silicon dioxide

The average C–H bond energy in methane is one-quarter of the energy required for the following process:

$$H\text{—}C\text{—}H(g) \longrightarrow C(g) + 4H(g)$$

The strength of a covalent bond is determined mainly by:

- the sum of the atomic radii of the two bonded atoms. Small atoms form stronger bonds than larger atoms. Thus the Cl–Cl bond is shorter and stronger than the Br–Br bond because chlorine is a smaller atom than bromine. An anomaly is the F–F bond. Because the two fluorine atoms are so small there is significant repulsion between the lone pairs of electrons on one atom and those on the other atom. The F–F bond energy is $+158 \, \text{kJ mol}^{-1}$, whereas the Cl–Cl bond energy is $+243 \, \text{kJ mol}^{-1}$.
- the number of electron pairs being shared. A double bond (two pairs shared) is stronger than a single bond (one pair shared). Nitrogen, N≡N, has the greatest covalent bond strength.

The strength of a covalent bond is similar to the strength of an ionic bond.

Figure 3.19 shows the relative strength of single bonds between hydrogen and the *p*-block elements.

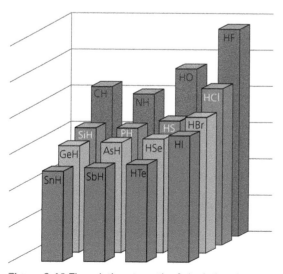

Figure 3.19 The relative strength of single bonds

Dative covalent bonds

Key term

A **dative covalent bond** is a covalent bond in which both electrons in the shared pair are provided by one atom.

In terms of the overlap of atomic orbitals, a **dative covalent bond** is the result of an overlap of an empty orbital in one atom and an orbital containing a lone pair of electrons in the other atom. An arrow from the atom with the lone pair to the atom with the empty orbital is used to represent a dative covalent bond.

Dative covalent bonds are sometimes called coordinate bonds.

Dative bonds with oxygen

The oxygen atom in a water molecule is able to use one of its two lone pairs to form a dative covalent bond. This occurs with H^+ ions and with many metal cations.

The hydronium ion, H_3O^+

The dot-and-cross diagram and structural formula of a hydronium ion are shown in Figure 3.20. The empty 1*s*-orbital in the H^+ ion overlaps with the orbital in oxygen that contains a lone pair of electrons. The H_3O^+ ion is the ion that makes a solution acidic. For simplicity, it is often written as $H^+(aq)$.

Figure 3.20

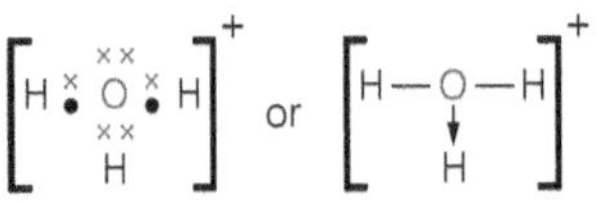

Tip

If you are asked to label the bonds, make sure that you label the covalent bonds within the water molecules as well as the dative covalent bonds.

The hydrated magnesium ion, $[Mg(H_2O)_6]^{2+}$

Magnesium has the electron configuration $1s^2\ 2s^2\ 2p^6\ 3s^2$ and that of the Mg^{2+} ion is $1s^2\ 2s^2\ 2p^6\ 3s^0$. Therefore, the Mg^{2+} ion has one empty 3*s*-orbital, three empty 3*p*-orbitals and five empty 3*d*-orbitals. It uses six of these by accepting six pairs of electrons to form six dative covalent bonds with the oxygen atoms in six water molecules (Figure 3.21).

Figure 3.21 Hydrated magnesium ion

Tip

Be careful when drawing the structure of hydrated ions. You must draw the arrow to the metal ion from the oxygen of the water molecule and not from the hydrogen.

Hydrated copper(II) ion

- Other metal cations, especially those in the *d*-block, form hydrated ions in the same way as magnesium.
- The blue colour of hydrated copper sulfate crystals is caused by the $[Cu(H_2O)_4]^{2+}$ ion.
- When hydrated copper sulfate is dissolved in water, two more water molecules bond datively to form the $[Cu(H_2O)_6]^{2+}(aq)$ ion.
- The anhydrous Cu^{2+} ion is colourless. When blue hydrated copper sulfate is heated, it loses the dative-bonded water molecules as steam and the solid turns white as anhydrous copper sulfate is formed.

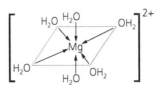

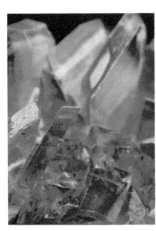

Hydrated copper sulfate crystals

Test yourself

4 Explain the difference between a covalent bond and a dative covalent bond.

Dative bonds with nitrogen

The nitrogen atom in ammonia, NH_3, has three pairs of covalently bonded electrons and one lone pair.

The ammonium ion, NH_4^+

The lone pair of electrons on the nitrogen atom is used to form a dative covalent bond with an H^+ ion. The result is the ammonium ion, NH_4^+ (Figure 3.22).

The H^+ ion has no electrons. Its empty $1s$-orbital overlaps with the orbital in the nitrogen atom that contains a lone pair. Once the dative covalent bond has formed, all four N−H bonds are identical.

Ammines

When excess ammonia solution is added to a precipitate of copper hydroxide, a dark blue solution is formed. This colour is due to the $[Cu(NH_3)_4(H_2O)_2]^{2+}$ ion, in which four ammonia molecules and two water molecules are datively bonded to the central copper ion.

Other examples of the formation of soluble datively bonded ions include the 'dissolving' of zinc hydroxide, silver oxide and silver halides in ammonia solution.

Dative bonds with chlorine

Both covalently bonded chlorine and chloride ions are able to use a lone pair to form a dative covalent bond.

Anhydrous aluminium chloride

Anhydrous aluminium chloride is covalent because the difference in the electronegativities of aluminium and chlorine is only 1.5 (see page 44).

- In the gas phase, just above its boiling temperature, it exists as Al_2Cl_6 molecules.
- The aluminium in a covalently bonded $AlCl_3$ molecule has only six electrons in its outer orbit and so has an empty orbital.
- Two $AlCl_3$ molecules bond together. The lone pair on one chlorine atom in one $AlCl_3$ bonds into the empty orbital of the aluminium atom in the other $AlCl_3$ molecule.
- One chlorine atom from each $AlCl_3$ molecule acts as a bridge, connecting the two molecules with dative covalent bonds (Figure 3.23). In three dimensions this has the structure shown in Figure 3.24, with bond angles of 109.5°.

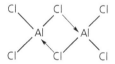

Figure 3.23

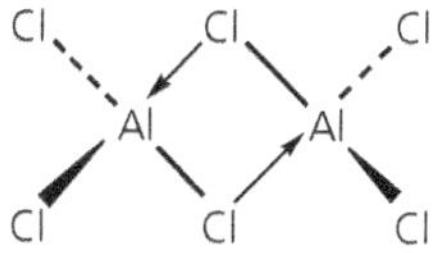

Figure 3.24

The PCl_6^- ion

The phosphorus atom in PCl_5 has ten electrons in its outer orbit (page 45), but it also has four empty $3d$-orbitals. Solid phosphorus pentachloride is not PCl_5, but an ionic compound, $PCl_4^+PCl_6^-$. One PCl_5 molecule loses a Cl^- ion, which uses one of its lone pairs of electrons to form a dative covalent bond with an empty orbital of a phosphorus atom in another PCl_5 molecule (Figure 3.25). On heating, the dative bond breaks and two molecules of PCl_5 are formed.

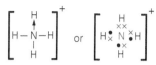

Figure 3.22 Ammonium ion

> **Tip**
>
> Do not confuse ammonia, NH_3, with the ammonium ion, NH_4^+.

> **Tip**
>
> Make sure that you have the arrows going the correct way — from the chlorine to the aluminium. There are no Al−Al bonds in Al_2Cl_6.

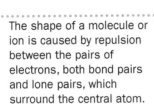

Figure 3.25

Shapes of molecules and ions

The shape of a molecule or ion is caused by repulsion between the pairs of electrons, both bond pairs and lone pairs, which surround the central atom.

In biochemistry, knowledge of the shapes of molecules is important in understanding many reactions. For example, when light strikes a rod cell in the retina of the eye, the light energy causes a molecule of 11-*cis*-retinal to change its shape, which triggers an impulse along the optic nerve to the brain. Animal fats and vegetable oils are esters of fatty acids, some of which are unsaturated. The *cis*-isomers of these fatty acids are less harmful than the *trans*-isomers.

The shapes of molecules such as DNA, proteins and enzymes are extremely complicated. However, the rules that govern the shapes of such molecules are the same as those used to predict the shapes of simple molecules and ions, such as water, H_2O, and ammonium, NH_4^+. The shape is determined according to the valence shell electron pair repulsion (VSEPR) theory.

The electron pairs repel each other to the position of minimum repulsion, which is also the position of maximum separation.

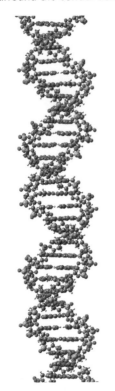

A model of DNA

Predicting the shapes of molecules

Molecules with single bonds only

The shape of a covalent molecule with no double bonds is determined by the number of bonds and lone pairs. The method for predicting the shape is as follows:

1 Count the number of bond pairs around the central atom. This is equal to the number of bonds formed by the central atom.

2 Count the number of lone pairs on the central atom. The number of non-bonding electrons is found by subtracting the number of electrons used in bonding from the group number of the element. The number of lone pairs is half this number.

3 Add these numbers together to get the total number of electron pairs; this determines the arrangement of the electron pairs.

4 The name of the shape depends on the position of the *atoms* around the central atom.

> **Tip**
>
> An alternative way is to draw a dot-and-cross diagram and then count the number of bonds and lone pairs.

> **Worked example**
>
> a) How many bond pairs and lone pairs are there around a sulfur atom in:
>
> I) hydrogen sulfide, H_2S
>
> II) sulfur hexafluoride, SF_6?
>
> b) How many bond and lone pairs are there around the nitrogen atom in ammonia, NH_3?

a) Sulfur is in group 6, so it has six outer electrons.

   i) Sulfur forms two bonds in H_2S, so has two bond pairs.
     There are $\frac{1}{2} \times (6 - 2) = 2$ lone pairs.

   ii) Sulfur forms six bonds, so has six bond pairs.
     There are $\frac{1}{2} \times (6 - 6) = 0$ lone pairs.

b) Nitrogen is in group 5, so it has five outer electrons and forms three bonds in NH_3.
   There is $\frac{1}{2} \times (5 - 3) = 1$ lone pair.

Test yourself

5 State the number of lone pairs of electrons on:

   a) the iodine atom in ICl_3

   b) the oxygen atom in F_2O

   c) the carbon atom in CO_2

Molecules and ions with double bonds

A double bond consists of a σ-bond and a π-bond and, therefore, can be regarded as one 'lot' of electrons.

The shape of a covalent molecule with one or more double bonds is determined by the number of σ-bonds and lone pairs.

The number of lone pairs is calculated as in steps 1 and 2 above. However, the arrangement of electrons around the central atom is determined by the number of σ bond pairs and the number of lone pairs.

Tip

Stereochemically, a double bond is equivalent to a single bond because they are between the same two atoms. Either count a double bond as one bond or count the number of σ-bonds around the central atom. Remember that each σ-bond is *one* pair of electrons.

Worked example

How many bonds are there around the sulfur atom in the sulfate ion, SO_4^{2-}, and how many lone pairs?

Tip

The number of electrons not used in bonding is the group number of the element minus the number of electrons that have been used in bonding.

Answer

The structural formula is:

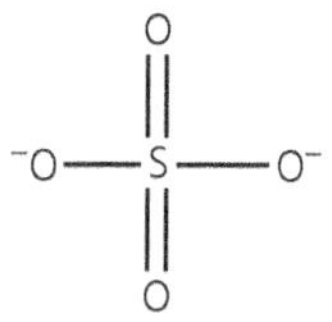

It uses six electrons to form two single and two double bonds, which is four σ- (and two π-) bonds. Sulfur is in group 6, so the number of lone

pairs $= \frac{1}{2} \times (6 - 6) = 0$.

Species with two σ-bond pairs and no lone pairs

- The two electron pairs repel each other to a position of minimum repulsion (maximum separation) and so take up a **linear** arrangement.
- Gaseous beryllium chloride, $BeCl_2$, is covalent. Its structural formula is Cl–Be–Cl. There are two bond pairs of electrons around the central beryllium atom. It is in group 2, so the number of lone pairs $= \frac{1}{2} \times (2 - 2) = 0$. The two electron pairs repel each other to a position of maximum separation, so the molecule is linear (Figure 3.26). The Cl–Be–Cl bond angle is 180°.
- Carbon dioxide is O=C=O and has two σ-bonds and two π-bonds. All four electrons of the carbon atom are used in bonding. There are two σ-bond pairs and no lone pairs, so the molecule is also linear, with a O–C–O bond angle of 180°.

Species with three electron pairs

The position of minimum repulsion caused by three pairs of electrons is a planar triangle around the central atom, with bond angles of 120°. This arrangement is called **trigonal planar**.

Three σ-bond pairs

Boron trichloride, BCl_3, is covalent. Boron is in group 3 and has three valence electrons, which are used to form three bonds. There are no lone pairs around the boron atom, so the position of minimum repulsion of the electron pairs is trigonal planar (triangular) with a bond angle of 120° (Figure 3.27).

In sulfur trioxide, SO_3, there are three σ- and three π-bonds. These use all six valence electrons, so there are no lone pairs. The three σ-pairs of electrons move as far apart as possible and take up the trigonal planar shape (Figure 3.28).

The carbonate ion is more complicated. As with all anions containing oxygen, the minus charges are on oxygen atoms. The structural formula is shown in Figure 3.29.

The carbon atom has used all *four* of its electrons in bonding and has no lone pairs (group $4 - 4 = 0$). It has formed three σ-bonds (and one π-bond). Therefore, the ion is trigonal planar because the three σ-bond electron pairs repel each other to a position of maximum separation.

Alkenes are planar around the C=C group. Each carbon atom in the C=C group forms three σ-bonds and one π-bond. The three σ-bond pairs repel each other to a position of maximum separation and, therefore, the two carbon atoms and the four atoms directly attached to them lie in the same plane. Ethene is planar.

Cis-but-2-ene is planar around the C=C group, so the –CH₃ groups and the hydrogen atoms should be drawn with 120° bond angles to the C=C group (Figure 3.30).

Two bond pairs and one lone pair

Sulfur dioxide, SO_2, has the structural formula O=S=O. Four of the six valence electrons are used in bonding, so there is one lone pair (group $6 - 4 = 2$ electrons = 1 lone pair). The three electron pairs (two σ-bonds and the lone pair) are in a trigonal planar arrangement. However, the shape of the molecule is described by the position of the *atoms* around the central sulfur atom. The sulfur dioxide molecule is V-shaped or bent (Figure 3.31).

Figure 3.26

Note that the beryllium atom does not have an octet of electrons.

Figure 3.27

Figure 3.28

Figure 3.29

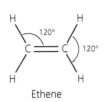

Ethene

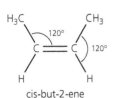

cis-but-2-ene

Figure 3.30

Figure 3.31

Species with four electron pairs

The electron pairs are in a three-dimensional **tetrahedral** arrangement, the internal angle of which is 109.5°.

Four σ-bond pairs and no lone pairs

- A simple example is methane, CH_4. The carbon forms four σ-bonds and, as all the valence electrons are used in bonding, it has no lone pairs. The four bond pairs repel each other and the molecule has a **tetrahedral** shape, with H–C–H bond angles of 109.5° (Figure 3.32). All covalent singly bonded carbon compounds have this shape around the carbon atom.

    Carbon atoms in alkanes are tetrahedrally bonded. A skeletal formula shows the bond angles more correctly than the displayed formula, as is illustrated by the skeletal and displayed formulae of pentane (Figure 3.33).

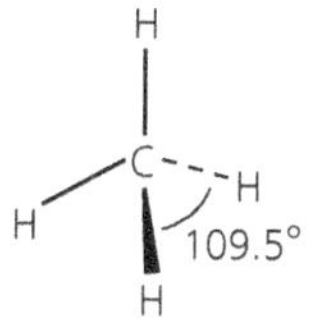

Figure 3.32

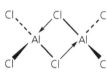

Skeletal

Displayed

C_5H_{12}

Molecular

Figure 3.33

A model of methane, CH_4

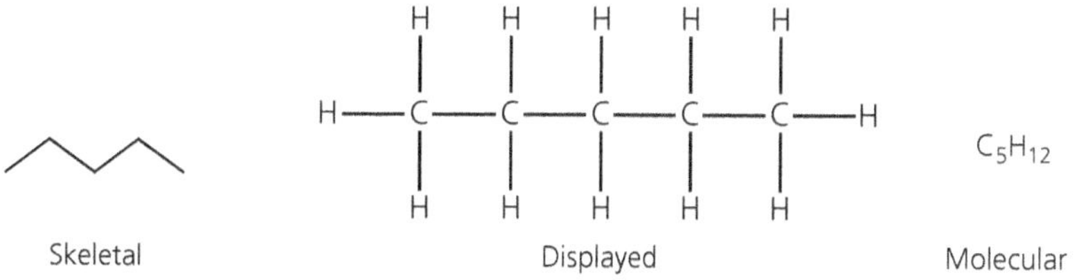

In skeletal formulae neither carbon atoms nor hydrogen atoms attached to them are shown. It is assumed that there are carbon atoms at the end of each line and at each bend.

- Silicon is also in group 4, so compounds such as SiH_4 and $SiCl_4$ are tetrahedral.
- The ammonium ion, NH_4^+, is tetrahedral. Three of the five valence electrons of nitrogen are used in forming single covalent bonds with three hydrogen atoms and two are used in forming a dative covalent bond with an H^+ ion. The four bond pairs of electrons repel each other and the ion is tetrahedral.
- The dimer, Al_2Cl_6, is a complicated example. Four bond pairs of electrons surround each aluminium, so the four chlorine atoms are arranged in a tetrahedron around the aluminium atoms, with a bond angle of 109.5° (Figure 3.34).
- The sulfate ion has the structural formula and shape shown in Figure 3.35. There are four σ-bonds and two π-bonds. Therefore, all six valence electrons of sulfur are used in bonding. The four σ-bonds repel equally and the ion is tetrahedral.

Figure 3.34

Figure 3.35

> ### Tip
>
> The best way to draw a tetrahedral molecule is by using two ordinary lines, one wedge and one dashed line coming from the central atom. A double bond is represented by a pair of lines.
>
> A wedge indicates a bond coming out of the paper and a dashed line indicates a bond going behind the paper, thus creating a three-dimensional effect.
>
>

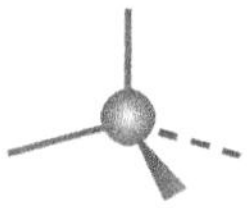

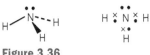

Figure 3.36

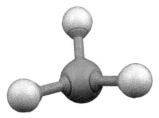

A model of ammonia, NH_3

. . . .
Do not confuse the shape of the *ammonia* molecule, NH_3 (pyramidal), with that of the *ammonium* ion, NH_4^+ (tetrahedral). Ammonia has three bond pairs and one lone pair; ammonium has four bond pairs and no lone pairs.

Three σ-bond pairs and one lone pair

The four pairs of electrons are arranged tetrahedrally around the central atom. However, the name of the shape is determined by the position of the **atoms**. The shape is **pyramidal** — a triangular-based pyramid around the central atom, with the lone pair on the opposite side of the central atom to the three bonded atoms.

Ammonia, NH_3, molecules are this shape. Nitrogen is in group 5, so the nitrogen atom has five valence electrons. Three of these are used in forming covalent bonds with the three hydrogen atoms. This leaves a lone pair. The electrons are arranged tetrahedrally, but the shape of the molecule is pyramidal (Figure 3.36).

> **Tip**
>
> The best way to draw a pyramidal molecule is with one ordinary line, one wedge and one dashed line.
>
>

The repulsion between the lone pair and the bond pairs is *greater* than the repulsion between bond pairs. This is because the electron density in a lone pair is greater than that in a bond pair. This forces the bonds closer together and reduces the H−N−H bond angle from the tetrahedral angle of 109.5° to 107°.

The sulfate(IV) ion, SO_3^{2-}, is also pyramidal (Figure 3.37). The sulfur atom forms two single bonds with two oxygen atoms and one double bond with the third oxygen atom. Therefore, four of the six valence electrons are used and there is one lone pair (group 6 − 4 = 2 electrons = 1 lone pair).

Figure 3.37

Two σ-bond pairs and two lone pairs

The four pairs of electrons are arranged tetrahedrally. However, as there are only two atoms bonded to the central atom, the molecule is **V-shaped** or bent.

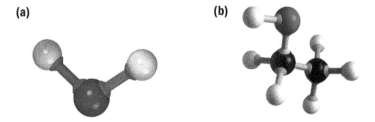

Models of (a) water, H_2O and (b) ethanol, C_2H_5OH

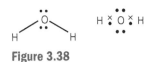

Figure 3.38

An example of this is water. Two of the six valence electrons of oxygen are used in bonding, so there are two lone pairs (6 − 2 = 4 unused electrons = 2 lone pairs). The four electron pairs repel to a position of minimum repulsion, so the molecule is V-shaped (Figure 3.38).

The repulsion between the two lone pairs is greater than that between the bond pairs, so the tetrahedral angle is further compressed to 104.5°.

In ethanol, CH_3CH_2OH, the oxygen atom has two σ-bonds and two lone pairs. This means that the C−O−H bond angle is the same as that in water at 104.5°. The other bond angles in the molecule are the normal tetrahedral angles of 109.5°.

Lone pair/lone pair repulsion is greater than lone pair/bond pair, which is greater than bond pair/bond pair repulsion.

Species with five σ-bond pairs and no lone pairs

The position of maximum separation is a planar triangle with one atom above and one below the plane. This shape is called **trigonal bipyramidal**. For example, gaseous phosphorus pentachloride, PCl_5, has five bonding pairs and no lone pairs of electrons around the phosphorus atom (Figure 3.39).

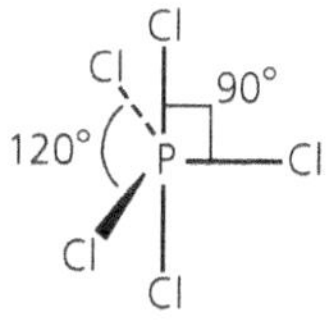

Figure 3.39

> **Tip**
>
> The best way to draw this complex shape is to have three ordinary lines at 90° to each other with one wedge and one dashed line on the opposite side.

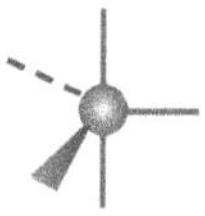

The bond angles between the chlorine atoms and the phosphorus atom in the triangular plane are all 120°. The angle between the top or bottom chlorine atom and those in the plane is 90°.

Species with six electron pairs

Six electron pairs repel and take up an octahedral arrangement with 90° bond angles between the bonding atoms and the central atom.

In SF_6, all six valence electrons of sulfur are used in bonding, so the shape of the molecule is octahedral (Figure 3.40).

> **Tip**
>
> Another way of drawing this shape is to have one line going vertically upwards from the central atom, one line going vertically downwards, two wedges bottom left and right, and two dashed lines top left and right.

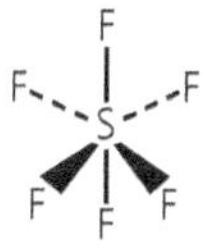

Many metal ions are hydrated, with the oxygen of six water molecules dative-covalently bonded to the central metal ion. These ions are octahedral, for example $[Cr(H_2O)_6]^{3+}$ and $[Mg(H_2O)_6]^{2+}$ (Figure 3.41).

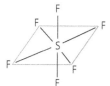

Figure 3.40 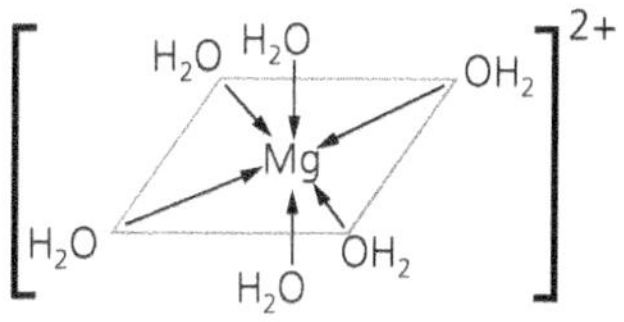   **Figure 3.41**

Summary

- Work out the number of σ-bonds and lone pairs of electrons around the central atom. This gives the *arrangement* of electrons.
- The *shape* of the molecule is this arrangement, modified by any lone pairs.
- Repulsion of the bond pairs by any lone pairs reduces the bond angle.

Examples are given in Table 3.3.

Table 3.3 Shapes of molecules and ions

Total number of electron pairs	Number of σ-bond pairs	Number of lone pairs	Arrangement of electron pairs (lone pairs in red)	Shape of molecule	Bond angle	Examples
2	2	0	Linear	Linear	180°	$BeCl_2$ CO_2
3	3	0	Trigonal planar	Trigonal planar	120°	BCl_3 CO_3^{2-} SO_3 NO_3^-
	2	1		V-shaped	<120°	SO_2 NO_2^-
4	4	0	Tetrahedral	Tetrahedral	109.5°	NH_4^+ CH_4 CCl_4 $SiCl_4$ PCl_4^+ SO_4^{2-}
	3	1		Pyramidal	<107°	NH_3 SO_3^{2-} H_3O^+
	2	2		V-shaped	<104.5°	H_2O
5	5	0	Trigonal bipyramidal 90° 120°	Trigonal bipyramidal	120° and 90°	$PCl_5(g)$
6	6	0	Octahedral 90° 90°	Octahedral	90°	SF_6 $[Mg(H_2O)_6]^{2+}$ and other hydrated cations

Polarity of molecules

In a covalent bond between two atoms of the same element (e.g. H_2 or Cl_2), the average position of the bonding electrons is exactly halfway between the centres of the two atoms. However, in the bond between atoms of different elements (e.g. HF or H_2O) this is not the case. In the H–F bond, the electrons are nearer to the fluorine atom. The ability of an atom in a covalent bond to draw the shared electrons nearer to itself is measured by the electronegativity of the element.

In the periodic table, electronegativity increases across a period and decreases down a group. The electronegativities (estimated using the Pauling scale) of some elements are shown in Table 3.4.

Fluorine is the most electronegative element.

Key term

Electronegativity is the ability of an element to attract the pair of electrons in a covalent bond.

Table 3.4 Electronegativities of some elements

H						
2.1						
Li	Be	B	C	N	O	F
1.0	1.5	2.0	2.5	3.0	3.5	4.0
Na	Mg	Al	Si	P	S	Cl
0.9	1.2	1.5	1.8	2.1	2.5	3.0
K						Br
0.8						2.8
Rb						I
0.8						2.5

When two covalently bonded elements have different electronegativities, small positive (δ^+) and small negative (δ^-) charges are present and the bond is said to be polar. The bonding electrons are drawn towards the more electronegative element, making it δ^-. The less electronegative element becomes δ^+. Some examples of polar bonds are shown in Figure 3.42.

$$\overset{\delta^+}{H}\!-\!\overset{\delta^-}{O} \qquad \overset{\delta^+}{H}\!-\!\overset{\delta^-}{Cl} \qquad \overset{\delta^+}{C}\!-\!\overset{\delta^-}{Cl} \qquad \overset{\delta^-}{N}\!-\!\overset{\delta^+}{H} \qquad \overset{\delta^-}{C}\!-\!\overset{\delta^+}{H}$$

Figure 3.42

Polar covalent bonds can be regarded as being between two ideals — a 100% covalent and hence non-polar bond and a 100% ionic bond. The relationship between the difference in electronegativity and the percentage ionic character is shown in Figure 3.43.

This graph shows that ionic and covalent bonds are the ends of a continuum stretching from purely ionic, through polarised ionic, to polar covalent and finally to pure (non-polar) covalent. An approximation can be used to predict the type of bonding — an electronegativity difference of more than 1.5 results in a predominantly ionic bond. A difference of less than this results in a polar covalent bond and no difference (as in C–I) results in a non-polar covalent bond.

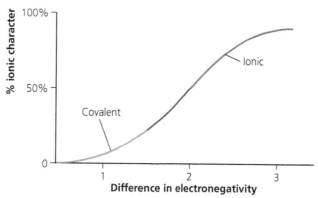

Figure 3.43 Relationship between difference in electronegativity and percentage ionic character

Shape and polarity

> **Tip**
> It is important to distinguish between a polar *molecule* and a polar *bond.*

The bonds in both CH_3Cl and CCl_4 are polar. The CH_3Cl molecule is polar, because the polarity of the C–Cl bond is not cancelled out. However, the CCl_4 molecule is not polar because the polarities of the four C–Cl bonds cancel since the molecule is symmetrical.

- Tetrahedral molecules of formula AB_4, in which all four B atoms are the same, are not polar.
- If one of the B atoms is replaced by an atom of different electronegativity or by a lone pair, the molecule is polar. Ammonia, NH_3, has three polar bonds and one lone pair (Figure 3.44a). The polarities do not cancel, so the molecule is polar.
- Trigonal planar molecules, such as SO_3 and BCl_3 (Figure 3.44b), are not polar because the bond polarities cancel.
- Linear molecules, such as CO_2 (Figure 3.44c), are also non-polar since the dipoles cancel. However, H_2O is V-shaped (Figure 3.44d), so the polarities do not cancel.
- Symmetrical molecules are non-polar even if the bonds are polar.

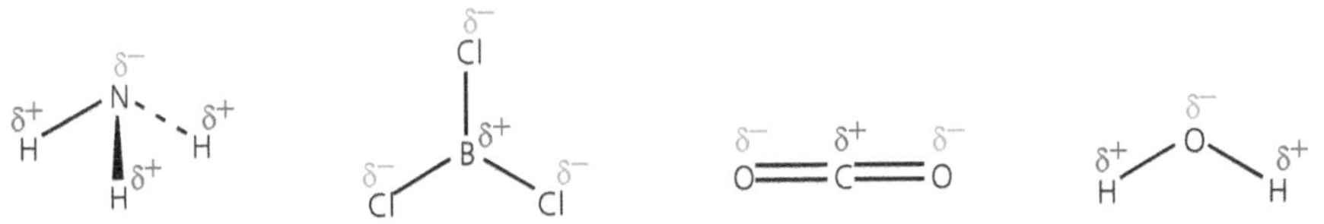

(a) is polar NH_3 (b) is non-polar BCl_3 (c) is non-polar CO_2 (d) is polar H_2O

Figure 3.44

> **Test yourself**
> 6 Decide whether the following bonds are polar or non-polar. If the bond is polar, state which is the δ^+ atom, and explain whether or not the molecule is polar:
> a) C=O as in CO_2
> b) C–I as in CH_3I

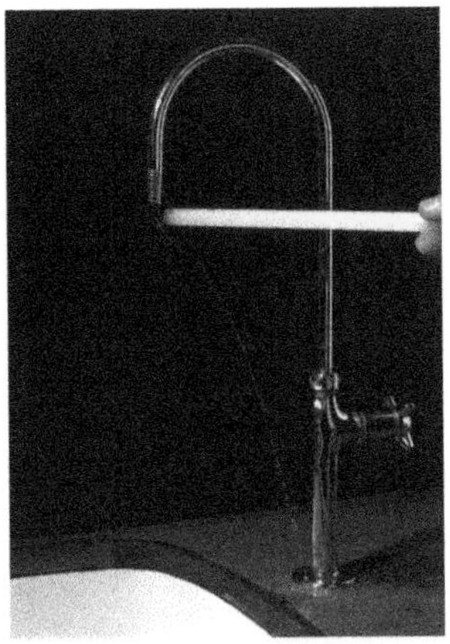
Stream of polar liquid deflected by a charged rod

A simple test to find whether or not a liquid consists of polar molecules is to run a stream of the liquid from a burette close to a charged rod or to a balloon that has been rubbed on wool and become charged with static electricity. A polar substance will be attracted towards the high charge of the rod or balloon, whereas a non-polar substance will not be deflected.

The polarity of a molecule is measured by its **dipole moment** (see Table 3.5). For a diatomic molecule such as hydrogen chloride, HCl, this is defined as the charge difference (how δ^+ and δ^- the atoms are) multiplied by the distance between the hydrogen and chlorine atoms. For a polyatomic molecule, it is more complex because the polarities of each bond have to be taken into account, as well as any lone pairs.

The polarity of a bond is sometimes shown as an arrow with a plus at one end. The arrow points to the δ^- atom in the bond — see Figure 3.45 for example.

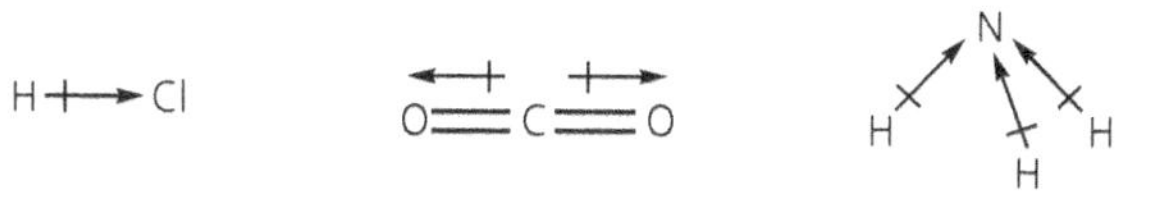

Figure 3.45

The polarity of the *molecule* is a combination of all the bond polarities and those due to any lone pairs.

Table 3.5 Dipole moments of some covalent molecules

Molecule	Dipole moment	Molecule	Dipole moment
HF	1.91	O_3	0.53
HCl	1.08	CH_4	0
HBr	0.80	BF_3	0
HI	0.42	CO_2	0
NH_3	1.47	*trans*-CHCl=CHCl	0
H_2O	1.85	*cis*-CHCl=CHCl	1.90

Summary tasks

Make sure that you can:

- describe metallic, ionic, covalent and dative covalent bonding
- explain the difference in the physical properties of the group 1 and 2 metals
- describe the reactions of metals with acids, water and other cations
- explain how the strength of ionic and covalent bonds varies according to the elements involved
- draw dot-and-cross diagrams of ionic and of covalent substances and explain the formation of σ- and π-bonds and the expansion of the octet

Check that you can:

- work out the number of bond pairs and lone pairs in a molecule or ion
- draw the shapes of molecules with two σ-bond pairs and no lone pairs, two σ-bond pairs and one lone pair, two σ-bond pairs and two lone pairs, three σ-bond pairs and no lone pairs, three σ-bond pairs and one lone pair, four σ-bond pairs and no lone pairs, five σ-bond pairs, and six σ-bond pairs
- estimate and explain the values of bond angles in molecules and polyatomic ions
- define electronegativity
- explain whether a molecule is polar or not

Questions

1 Explain why magnesium has a higher melting temperature than sodium.

2 Carbon monoxide can be thought of as having two covalent bonds and one dative covalent bond between the carbon and oxygen atoms. Draw the dot-and-cross diagram for carbon monoxide.

3 Explain why phosphorus can form five covalent bonds whereas nitrogen can form only three covalent bonds.

4 Explain the difference between a σ-bond and a π-bond.

5 Draw dot-and-cross diagrams for:
   a) carbon tetrachloride, CCl_4
   b) carbon dioxide, CO_2
   c) the sulfate ion, SO_4^{2-}
   d) xenon tetrafluoride, XeF_4

6 Draw and explain the shapes of the following:
   a) PH_3
   b) SCl_2
   c) PO_4^{3-}
   d) AsF_5
   e) HCN (H−CN)

7 Give the bond angles of species a−e in Question 6.

8 Decide whether the following bonds are polar or non-polar. If the bond is polar, state which is the δ^+ atom, and explain whether or not the molecule is polar.
   a) I−Cl as in ICl_3
   b) F−O as in F_2O

Exam practice questions

1 a) Explain why solid metals conduct electricity but solid ionic solids do not. (3)

b) Which metal forms the strongest metallic bond?
- **A** aluminium
- **B** magnesium
- **C** potassium
- **D** sodium (1)

c) Which is a property of *all* metals?
- **A** They form cations.
- **B** They have high first ionisation energies.
- **C** They react with acids to produce hydrogen.
- **D** They react with oxygen to give acidic oxides. (1)

d) The ionic radius of Na^+ is:
- **A** the sum of the ionic radii in sodium chloride
- **B** smaller than the metallic radius of sodium
- **C** larger than the metallic radius of sodium
- **D** smaller than the ionic radius of the Mg^{2+} ion (1)

(Total 6 marks)

2 a) Define the term **σ-bond**. (2)

b) A double bond is:
- **A** two σ-bonds
- **B** one σ-bond and one π-bond
- **C** the sideways overlap of two *p*-orbitals
- **D** when the four shared electrons are on the line between the two nuclei (1)

c) Which is the strongest covalent bond?
- **A** N–H
- **B** P–H
- **C** O–H
- **D** S–H (1)

d) Draw a dot-and-cross diagram of phosphorus(III) chloride, showing the outer electrons only. (2)

e) Which does **not** contain a dative covalent bond?
- **A** PCl_4^+
- **B** NH_4^+
- **C** PCl_6^-
- **D** Al_2Cl_6 (1)

(Total 7 marks)

3 a) Explain what is meant by valence shell electron pair repulsion theory. (2)

b) The shape of the hydrogen sulfide molecule, H_2S, is:
- **A** tetrahedral
- **B** linear
- **C** V-shaped
- **D** non-planar (1)

c) The shape of the sulfur trioxide molecule, SO_3, is:
- **A** tetrahedral
- **B** pyramidal
- **C** planar
- **D** V-shaped (1)

d) The number of lone pairs around the xenon atom in XeF_4 is:
- **A** 4
- **B** 2
- **C** 1
- **D** 0 (1)

(Total 5 marks)

4 a) Explain why a metal such as calcium conducts electricity whereas a non-metal such as sulfur does not. (3)

b) Draw a dot-and-cross diagram, showing outer electrons only, for calcium oxide. (3)

c) Write ionic equations for the reaction of calcium with:
- **i)** water
- **ii)** dilute hydrochloric acid (2)

d) Suggest why bubbles soon cease when excess dilute sulfuric acid is added to a piece of calcium. (2)

(Total 10 marks)

5 Phosphorus reacts with chlorine to form either PCl_3 or, with excess chlorine, PCl_5, but only forms PI_3 with iodine.

a) Draw a dot-and-cross diagram of PI_3, showing outer electrons only. (2)

b) Explain why PCl_5 can be formed whereas PI_5 cannot be formed. (4)

(Total 6 marks)

4

Bonding and structure II (Topic 2)

Forces between ions, atoms and molecules

The seven types of interaction that we need to consider are summarised in Table 4.1.

Table 4.1 Forces between ions, atoms and molecules

Type of interaction	Typical strength/ kJ mol^{-1}	Example
Ion–ion	250	Between two ions
Atom–atom	400	Between two atoms in a covalent bond
Ion–electron	Very varied	Metals
Ion–water molecule	100	Hydrated ions
Permanent dipole–dipole	1 to 10	Between polar molecules
Instantaneous induced dipole–induced dipole (London)	5 to 25	Between all types of molecules
Hydrogen bonding	20	Between δ^+ H and δ^- N, O or F in other molecules

The interactions in green are chemical bonds; those in red are intermolecular forces.

Chemical bonds

Ion–ion bonds
- Ion–ion bonds are simple electrostatic forces of attraction between a positive and a negative ion.
- They are non-directional.
- The strength is proportional to the product of the charges and inversely proportional to the sum of the ionic radii.

Atom–atom bonds
- Atom–atom bonds are covalent bonds.
- A covalent bond is the attraction of the two nuclei for the shared electrons in the bond.
- Short bonds are stronger than long bonds.

Ion–electron bonds
- Ion–electron bonds are the forces that act in a metal.
- They are also non-directional.

- Small metal ions bond more strongly than large ones.
- Metals that have more delocalised electrons have stronger bonds than those that release fewer electrons.

Ion–water molecule bonds

- Water is a polar molecule that consists of δ^+ hydrogen atoms and δ^- oxygen atoms.
- The δ^- oxygen atoms are attracted to positive metal ions and the δ^+ hydrogen atoms to negative anions.
- One of the lone pairs of electrons in the oxygen forms a dative covalent bond with an empty orbital in a metal cation, producing a hydrated ion.

Forces between covalently bonded molecules

Intermolecular forces exist between two covalently bonded molecules. These are of three types:

- **Permanent dipole forces** exist between polar molecules.
- **Instantaneous induced dipole (London) forces** exist between all molecules.
- **Hydrogen bonds** exist between a δ^+ hydrogen atom in one molecule and the lone pair of electrons on a δ^- oxygen, nitrogen or fluorine atom in another molecule.

Permanent dipole–dipole forces

- Molecules with a permanent dipole can attract neighbouring molecules.
- The dipoles line up so that the δ^+ end of one molecule is next to the δ^- end of another molecule (Figure 4.1).
- This is an example of an intermolecular force.

> An intermolecular force exists *between* separate covalent molecules.

represents the intermolecular force of attraction

Figure 4.1

Instantaneous induced dipole–induced dipole forces

Instantaneous induced dipole–induced dipole forces are normally called **London forces**.

The electrons in a covalent molecule oscillate within their atomic orbitals or covalent bonds. This random motion causes a temporary dipole in the molecule. The electrons in neighbouring molecules oscillate in phase, each inducing a dipole in the molecule next to it (Figure 4.2) so that, at any instant, the δ^+ end of one molecule is next to the δ^- end of a neighbouring molecule. A fraction of a second later the polarity will change, but again the new δ^+ end will induce a δ^- charge on the end of the molecule next to it.

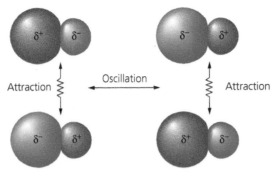

Figure 4.2

Instantaneous induced dipole–induced dipole forces are quite strong — usually stronger than permanent dipole–dipole attractions. The strength depends mainly upon the number of electrons in the molecule. For example, at room temperature, iodine is a solid and chlorine is a gas because the London forces between iodine molecules (106 electrons) are much stronger than the London forces between chlorine molecules (34 electrons).

It has been estimated that the energy required to overcome the permanent dipole forces between hydrogen chloride molecules at room temperature is about $1\,kJ\,mol^{-1}$ and that required to overcome the London forces between the non-polar methane molecules is nearly $5\,kJ\,mol^{-1}$. The highly polar chloromethane molecule has dipole–dipole forces of about $10\,kJ\,mol^{-1}$, but this is still just less than its London forces. The strength of London forces between multi-atom molecules also depends upon their shape and hence the number of points of contact between neighbouring molecules. For example, the almost spherical molecule $C(CH_3)_4$ has fewer points of contact with other molecules than the zigzag molecule $CH_3CH_2CH_2CH_2CH_3$. The first, 2,2-dimethylpropane, boils at 10°C and the other, pentane, at 36°C. Both are non-polar molecules with the same number of electrons.

London forces exist between *all* covalent molecules. Even atoms of noble gases have these forces between them. However, as non-bonding electrons are less able than bonding electrons to form instantaneous dipoles, the boiling temperatures of noble gases are very low.

Hydrogen bonds

Although the word 'bond' implies a chemical bond, a hydrogen bond is a type of intermolecular force. A hydrogen bond forms between a δ^+ hydrogen atom in one molecule and the **lone pair of electrons** on a δ^- fluorine, oxygen or nitrogen atom in another molecule. This happens when the hydrogen atom is covalently bonded to a fluorine, oxygen or nitrogen atom. The bond angle around the hydrogen atom in a hydrogen bond is always 180°.

Hydrogen bonding occurs between a δ^+ hydrogen atom, which is extremely small, and the next smallest atoms (fluorine, oxygen or nitrogen), which must be δ^-.

A hydrogen bond is a relatively strong intermolecular force. Hydrogen is the smallest atom and has no shielding electrons. Therefore, a δ^+ hydrogen atom is like a partially exposed nucleus and can form a strong interaction with the lone pair on a small δ^- atom, such as fluorine, oxygen or nitrogen. In hydrogen chloride the chlorine atom is too large to get close enough to a hydrogen atom to form a hydrogen bond. Therefore, although chlorine in hydrogen chloride is as δ^- as nitrogen is in ammonia, hydrogen chloride molecules do not form hydrogen bonds with each other.

Hydrogen bonding through fluorine

The only fluorine compound with intermolecular hydrogen bonds is hydrogen fluoride. The δ^+ hydrogen atoms in one molecule form hydrogen bonds with δ^- fluorine atoms in an adjacent molecule. The F—H—F bond angle is 180°; the H—F—H bond angle is 109.5°. The result is a zigzag chain of HF molecules (Figure 4.3).

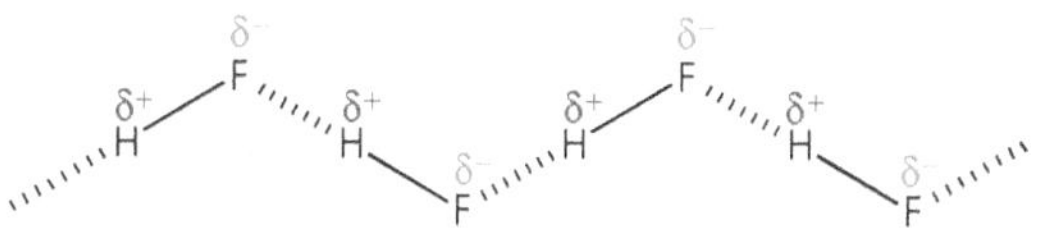

Figure 4.3

Hydrogen bonding through oxygen

- All compounds containing an —OH group form hydrogen bonds.
- The most important example is water. The hydrogen atoms are δ^+ and form hydrogen bonds with a lone pair on the δ^- oxygen atoms in other water molecules (Figure 4.4).

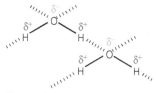

Figure 4.4

Hydrogen bonding between water molecules is stronger than that between hydrogen fluoride molecules. Although a given hydrogen bond is stronger between a δ^+ hydrogen atom and a δ^- fluorine atom than between a δ^+ hydrogen and a δ^- oxygen atom, there are more hydrogen bonds per molecule in water than in hydrogen fluoride. Water boils at 100°C, whereas hydrogen fluoride boils at 20°C. This shows that the sum of the intermolecular forces in water is higher than the sum of those in hydrogen fluoride.

Tip

The bond angle around a hydrogen atom in a hydrogen bond is 180°.

Water has the unusual property of the solid being less dense than the liquid. This is because ice crystals contain interlocking rings of six water molecules held together by hydrogen bonds (Figure 4.5). The distance between molecules opposite each other in the ring is quite large relative to the close approach of neighbouring molecules.

When ice melts, the ring structure is destroyed and the *average* distance apart of the molecules decreases, causing the density to increase.

Alcohol molecules contain —OH groups. Therefore, they can form hydrogen bonds with other alcohol molecules or, when dissolved in water, with water molecules (Figure 4.6). Carboxylic acid molecules also contain —OH groups and behave similarly (Figure 4.7).

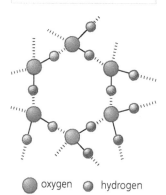

● oxygen ● hydrogen

Figure 4.5

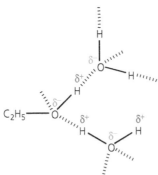

Figure 4.6

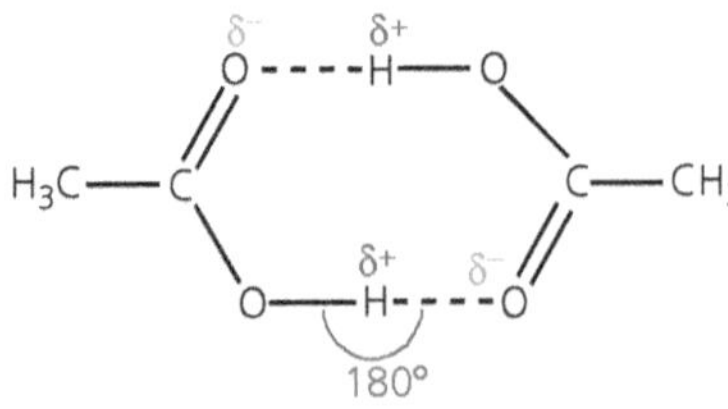

Figure 4.7

Hydrogen bonding through nitrogen

When nitrogen forms three covalent bonds, it has a lone pair of electrons. If the nitrogen is bonded to hydrogen, it becomes δ^- and the hydrogen becomes δ^+. This allows hydrogen bonding to occur between molecules. This is true for all nitrogen compounds with an −NH group. An example is ammonia, NH_3, in which the δ^+ hydrogen atom in one molecule hydrogen-bonds to the lone pair on the δ^- nitrogen atom in another molecule (Figure 4.8).

Organic compounds containing the primary amine group, $-NH_2$, such as ethylamine, $C_2H_5NH_2$, and those with the NH group, such as diethylamine, $(C_2H_5)_2NH$, also form intermolecular hydrogen bonds.

Proteins and DNA

Proteins are long chains of amino acids arranged either in a helix or in a pleated sheet. Both structures are held in shape by hydrogen bonds between the δ^+ hydrogen atom in an −NH group and the δ^- oxygen in a C=O group, which is four amino acid residues away on the chain in a helix, or on an adjacent chain in a pleated sheet.

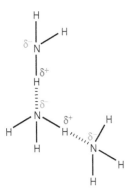

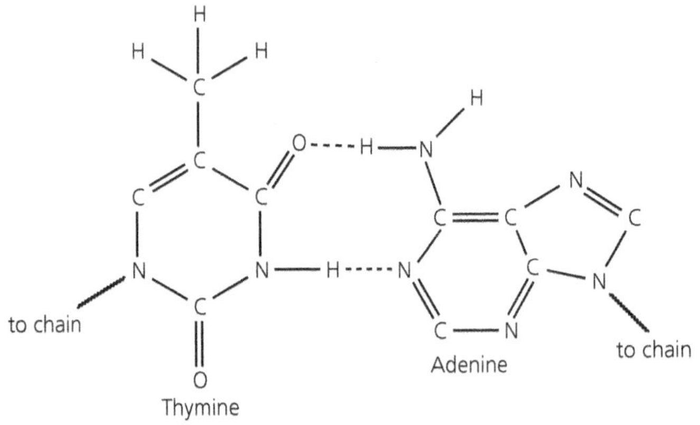

Figure 4.8

Figure 4.9 Hydrogen bonding between base pairs in DNA

A DNA molecule is a double helix. Each strand of the helix is made up of a pattern of base–sugar–phosphate units. Each strand is held to the other strand by hydrogen bonds. The base adenine in one strand is linked to thymine in the other strand by two hydrogen bonds (Figure 4.9) and the base cytosine to guanine by three hydrogen bonds.

Forces and physical properties

The physical properties of an element or compound depend upon the nature of the forces between the particles.

Melting a solid

- A solid consists of a regular arrangement of particles (ions, atoms or molecules), which vibrate about a fixed position and cannot move through the solid.
- When a solid is heated, the vibration increases and the temperature rises. When the melting temperature is reached, the structure of the solid begins to break down and it starts to melt.
- As the heating continues, more solid melts. However, the temperature stays constant until all the solid has melted.
- When molten, the particles are free to move around through the liquid; they are not fixed in position.
- If the forces between the particles are strong, much energy is required to break down the structure of the solid. Therefore, it will have a high melting temperature.

Boiling a liquid

- In a liquid, the particles (ions, atoms or molecules) are close together, but their positions are random and they tumble over each other. Particles move at different speeds and continually collide with each other.
- When a liquid is heated, the particles gain kinetic energy and their average speed increases.
- Some particles move fast enough to escape from the surface as a gas. This is called **evaporation**.
- When the boiling temperature is reached, some particles have the necessary energy to escape from the middle of the liquid. Bubbles of gas are produced and the liquid boils.
- If the forces between the particles are strong, much energy is required to separate the particles. Therefore, the liquid will have a high boiling temperature.

Structure

The types of solid structure are:

- metallic (see page 37)
- giant ionic lattice
- giant covalent lattice
- simple molecular, including hydrogen-bonded molecular
- polymeric

Ionic solids

Ionic solids consist of a regular arrangement of charged ions. This arrangement is called a **lattice**.

Melting

- The melting temperature is dependent on the strength of the ion–ion forces. As these forces are strong a lot of energy is required to separate the ions and melt the solid.
- Ions with a 2+ or 2− charge exhibit stronger forces than those that are singly charged.
- Ions with a small radius give rise to stronger forces of attraction than those with a large radius.
- The melting temperature also depends upon the lattice structure. Lattices in which the ion ratio is 2:1 melt at a lower temperature than that expected from their charge and radius values.

The melting temperatures of some ionic substances are shown in Table 4.2.

Table 4.2 Melting temperatures of some ionic substances

	Ions	Ionic radius/nm	Melting temperature/°C
Sodium chloride	Na^+	0.095	801
	Cl^-	0.181	
Potassium chloride	K^+	0.133	776
	Cl^-	0.181	
Calcium chloride	Ca^{2+}	0.010	782
	Cl^-	0.181	
Calcium oxide	Ca^{2+}	0.099	2614
	O^{2-}	0.140	
Magnesium oxide	Mg^{2+}	0.065	2800
	O^{2-}	0.140	

> Ionic compounds conduct electricity by the movement of charged ions; metals conduct by the movement of electrons.

Electrical conductivity

Ionic solids do not conduct electricity because the ions are fixed in the lattice and cannot move through the solid.

When molten or dissolved, the lattice is broken down and the ions are able to move freely, allowing electricity to be conducted.

> **Tip**
>
> Do not answer this question in terms of the movement of electrons. That applies only to metals and graphite.

> **Worked example**
>
> Why does molten calcium oxide conduct electricity whereas solid calcium oxide does not?
>
> **Answer**
>
> In the solid state the ions are fixed in position, so there are no charge carriers that can move. When molten, the solid lattice breaks down. The ions become free to move and are able to carry the current.

Giant covalent substances

Giant covalent substances are also called giant atomic or network covalent. They are solids that consist of a giant lattice of atoms linked to each other by covalent bonds.

Diamond and graphite

Carbon exists in two main forms — diamond and graphite.

In diamond, each carbon atom has four σ-bonds to four other carbon atoms, in a giant three-dimensional tetrahedral arrangement, with all bond angles 109.5° (Figure 4.10). Diamond has an extremely high melting temperature because each carbon atom is covalently bonded to four others. Millions of strong covalent bonds have to be broken in order to melt it.

Damien Hirst's diamond-encrusted skull

Graphite has a layered structure (Figure 4.11). Each carbon atom is bonded to three others by σ-bonds, forming interlocking hexagonal rings. The fourth electron is in a *p*-orbital, which forms a delocalised cloud above and below the plane of the rings. The planar rings are weakly bonded to the ones above and below by London forces, so they can slide over each other easily. This is why a pencil leaves a mark of graphite on paper. The delocalised electrons are the reason why graphite conducts electricity when solid, as they can move across the surface of the planes.

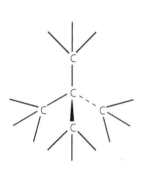

Figure 4.10

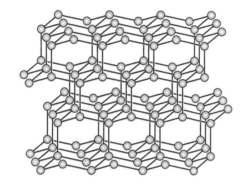

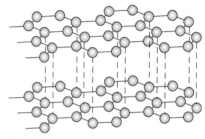

Figure 4.11

Other types of solid carbon

Graphene, discovered in 2004, is pure carbon in the form of a very thin, nearly transparent sheet, just one atom thick. It can be described as a one-atom-thick layer of graphite. It is remarkably strong for its very low weight (100 times stronger than steel) and it is a good conductor of heat and electricity.

Sir Harry Kroto of the University of Sussex and Richard Smalley of Rice University, Texas, discovered the C_{60} molecule by firing a laser at a disc of carbon and condensing the vapour formed. The molecule consists of 20 interconnecting hexagons and twelve pentagons. Each carbon atom has three σ-bonds and the fourth electron is delocalised in the structure in a similar way to graphite. The molecule has the same basic geometry as the geodesic dome designed by Richard Buckminster Fuller and so the C_{60} molecule is colloquially called a buckyball (Figure 4.12).

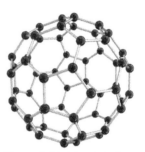

Figure 4.12 A buckyball

Further studies have shown the existence of a C_{70} molecule. This has 25 hexagons and the molecule is shaped like a rugby ball. Evaporation of a solution of C_{60} or C_{70} in benzene produces red crystals.

Molecules such as C_{60} and C_{70} are called **fullerenes**. Their chemistry is similar to that of alkenes — for example, they undergo addition reactions with hydrogen and halogens; C_{60} can be polymerised. An atom or an ion can even be trapped inside the carbon ball. This has an important medical application. Radioactive radon-224 atoms are trapped inside C_{60} molecules, which are coated with tumour-targeting antibodies. The molecules are injected into a patient suffering from cancer. The treated C_{60} is adsorbed by the cancer cells. The radon atoms emit α-rays, which destroy the cancer cells in the tumour but do not affect other organs in the body because the range of α-rays is short.

A further development was the discovery of carbon **nanotubes**. A nanotube consists of a cylinder of interlocking hexagons of carbon atoms (Figure 4.13). One end of the cylinder is sealed with a fullerene molecule. The internal radius of

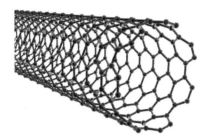

Figure 4.13 A nanotube

Sublimation is when a solid is heated and turns straight into a gas without melting.

Tip

The only time *covalent* bonds are broken on melting is when a giant atomic solid is heated.

carbon nanotubes is a few nanometres. Nanotubes can be used to deliver drugs to specific parts of the body.

Clusters of carbon nanotubes are one hundred times as strong as steel wire. They contain delocalised electrons and can conduct electricity.

Silicon

- Silicon has a structure similar to that of diamond.
- Silicon carbide, SiC, has a diamond-like structure in which each silicon atom is surrounded tetrahedrally by four carbon atoms, which, in turn, are surrounded by four silicon atoms. The whole is a giant covalently bonded network of alternating silicon and carbon atoms.
- Quartz, SiO_2, is also a giant covalent lattice. Each silicon atom is bonded to four oxygen atoms and each oxygen atom to two silicon atoms (see page 47).

Melting

Since covalent bonds have to be broken when the solid is melted or sublimed, all giant atomic substances have very high melting or sublimation temperatures. Diamond and graphite sublime at over 3500°C and quartz melts at 1610°C.

Hardness

Giant atomic substances are very hard, because of the strong covalent bonds in the lattice. This makes them useful as abrasives. For example, sandpaper is coated with grains of quartz, while the abrasive carborundum is made of silicon carbide.

Simple molecular substances

Most covalent substances belong to this category. Many non-metallic elements form simple molecules. They include:

- nitrogen, N_2, and phosphorus, P_4, in group 5
- oxygen, O_2, and sulfur, S_8, in group 6
- the halogens, in group 7, which are all diatomic

The forces between elemental molecules are London forces only.

Compounds of non-metallic elements also form simple molecular structures. Examples include:

- organic compounds, such as alkanes, alkenes and halogenoalkanes
- hydrogen sulfide, H_2S
- phosphorus(iii) chloride, PCl_3, and phosphorus(v) chloride, PCl_5
- many halogen compounds, such as SF_6

The forces between molecules of a compound are London forces and, if the molecule is polar, permanent dipole–dipole forces.

Melting and boiling

The intermolecular forces are weak, so simple molecular substances have low melting and boiling temperatures.

Tip

Covalent bonds are *not* broken when a molecular substance is melted or boiled. The strength of the covalent bonds within the molecules has nothing to do with the boiling temperature of the substance. This is a common misunderstanding in answers at AS and A-level.

The noble gases consist of monatomic molecules and their boiling temperatures increase down the group. Helium has the lowest value and radon the highest. This is because there are London forces between the atoms, and the strength of these forces increases as the number of electrons in the atom increases.

The boiling temperature of members of the homologous series of alkanes increases as the number of carbon atoms increases. The larger molecules have more electrons and so their London forces are stronger. However, a branched-chain alkane such as methylpropane, $(CH_3)_3CH$, has a lower boiling temperature than its isomer butane, $CH_3CH_2CH_2CH_3$. This is because branching hinders the packing of the molecules.

The boiling temperatures of the hydrogen halides, from hydrogen chloride, HCl, to hydrogen iodide, HI, increase because the strength of the London forces increases as the number of electrons increases. This outweighs the decrease in the strength of the permanent dipole–dipole forces. However, hydrogen fluoride is anomalous because it forms intermolecular hydrogen bonds. The variation is shown in Figure 4.14.

Hydrogen-bonded molecular substances

This is a subset of simple molecular. Hydrogen fluoride, water, alcohols, carboxylic acids, ammonia and organic amines are examples of hydrogen-bonded molecular substances.

Boiling

For a hydrogen-bonded substance to boil, the molecules have to be separated. This involves breaking the hydrogen bonds *and* the London forces between the molecules. Hydrogen bonds are quite strong. Therefore, the boiling temperatures of hydrogen-bonded substances are much higher than those of similar compounds that are not hydrogen-bonded.

Hydrogen fluoride has intermolecular hydrogen bonds. These are much stronger than the London and dipole–dipole forces that exist between molecules of the other group 7 hydrogen halides. This means that the boiling temperature of hydrogen fluoride is higher than the boiling temperatures of the other hydrogen halides.

The boiling temperature of water is also anomalous, being higher than that of other group 6 hydrides. This is also caused by hydrogen bonding in water but not in the other group 6 hydrides. Similarly, the boiling temperature of ammonia, NH_3, is higher than that of phosphine, PH_3.

However, the group 4 hydrides do not show this anomalous behaviour of the first member. The carbon atom in methane is only slightly δ^- and the hydrogen atoms are only slightly δ^+, so hydrogen bonding is not possible. This is shown by the graphs in Figure 4.14. The anomalous high values for NH_3, H_2O and HF are due to hydrogen bonding. The steady increase in the boiling temperatures of the other compounds is caused by an increase in the strength of the London forces because of the increase in the number of electrons in the molecule.

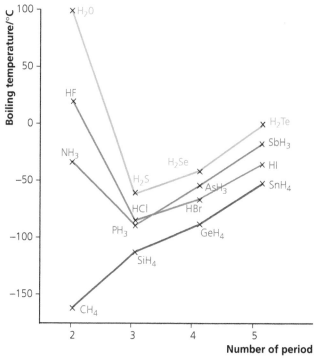

Figure 4.14 Variation in boiling temperature down groups and across periods

Ethanol, CH_3CH_2OH, has a much higher boiling temperature than its isomer methoxymethane, CH_3OCH_3. Ethanol has an $-OH$ group, so the δ^+ hydrogen atom in one molecule can hydrogen bond with the δ^- oxygen atom in another molecule. Methoxymethane does not have a δ^+ hydrogen atom and so cannot form any hydrogen bonds.

Polymeric substances

Polymers such as poly(ethene) and PVC are examples of polymeric solids. The molecules have varying chain lengths and are arranged in a semi-regular fashion — between a true solid, with a regular pattern of molecules, and a liquid, with a random arrangement.

Melting

- The chain length of a polymer is variable and the solid is not fully crystalline, so polymers soften rather than melt at a fixed temperature.
- Thermosetting polymers, which are highly cross-linked, decompose rather than melt. Examples include melamine and polyurethane, which are used as surfaces that must not deform when a hot object is placed on them.

Answering questions on melting and boiling temperatures

To answer a question comparing the melting or boiling temperatures of different substances, adopt the following procedure:

- Work out the type of structure.
- List all the forces between the particles in the substances being compared.
- If they are different, explain why one has one type of force and the others do not.
- State and explain the relative strengths of the forces.
- Relate the strength of the forces to the energy required to separate the particles.

Test yourself

2 Identify the type of solid structure in:

  a) chlorine   d) glucose, $CHO(CHOH)_4CH_2OH$

  b) vanadium   e) silicon tetrachloride, $SiCl_4$

  c) lithium fluoride

Worked example 1

Explain why sulfur has a higher melting temperature than phosphorus, and why silicon has a much higher melting temperature than both sulfur and phosphorus.

Both sulfur and phosphorus have simple molecular structures, with instantaneous induced dipole–induced dipole (London) forces between the molecules.

Sulfur is S_8 and so has more electrons in a molecule than does phosphorus, which is P_4. This means that the London forces between sulfur molecules are stronger than those between phosphorus molecules. Therefore, more energy is needed to separate them. This results in sulfur having a higher melting temperature than phosphorus.

Silicon has a giant atomic structure with strong covalent bonds between the atoms. These have to be broken for silicon to melt and so a very much higher temperature is required.

Worked example 2

Explain why, in comparison with the other group 6 hydrides, water has an anomalous boiling temperature.

Answer

All the group 6 hydrides are covalent molecules. However, only oxygen atoms are both small and δ^-. In water, hydrogen bonds form between the lone pair of electrons on the δ^- oxygen and δ^+ hydrogen atoms. Therefore, the intermolecular forces between water molecules are hydrogen bonds and London forces.

The atoms of other group 6 elements are too large and not sufficiently electronegative for hydrogen bonding to be possible. The important intermolecular forces between molecules of these hydrides are London forces, which increase as the number of electrons in the molecule increase.

Hydrogen bonds are stronger than London forces, so more energy has to be supplied to separate water molecules than is needed to separate molecules of the other group 6 hydrides. Therefore, water has a much higher boiling temperature than the other hydrides, the boiling temperatures of which steadily increase as the strengths of the London forces increase.

Test yourself

3 Explain why propanone, CH_3COCH_3, has a higher boiling temperature than butane, C_4H_{10}.

Solubility

- For a substance to dissolve, the solute particles must be separated from each other and the individual solute particles become surrounded by solvent particles.
- The forces between solute and solvent must be strong enough to overcome the solvent–solvent and solute–solute forces.

Solubility of ionic solids

Many ionic solids dissolve in water. The energy required to separate the ions in the solid is compensated for by the energy released by the hydration of the ions.

The positive cations are surrounded by the δ^- oxygen atoms of water molecules and the negative anions are surrounded by the δ^+ hydrogen atoms. This process is called **hydration** and the energy released is called the **hydration energy**.

Ionic solids dissolve in other ionic compounds when they are molten. The extraction of aluminium metal from aluminium oxide uses a solution of aluminium oxide in molten cryolite, which is an ionic compound of formula Na_3AlF_6.

Solubility of compounds that can form hydrogen bonds with the solvent

Compounds that can form hydrogen bonds are soluble in water. The δ^+ hydrogen atoms in the compound form hydrogen bonds with a lone pair of the δ^- oxygen atoms in the water molecules. The δ^- oxygen or nitrogen atoms in the compound form hydrogen bonds with the δ^+ hydrogen atoms in the water molecules.

Both ethanol, CH_3CH_2OH, and ethanoic acid, CH_3COOH, mix in all proportions (are **miscible**) with water.

The lone pair of electrons on the δ^- oxygen atom in ethanol forms a hydrogen bond with the δ^+ hydrogen atom in water. The δ^+ hydrogen atom in ethanol forms a hydrogen bond with the lone pair on the δ^- oxygen atom in water.

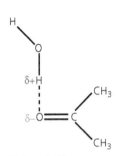

Figure 4.15

Molecules of propanone, CH_3COCH_3, cannot hydrogen-bond with each other because they do not have a δ^+ hydrogen atom. However, propanone is very water-soluble because its δ^- oxygen atom can form hydrogen bonds with the δ^+ hydrogen atoms in the water (Figure 4.15).

Note that the O—H—O angle around the hydrogen atom that is hydrogen-bonded is 180°. This is because it is surrounded by one pair of σ-bonded electrons and one lone pair from the δ^- oxygen atom forming the hydrogen bond.

Ethanoic acid, CH_3COOH, is miscible with water in all proportions. However, pentanoic acid, $CH_3CH_2CH_2CH_2COOH$, is almost insoluble because of its hydrocarbon chain of four carbon atoms. There are only two sites (C=O and OH) for hydrogen bonding and there are four other non-polar groups.

Solubility of non-hydrogen-bonding substances

If a substance can neither form hydrogen bonds with water nor react with it, it is likely to be insoluble, whether or not the molecule is polar. The highly polar fluoromethane, CH_3F, is insoluble, as are the non-polar alkanes and alkenes.

Solubility in non-aqueous solvents

This depends on the similarities between the intermolecular forces of the solvent and the solute. Thus, non-polar solvents tend to dissolve non-polar solutes and polar solvents dissolve polar solutes.

Alkanes are soluble in each other. Crude oil is a complex mixture of alkanes dissolved in each other. Non-polar hexane dissolves non-polar bromine.

Ethoxyethane, $C_2H_5OC_2H_5$, is polar and is a good solvent for many organic substances.

The solubility of drugs in water and in the lipids that make up the membranes of animal cells is important. Balms rubbed on the skin must be lipid-soluble; those injected into the bloodstream or ingested orally must be water-soluble. The presence of −OH, >NH and >C=O groups increases water solubility. The presence of hydrocarbon chains and rings increases lipid solubility.

Summary tasks

Make sure that you can:

- identify and explain the forces between covalent molecules
- relate the values of the melting or boiling temperatures to the strengths of forces between ions, between atoms and between molecules as well as to the strength of forces in metals
- draw and explain graphs of boiling temperatures versus period number of the hydrides in groups 4, 5, 6 and 7
- relate solubility to the forces between the solute and the solvent

Questions

1 a) Explain why graphite conducts electricity whereas diamond does not.
  b) Would you expect the fullerene C_{60} to conduct electricity? Justify your answer.

2 Other than the delivery of radon to a tumour, describe a use of either a fullerene or carbon nanotubes.

3 Explain the following:
  a) Silicon and phosphorus are both covalent substances, but silicon has a much higher melting temperature than phosphorus.
  b) Solid sodium and solid sodium chloride both have lattice structures involving ions. Solid sodium conducts electricity, but solid sodium chloride does not.

4 Explain why hydrogen bromide has a lower boiling temperature than hydrogen iodide.

5 Explain why ammonia is soluble in water whereas chloromethane is not. Both are gases. Chloromethane is more polar (dipole moment 1.9 D) than ammonia (dipole moment 1.5 D).

6 Explain why magnesium chloride is soluble in water, even though its lattice energy is $-526\,\text{kJ mol}^{-1}$.

7 Discuss the solubility of aspirin and ibuprofen in water and in lipids.

Aspirin

Ibuprofen

Aspirin	Ibuprofen
$C_6H_4(OCOCH_3)CO_2H$	$C_{13}H_{18}O_2$

8 a) Draw a dot-and-cross diagram of the SF_5^- ion.
  b) Suggest the shape of this ion. Justify your answer.

Exam practice questions

1 a) Explain the variation of boiling temperatures among the hydrides in group 5 (NH_3 to BiH_3). (3)

b) The difference in electronegativity of nitrogen and hydrogen is the same as that between hydrogen and chlorine. Explain why ammonia forms intermolecular hydrogen bonds whereas hydrogen chloride does not. (2)

c) Water has a higher boiling temperature than hydrogen fluoride because:
  A the covalent bonds are stronger in water than in hydrogen fluoride
  B water forms more hydrogen bonds than hydrogen fluoride does
  C an H…O hydrogen bond in water is stronger than an H…F hydrogen bond in hydrogen fluoride
  D the oxygen atom is less δ^- than the fluorine atom (1)

d) The bond angle around the hydrogen-bonded hydrogen in liquid ammonia is:
  A 180°   **C** 109.5°
  B 120°   **D** 107°   (1)
  (Total 7 marks)

2 a) Explain why the highly polar chloromethane, CH_3Cl, has a lower boiling temperature than the non-polar butane, C_4H_{10}. (3)

b) Silicon carbide has a similar structure to diamond. It has a high melting temperature because:
  A the silicon–carbon covalent bonds are strong
  B there are strong intermolecular forces between silicon carbide molecules
  C it is an ionic compound with strong forces between the silicon cations and the carbon anions
  D the silicon carbide molecules are three dimensional (1)

c) Hydrogen chloride has a lower boiling temperature than hydrogen iodide because:
  A the mass of a hydrogen chloride molecule is less than that of the hydrogen iodide molecule
  B there are fewer protons in a hydrogen chloride molecule than in a hydrogen iodide molecule
  C there are fewer electrons in a hydrogen chloride molecule than in a hydrogen iodide molecule
  D hydrogen chloride is less polar than hydrogen iodide (1)

d) Which has the strongest intermolecular forces?
  A $CH_3CH_2CH_2CH_2CH_3$
  B $CH_3CH_2CH_2CH_3$
  C $(CH_3)_4C$
  D $(CH_3)_2CHCH_2CH_3$ (1)
  (Total 6 marks)

3 a) Phosphorus and iodine react to form phosphorus triiodide, PI_3. Draw the shape of the PI_3 molecule and explain why it is this shape. (3)

b) Is the PI_3 molecule polar? Explain your answer. (Electronegativities: phosphorus 2.1; iodine 2.5) (2)

c) Phosphorus triiodide is a solid at room temperature whereas phosphorus trichloride is a liquid. Explain why the melting temperature of phosphorus trichloride is lower than that of phosphorus triiodide. (3)
  (Total 8 marks)

5 Oxidation and reduction: redox (Topic 3)

At first sight, chemistry appears to be a huge collection of reactions. To bring order out of this chaos, chemical reactions are categorised. One such category includes oxidation, together with its opposite, reduction.

Everyday examples of oxidation include the burning of fuels, the rusting of iron and the bleaching of dyes.

Oxidation in action

The extraction of a metal, such as iron, from its ore is an example of reduction.

Neither oxidation nor reduction can take place on its own. They always happen together. When a fuel, such as methane, is burnt in oxygen, methane is oxidised and oxygen is reduced. Such a reaction is called a **redox reaction**.

In a redox reaction, one substance is oxidised and another is reduced.

Oxidation was originally defined as the addition of oxygen to a species and reduction as the removal of oxygen from a species. The reaction between carbon monoxide and iron(III) oxide that takes place in a blast furnace in the extraction of iron is an example:

$$Fe_2O_3 + 3CO \rightarrow 2Fe + 3CO_2$$

The iron(III) oxide loses oxygen and is therefore reduced. The carbon monoxide gains oxygen and is therefore oxidised.

The definition was expanded to include the removal of hydrogen as an example of oxidation. When chlorine gas is bubbled into aqueous hydrogen sulfide, the hydrogen sulfide is oxidised to sulfur by the removal of hydrogen. The chlorine is reduced to HCl by the addition of hydrogen:

$$H_2S + Cl_2 \rightarrow S + 2HCl$$

When it became accepted that atoms consist of protons, neutrons and electrons, chemists understood what was happening in oxidation reactions and the electron transfer theory was put forward. This is the approach that is used by chemists today.

Electron transfer in redox reactions

The combustion of magnesium in oxygen is an oxidation reaction:

$$Mg + \tfrac{1}{2}O_2 \rightarrow MgO$$

This involves the addition of oxygen.

Magnesium has the electron configuration [Ne] $3s^2$. In this reaction, each magnesium atom loses its two outer electrons, becoming [Ne] $3s^0$. The electrons are gained by an oxygen atom. The result is the formation of an Mg^{2+} ion and an O^{2-} ion:

$$Mg(s) + \tfrac{1}{2}O_2(g) \rightarrow Mg^{2+}O^{2-}(s)$$

What happens to the magnesium in this reaction is identical to what happens to it in the reaction with chlorine:

$$Mg(s) + Cl_2(g) \rightarrow Mg^{2+}2Cl^-(s)$$

The magnesium is oxidised because it has lost electrons. Oxygen in the first equation, and chlorine in the second, are reduced because they have gained electrons.

The reduction of iron oxide in the blast furnace can be seen as the gain of three electrons by the Fe^{3+} ions in the oxide:

$$Fe^{3+} + 3e^- \rightarrow Fe$$

When one substance is reduced by gaining electrons, the electrons have been supplied by another species, which lost them and so became oxidised. When chlorine gas is passed through a solution of potassium bromide, the bromide ions lose electrons (are oxidised) and become bromine. The chlorine molecule gains the electrons (is reduced) and becomes chloride ions:

$$2Br^- + Cl_2 \rightarrow Br_2 + 2Cl^-$$

Bromide ions are oxidised to bromine and chlorine is reduced to chloride ions.

Oxidation numbers

Key term

The **oxidation number** of an element in a compound or ion is the charge that the element would have if the compound were fully ionic.

Redox reactions can also be described in terms of the oxidation numbers of the elements concerned. The oxidation number of the species in a simple ionic compound is the charge on the ion. For example, in magnesium chloride, the magnesium ions are 2+, so the oxidation number of magnesium is +2. The charge on each chloride ion is 1−, so the oxidation number of each chlorine in $MgCl_2$ is −1. This concept can be extended to covalent substances and to polyatomic ions such as sulfate, SO_4^{2-}.

The oxidation number is calculated on the basis that the bonding electrons are assigned to the more electronegative atom in a covalent bond. Consider hydrogen sulfide, H_2S. The bonding is covalent and the sulfur atom shares a pair of electrons with each hydrogen atom. However, sulfur is more electronegative than hydrogen, so the bond pair is assigned to the sulfur in both H−S bonds. In this way, the sulfur atom 'gains' one electron from each of the two H–S bonds, giving it an assigned charge of 2−. The compound is not ionic, but the sulfur is δ^- and is said to have an oxidation number of −2, or to be in the −2 oxidation state.

If there is a covalent bond between two atoms of the same element, neither 'gains' an electron from the bond. Thus in hydrogen peroxide, H–O–O–H, the O–H bonding electrons are assigned to the more electronegative oxygen atom, making each hydrogen +1 and each oxygen −1, but the O–O bonding electrons go back to their 'own' oxygen, which neither gains nor loses extra electrons, and so the oxidation number of each oxygen atom remains as −1.

Deduction of oxidation numbers

Oxidation numbers can be deduced using a series of rules:

- The oxidation number of an uncombined element is zero. For example, the bonding electrons in chlorine, Cl_2, 'go' one to each chlorine atom. Neither gains an electron, so both chlorine atoms have an oxidation number of 0.
- The oxidation number of the element in a monatomic ion is the charge on the ion. For example, the oxidation number of copper in the Cu^{2+} ion is +2 — it is in the +2 state. The name of a compound, such as copper(II) oxide, indicates that the copper is in the +2 oxidation state.
- All group 1 metals have an oxidation number of +1 in their compounds; all group 2 metals have an oxidation number of +2 in their compounds.
- Fluorine always has the oxidation number −1 in its compounds.
- Hydrogen has the oxidation number +1 in its compounds, apart from when it is combined with a metal, when the oxidation number is −1.
- Oxygen has the oxidation number −2 in its compounds, apart from in peroxides or when it is combined with fluorine.
- The sum of the oxidation numbers of the atoms in a neutral compound is zero. For example, in ammonia, NH_3, the oxidation number of nitrogen (−3) plus three times the oxidation number of hydrogen (+1) equals zero.
- The sum of the oxidation numbers in a polyatomic ion is the charge on that ion. For example, in the MnO_4^- ion, the oxidation number of manganese (+7) plus four times the oxidation number of oxygen (−2) equals −1.

The possible oxidation numbers of some elements in their compounds are shown in Table 5.1.

Tips

Fluorine is more electronegative than oxygen, so in F_2O the two fluorine atoms are −1 each and the oxygen +2.

Remember that the most electronegative element is fluorine, followed by oxygen and then chlorine. Electronegativity *increases* across a period and *decreases* down a group in the periodic table.

Tip

Remember that if an element is joined to a *more* electronegative element, it will have a positive oxidation number. So, bromine in BrO_3^- is in a positive oxidation state.

Table 5.1 Oxidation numbers

Element	Oxidation number
Lithium, sodium and potassium	+1
Magnesium, calcium, strontium and barium	+2
Aluminium	+3
Nitrogen (except in some oxides)	−3, +3 or +5
Oxygen (except in peroxides and superoxides or when combined with fluorine)	−2
Sulfur	−2, +1, +2, $+2\frac{1}{2}$, +4 or +6
Fluorine	−1
Chlorine, bromine and iodine	−1, +1, +3, +5 or +7

Worked example 1

Deduce the oxidation number of chlorine in:

a) $NaCl$ b) ClO^- c) ClO_3^-

Answer

a) The oxidation number of Na is +1. The two oxidation numbers must add up to zero. Therefore, Cl must be −1.

b) Let the oxidation number of chlorine = y.

The oxidation number of oxygen is −2 and the charge on the ion is −1, so:

$$-2 + y = -1$$
$$y = +1$$

The oxidation number of chlorine in the ClO^- ion is +1.

c) Let the oxidation number of chlorine = z.

The oxidation number of oxygen is −2 and the charge on the ion is −1, so:

$$(3 \times -2) + z = -1$$
$$z = -1 + 6 = +5$$

The oxidation number of chlorine in the ClO_3^- ion is +5.

Tip

Remember that you must always put the sign of the oxidation number *before* the number. The sign must *never* be omitted. If it is omitted, the answer may be marked as wrong.

Worked example 2

Deduce the oxidation number of sulfur in:

a) SCl_2 b) SO_2 c) SO_4^{2-}

Answer

a) Chlorine is more electronegative than sulfur. Therefore, (2×-1) and the oxidation number of sulfur add up to zero.

The oxidation number of sulfur in SCl_2 is +2.

b) The oxidation number of sulfur and 2× the oxidation number of oxygen add up to zero. The oxidation number of oxygen is −2.

Therefore, the oxidation number of sulfur in SO_2 is +4.

c) Let the oxidation number of sulfur = z.

The oxidation number of sulfur and 4× the oxidation number of oxygen add up to −2.

$$z + (4 \times -2) = -2$$
$$z = -2 + 8 = +6$$

The oxidation number of sulfur in the SO_4^{2-} ion is +6.

Worked example 3

Deduce the oxidation number of manganese in:

a) MnO_4^- b) MnO_4^{2-}

Answer

Let the oxidation number of manganese = z.

a) $z + (4 \times -2) = -1$

$z = -1 + 8 = +7$

The oxidation number of manganese in the MnO_4^- ion is +7.

b) $z + (4 \times -2) = -2$

$z = -2 + 8 = +6$

The oxidation number of manganese in the MnO_4^{2-} ion is +6.

Worked example 4

Deduce the oxidation number of vanadium in VO_2^+.

Answer

$z + (2 \times -2) = +1$

$z = 1 + 4 = +5$

The oxidation number of vanadium in the VO_2^+ ion is +5.

Test yourself

1 Deduce the oxidation numbers of oxygen in:

a) F_2O b) H_2O_2 c) K_2O d) KO_2

Redox in terms of oxidation numbers

Consider the reaction:

$$2H_2S(g) + SO_2(g) \rightarrow 3S(s) + 2H_2O(l)$$

The H_2S has been oxidised (loss of hydrogen) and the SO_2 reduced (loss of oxygen). The oxidation number of sulfur in H_2S is −2, in SO_2 is +4 and in S is zero. The H_2S has been oxidised and the oxidation number of S in H_2S has increased from −2 to 0. The SO_2 has been reduced and the oxidation number of sulfur has decreased from +4 to 0.

This leads to another definition of oxidation and reduction:

Oxidation occurs when the oxidation number of an element increases.

Reduction occurs when the oxidation number of an element decreases.

The element can be uncombined or in an ion or molecule.

Names of compounds in terms of oxidation number

The names of compounds and ions that contain an element that can have more than one oxidation number include the oxidation number. This is written as a Roman numeral in brackets:

- Manganese in the MnO_4^- ion is in the +7 state. Therefore, the ion is manganate(VII).
- Chromium in the $Cr_2O_7^{2-}$ ion is in the +6 state. Therefore, the ion is dichromate(VI).
- $FeCl_3$ is iron(III) chloride; $FeSO_4$ is iron(II) sulfate.

Worked example

Name the following ions:

a) ClO^- b) ClO_3^-

Answer

a) The chlorine is in the +1 oxidation state, so the ion is chlorate(I).

b) The chlorine is in the +5 oxidation state, so the ion is chlorate(V).

Polyatomic anions containing oxygen have names ending in -ate. The exception is the OH^- ion, which is called the hydroxide ion.

Test yourself

2 Name the following substances or ions:

a) $CrCl_2$ b) Cu_2O c) N_2O d) MnO_4^{2-}

Oxidising and reducing agents

Chlorine reacts with bromide ions to form bromine and chloride ions:

$$Cl_2 + 2Br^- \rightarrow Br_2 + 2Cl^-$$

Each chlorine atom in Cl_2 has gained one electron and so is reduced. Each bromide ion has lost an electron and so is oxidised. Chlorine has oxidised bromide ions. Therefore, chlorine is an **oxidising agent**. The bromide ions have reduced the chlorine. Therefore, the bromide ion is a **reducing agent**.

- An oxidising agent is a species (atom, molecule or ion) that oxidises another species by removing one or more electrons or increasing the oxidation number of an element in that species. When an oxidising agent reacts, it is itself reduced.
- A reducing agent reduces another species by giving it one or more electrons or by decreasing the oxidation number of an element in that species. When a reducing reagent reacts, it is itself oxidised.

Consider a redox reaction in which substance X oxidises substance Y:

e^-

$X + Y \rightarrow$ products

Substance X has removed an electron from substance Y and so has oxidised it. Substance X is the oxidising agent. It has gained an electron and has itself been reduced. Substance Y has given an electron to substance X and so has reduced it. Substance Y is the reducing agent. It has lost an electron and has itself been oxidised.

Some common oxidising and reducing agents and the products formed when they react are given in Table 5.2.

Table 5.2 Common oxidising and reducing agents

Oxidising agents	Product when reduced
Chlorine, Cl_2	Chloride ions, Cl^-
Bromine, Br_2	Bromide ions, Br^-
*Manganate(VII) ions, MnO_4^-	Manganese(II) ions, Mn^{2+}
*Dichromate(VI) ions, $Cr_2O_7^2$	Chromium(III) ions, Cr^{3+}
*Hydrogen peroxide, H_2O_2	Water, H_2O
Iron(III) ions, Fe^{3+}	Iron(II) ions, Fe^{2+}
Concentrated sulfuric acid, H_2SO_4	Sulfur dioxide, SO_2
Concentrated nitric acid, HNO_3	Nitrogen dioxide, NO_2
Hydrogen ions, H^+, in dilute acid	Hydrogen, H_2

Reducing reagents	Product when oxidised
Iodide ions, I^-, or hydrogen iodide, HI	Iodine, I_2
Hydrogen sulfide, H_2S	Sulfur, S
Sulfur dioxide, SO_2	Sulfate ions, SO_4^{2-}
Iron(II) ions, Fe^{2+}	Iron(III) ions, Fe^{3+}
Hydrogen peroxide, H_2O_2	Oxygen, O_2
Tin(II) ions, Sn^{2+}	Tin(IV) ions, Sn^{4+}
Carbon	Carbon monoxide or carbon dioxide
Carbon monoxide, CO	Carbon dioxide, CO_2
Metals (e.g. Mg)	Metal ions (e.g. Mg^{2+})

*The solution must be made acidic with dilute sulfuric acid.

Disproportionation reactions

When chlorine gas is bubbled into aqueous sodium hydroxide, a disproportionation reaction takes place. One atom in the Cl_2 molecule is oxidised to NaOCl and one is reduced to NaCl. The equation, with the oxidation numbers of chlorine, is:

$$Cl_2 + 2NaOH \rightarrow NaOCl + NaCl + H_2O$$
$$0 \qquad\qquad\qquad +1 \quad -1$$

> **Key term**
>
> **Disproportionation** is a redox reaction in which an element in a *single species* is simultaneously oxidised and reduced.

> To be involved in a disproportionation reaction, an element must have at least three oxidation states — the initial one, one higher and one lower.

Worked example 1

Chlorine reacts with hot aqueous potassium hydroxide:

$$3Cl_2 + 6KOH \rightarrow 5KCl + KClO_3 + 3H_2O$$

Explain why this is a disproportionation reaction.

Answer

The chlorine is in the zero state in Cl_2. In the products, the oxidation number of chlorine is −1 in KCl and in $KClO_3$ it is in the +5 oxidation state. The chlorine in the single species Cl_2 is oxidised from 0 to +5 and simultaneously reduced from 0 to −1.

Worked example 2

Explain why the following is not a disproportionation reaction:

$$OCl^-(aq) + Cl^-(aq) + 2H^+(aq) \rightarrow Cl_2(aq) + H_2O(l)$$

Answer

The chlorine in OCl^- is reduced from the +1 oxidation state to the zero state and the chlorine in Cl^- is oxidised from the −1 state to the zero state. However, the two chlorine atoms are not in the *same species*, and so it is not a disproportionation reaction.

This reaction is sometimes called 'reverse disproportionation'.

Worked example 3

Is the decomposition of hydrogen peroxide a disproportionation reaction?

$$2H_2O_2 \rightarrow 2H_2O + O_2$$

Answer

The oxidation number of both oxygen atoms in H_2O_2 is −1. The oxidation number of the oxygen in H_2O is −2 and of the oxygen in O_2 is zero. The oxygen in H_2O_2 has simultaneously been oxidised from −1 to zero and reduced from −1 to −2. Therefore, the decomposition is a disproportionation reaction.

Test yourself

3 Write the equation for the disproportionation reaction of copper(I) ions to copper metal and copper(II) ions.

Ionic half-equations

Ionic half-equations always have electrons on either the left-hand side or the right-hand side.

Oxidation reactions can be written as half-equations, which show the loss of electrons from a single species and its oxidation product. For example, the oxidation half-equation for the oxidation of zinc atoms to zinc ions is:

$$Zn(s) \rightarrow Zn^{2+}(aq) + 2e^-$$

There are four points to note about a half-equation such as this:

- This is an oxidation reaction, so the electrons are on the right-hand side of the equation.
- The equation must balance for charge as well as for numbers of atoms. In this example, both sides add up to a charge of zero $(0 = +2 - 2)$.
- State symbols should be included in half-equations.
- The reactant must always be on the left-hand side of the half-equation.

Reduction reactions can also be written as half-equations. When zinc is added to dilute hydrochloric acid, hydrogen ions are reduced to hydrogen. The half-equation is:

$$2H^+(aq) + 2e^- \rightarrow H_2(g)$$

This is a reduction reaction, so the electrons are on the left-hand side of the half-equation.

Tip

Remember that electrons are negative. It is advisable to put the charge as a superscript in the same way as the charge on an ion is shown.

Half-equations can be combined to give the overall equation for the reaction (page 87).

Worked example 1

Write an ionic half-equation for the oxidation of Fe^{2+} ions to Fe^{3+} ions.

Answer

Fe^{2+} ions each lose an electron and become Fe^{3+} ions. The half-equation is:

$$Fe^{2+}(aq) \rightarrow Fe^{3+}(aq) + e^-$$

As the Fe^{2+} ions have been oxidised, the electron appears on the right. The charges on both sides of the half-equation add up to +2.

Worked example 2

Write an ionic half-equation for the reduction of chlorine to chloride ions.

Answer

Chlorine atoms each gain one electron and are reduced to chloride ions. The half-equation is:

$$Cl_2(g) + 2e^- \rightarrow 2Cl^-(aq)$$

This equation can be halved:

$$\tfrac{1}{2}Cl_2(g) + e^- \rightarrow Cl^-(aq)$$

The chlorine has been reduced, so the electrons appear on the left.

Test yourself

4 Write half-equations for:

a) the reduction of Sn^{4+} to Sn^{2+}

b) the oxidation of iodide ions, I^-, to iodine, I_2

Tip

Reducing agents are *oxidised* when they react, so their half-equations must have electrons on the *right*

Oxidising agents are *reduced* when they react, so their half-equations must have the electrons on the *left*

More complex half-equations

Some oxidising agents require the presence of acid. For example, in the presence of dilute sulfuric acid, potassium manganate(VII) solution is a strong oxidising agent. The manganese in the MnO_4^- ion is reduced to Mn^{2+} ions. A first, but totally wrong, attempt at a half-equation would be:

$$MnO_4^- \rightarrow Mn^{2+} + 3e^-$$

This equation balances for charge but cannot be correct because the electrons are on the wrong side. They have to be on the left-hand side because MnO_4^- ions are being reduced.

The answer is to have hydrogen ions on the left-hand side. These pick up the oxygen atoms from the MnO_4^- ions and form water. There are four oxygen atoms, so eight hydrogen ions are needed and four water molecules are formed.

A second attempt at the half-equation is:

$$MnO_4^-(aq) + 8H^+(aq) + xe^- \rightarrow Mn^{2+}(aq) + 4H_2O(l)$$

where x is the number of electrons.

The value of x can be worked out in either of two ways:

1 The oxidation number of manganese changes from +7 to +2, which is a change of 5. Therefore there must be five electrons on the left. The correct ionic half-equation is:

$$MnO_4^-(aq) + 8H^+(aq) + 5e^- \rightarrow Mn^{2+}(aq) + 4H_2O(l)$$

2 The equation must balance for charge. The charge on the right-hand side is +2. The charge on the left-hand side is:

$$-1 + 8 - x = 7 - x$$

The charge on the left-hand side must equal the charge on the right-hand side, i.e. +2. Therefore:

$$7 - x = +2$$
$$x = 7 - 2 = 5$$

There are five electrons on the left-hand side, so the correct ionic half-equation is:

$$MnO_4^-(aq) + 8H^+(aq) + 5e^- \rightarrow Mn^{2+}(aq) + 4H_2O(l)$$

In acid solution, hydrogen peroxide, H_2O_2, acts as an oxidising agent. It is reduced to water (Table 5.2 on page 83). The half-equation will have H^+ and electrons on the left-hand side:

$$H_2O_2(aq) + 2H^+(aq) + 2e^- \rightarrow 2H_2O(l)$$

Two electrons are needed so as to make both sides of the equation neutral.

> **Worked example**
>
> Write the ionic half-equation for the reduction of dichromate(VI) ions to Cr^{3+} ions in acid solution.
>
> **Answer**
>
> Electrons must be on the left-hand side because the $Cr_2O_7^{2-}$ ions are being reduced. The solution is acidic and so H^+ ions are also on the left. There are seven oxygen atoms in the $Cr_2O_7^{-2}$ ion. Therefore, seven water molecules are produced and 14 hydrogen ions are needed on the left-hand side of the equation.
>
> A simple way of working out the number of electrons is by using oxidation numbers. Each chromium in $Cr_2O_7^{2-}$ is +6 and it is +3 in Cr^{3+}. Each chromium changes by 3 and, as there are two chromium atoms, the total change is +6. This means that there must be six electrons on the left.
>
> Alternatively the number can be found via charge.
>
> The charge on the right-hand side is +6, so the left-hand side must also be +6:
>
> $$-2 + 14 - x = 6$$
> $$x = -2 + 14 - 6 = 14 - 8 = 6$$
>
> Therefore the half-equation is:
>
> $$Cr_2O_7^{2-}(aq) + 14H^+(aq) + 6e^- \rightarrow 2Cr^{3+}(aq) + 7H_2O(l)$$

5 Write the half-equation for the reduction of BrO_3^- ions to Br^- ions in acid solution.

Summary: rules for writing half-equations

1 The electrons are on the left-hand side for a reduction equation and on the right-hand side for an oxidation equation.

2 If the reaction takes place in acid solution, add H^+ ions to the left-hand side and water molecules to the right-hand side.

3 Make sure that the equation balances for atoms.

4 Change the number of electrons so that the equation balances for charge.

Overall redox equations

Half-equations can be combined to give the overall equation for a redox reaction. This is done in two steps:

1 Multiply one or both half-equations by integers so that the number of electrons becomes the same in both.

2 Add the two half-equations together to obtain the overall equation.

Note that the electrons on the left-hand side cancel the electrons on the right-hand side.

The reaction between aqueous silver nitrate and copper metal is a redox reaction. The silver ions are reduced to silver atoms and the copper atoms are oxidised to copper ions. The two half-equations are:

$$Ag^+(aq) + e^- \rightarrow Ag(s)$$
$$Cu(s) \rightarrow Cu^{2+}(aq) + 2e^-$$

Copper wire dipping in a solution of silver nitrate. The silver ions preferentially replace the copper, leaving crystalline silver deposits and forming a solution of copper nitrate

The overall equation is found by multiplying the first equation by 2 and then adding it to the second equation:

$$2Ag^+(aq) + 2e^- + Cu(s) \rightarrow 2Ag(s) + Cu^{2+}(aq) + 2e^-$$

The electrons cancel, so the result is:

$$2Ag^+(aq) + Cu(s) \rightarrow 2Ag(s) + Cu^{2+}(aq)$$

The rules for deriving the overall equation from half-equations are:

1 Check that one half-equation has the electrons on the left-hand side and the other has them on the right-hand side.

2 Multiply the half-equations by integers so that the number of electrons is the same in both.

3 Add the two equations and cancel the electrons (and any spectator ions).

4 Check that both reactants are on the left-hand side of the overall equation.

Worked example 1

Acidified dichromate(VI) ions oxidise Fe^{2+} ions to Fe^{3+} ions. In this reaction, the acidified dichromate(VI) is itself reduced to Cr^{3+} ions. Write the two ionic half-equations and hence derive the overall equation.

Answer

The half-equations are:

$$Fe^{2+}(aq) \rightarrow Fe^{3+}(aq) + e^-$$
$$Cr_2O_7^{2-}(aq) + 14H^+(aq) + 6e^- \rightarrow 2Cr^{3+}(aq) + 7H_2O(l)$$

Multiply the first equation by 6 to obtain the same number of electrons in both equations. Then, add the two equations together and cancel the electrons. The overall equation is:

$$Cr_2O_7^{2-}(aq) + 14H^+(aq) + 6Fe^{2+}(aq) \rightarrow 2Cr^{3+}(aq) + 7H_2O(l) + 6Fe^{3+}(aq)$$

The Fe^{2+} ions are oxidised, so they lose electrons. As the dichromate(VI) ions are the oxidising agent, they are reduced and so the electrons are on the left.

Worked example 2

In the presence of dilute sulfuric acid, potassium manganate(VII) oxidises Sn^{2+} ions to Sn^{4+} ions and is itself reduced to Mn^{2+} ions. Write the two ionic half-equations and use them to derive the overall equation.

Answer

The half equations are:

$$Sn^{2+}(aq) \rightarrow Sn^{4+}(aq) + 2e^-$$
$$MnO_4^-(aq) + 8H^+(aq) + 5e^- \rightarrow Mn^{2+}(aq) + 4H_2O(l)$$

Multiply the first equation by 5 and the second equation by 2 to obtain the same number of electrons in each equation. Then, add the two equations and cancel the electrons. The overall equation is:

$$2MnO_4^-(aq) + 16H^+(aq) + 5Sn^{2+}(aq) \rightarrow 2Mn^{2+}(aq) + 8H_2O(l) + 5Sn^{4+}(aq)$$

Deduction of half-equations from the overall equation

The half-equations can be deduced from the overall equation because the latter shows the formulae of all the reactants and products. The redox reaction between nitric acid, HNO_3, and hydrogen sulfide, H_2S, is a suitable example:

$$2HNO_3 + H_2S \rightarrow 2NO_2 + S + 2H_2O$$

First, work out which substance has been oxidised and write electrons on the right-hand side of the half-equation.

The sulfur in H_2S loses hydrogen (or the oxidation number of sulfur is increased from -2 to 0) and so is oxidised. The half-equation is:

$$H_2S \rightarrow 2H^+ + S + 2e^-$$

The hydrogen sulfide is oxidised and therefore the nitric acid must be reduced. The number of electrons on the left-hand side in the half-equation for nitric acid reduction must be the same as the number on the right-hand side in the half-equation for hydrogen sulfide oxidation. Therefore, the half-equation for the reduction of nitric acid to nitrogen dioxide is:

$$2HNO_3 + 2H^+ + 2e^- \rightarrow 2NO_2 + 2H_2O$$

On addition of the two half-equations, the $2H^+$ on the left-hand side of the nitric acid reduction equation cancels with the $2H^+$ on the right-hand side of the hydrogen sulfide oxidation equation.

As the oxidation number of sulfur changes by two, there must be two electrons in the equation. They will be on the *right* as H_2S has been *oxidised*. The hydrogen in H_2S has been neither oxidised nor reduced. Therefore, it must still be in the $+1$ state and so H^+ and not H_2 is the product in the half-equation. Note that the equation balances for charge.

Note that nitric acid is the oxidising agent and hydrogen sulfide is the reducing agent.

Balancing equations using oxidation numbers

Half-equations

The number of electrons in a half-equation is equal to the total *change* in oxidation number of the element.

In acid solution, ferrate(VI) ions, FeO_4^{2-}, can be reduced to Fe^{2+} ions. The oxidation number of iron changes from +6 to +2. This is a decrease of four, so there are four electrons on the left-hand side of the reduction half-equation. The half-equation is:

$$FeO_4^{2-}(aq) + 8H^+(aq) + 4e^- \rightarrow Fe^{2+}(aq) + 4H_2O(l)$$

When potassium dichromate(VI), $Cr_2O_7^{2-}$, in dilute sulfuric acid, is reduced to Cr^{3+} ions, the oxidation number of each chromium decreases by three. However, there are two chromium atoms in the equation, so the total change is six. Therefore, the half-equation has six electrons on the left-hand side:

$$Cr_2O_7^{2-}(aq) + 14H^+(aq) + 6e^- \rightarrow 2Cr^{3+}(aq) + 7H_2O(l)$$

Overall redox equations

The total change in oxidation number of the element being reduced is equal to the total change in oxidation number of the element being oxidised.

When potassium manganate(VII) oxidises Sn^{2+} ions to Sn^{4+} ions, the oxidation number of the manganese changes from +7 to +2 — a decrease of five. The oxidation number of tin increases by two. To balance the change in oxidation numbers, $2MnO_4^-$ and $5Sn^{2+}$ are needed. In this way, the total change in oxidation number of both manganese and tin is 10. The overall equation is:

$$2MnO_4^-(aq) + 16H^+(aq) + 5Sn^{2+}(aq) \rightarrow 2Mn^{2+}(aq) + 8H_2O(l) + 5Sn^{4+}(aq)$$

Some students prefer to work out overall redox equations using half-equations as in the worked examples on page 88. However it is done, the final equation must balance for atoms and charge and *not* contain any uncancelled electrons.

Summary tasks

Make sure that you know the definitions of:

- oxidation and reduction in terms of electron transfer
- oxidising and reducing agents
- disproportionation

Check that you can:

- calculate the oxidation numbers of the elements in neutral molecules, simple ions and polyatomic ions
- name polyatomic ions such as ClO_2^- and MnO_4^{2-}
- write ionic half-equations
- write overall redox equations

Questions

1 State whether the following changes are oxidation or reduction. Explain your answers in terms of the transfer of electrons.
   a) Cr^{2+} to Cr^{3+}
   c) Sn^{4+} to Sn^{2+}
   b) HI to I_2
   d) Cl^- to Cl_2

2 Write ionic half-equations for the changes in Question 1, parts a to d.

3 Write ionic half-equations for the following, which take place in acidic solution:
   a) iodate(v) ions, IO_3^-, to iodine
   b) manganese dioxide, MnO_2, to Mn^{2+} ions
   c) VO_2^+ ions to VO^{2+} ions

4 Write overall equations for the following redox reactions:
   a) manganate(VII) ions in acid solution reacting with hydrogen iodide
   b) Fe^{3+} ions being reduced to Fe^{2+} ions by Sn^{2+} ions, which are oxidised to Sn^{4+} ions
   c) dichromate(VI) ions in acid solution oxidising nitrogen dioxide, NO_2, to nitrate ions, NO_3^-

5 Deduce the oxidation number of iodine in:
   a) I_2O_7
   c) KIO_4
   b) IO_3^-
   d) $Ba(IO_2)_2$

6 Deduce the oxidation number of vanadium in:
   a) V^{3+}
   c) VO^{2+}
   b) VO_2^+

7 Deduce the oxidation number of nitrogen in:
   a) NO_2
   c) N_2O_5
   b) NO_2^-
   d) N_2H_4

8 Potassium bromide, KBr, reacts with potassium bromate, $KBrO_3$, in the presence of dilute sulfuric acid according to the equation:

$$5KBr + KBrO_3 + 3H_2SO_4 \rightarrow 3Br_2 + 3K_2SO_4 + 3H_2O$$

   a) Give the oxidation numbers of bromine in KBr, $KBrO_3$ and Br_2.
   b) State, with a reason, which substance in the equation is the oxidising agent.

9 Calculate the total change in oxidation number of the carbon atoms when ethanedioate ions, $C_2O_4^{2-}$, are oxidised to carbon dioxide.

10 Write the ionic equation for the reaction of bromine with aqueous sodium hydroxide, to form $NaBr$, $NaOBr$ and water.

11 From each of the redox equations below, deduce the two half-equations and identify the oxidising agent and the reducing agent.
   a) $Cl_2 + 2NaBr \rightarrow 2NaCl + Br_2$
   b) $HSO_3^- + 2Fe^{3+} + H_2O \rightarrow SO_4^{2-} + 2Fe^{2+} + 3H^+$

12 Chlorine oxidises iron to Fe^{3+} ions.
   a) Write the half-equations for the oxidation of iron to Fe^{3+} ions and for the reduction of chlorine to Cl^- ions.
   b) Use your answer to a) to write the overall ionic equation.

Exam practice questions

1 a) Define:
  i) disproportionation
  ii) oxidation number (4)

b) Which of the following is a redox reaction?
  A $H^+(aq) + OH^-(aq) \rightarrow H_2O(l)$
  B $2CrO_4^{2-} + 2H^+(aq) \rightarrow$
    $\qquad Cr_2O_7^{2-}(aq) + H_2O(l)$
  C $SnCl_2(aq) + 2FeCl_3(aq) \rightarrow$
    $\qquad SnCl_4(aq) + 2FeCl_2(aq)$
  D $CuO(s) + H_2SO_4(aq) \rightarrow$
    $\qquad CuSO_4(aq) + H_2O(l)$ (1)

c) Which of the following is **not** a disproportionation reaction?
  A $2H_2O_2(l) \rightarrow 2H_2O(l) + O_2(g)$
  B $Cl_2(g) + H_2O(l) \rightarrow$
    $\qquad Cl^-(aq) + OCl^-(aq) + 2H^+(aq)$
  C $CuCl_2(aq) + Cu(s) + 2Cl^-(aq) \rightarrow$
    $\qquad 2CuCl^-(aq)$
  D $3MnO_4^{2-}(aq) + 2H_2O(l) \rightarrow$
    $MnO_2(s) + 2MnO_4^-(aq) + 4OH^-(aq)$ (1)

d) When iodine reacts with sodium thiosulfate, sodium tetrathionate, $Na_2S_4O_6$, is produced. The oxidation number of sulfur in the product is:
  A +2   **C** +4
  B +2.5   **D** +6 (1)

e) The oxidation number of oxygen in potassium superoxide, KO_2, is:
  A $-\frac{1}{2}$ **C** -2
  B -1 **D** -4 (1)
  (Total 8 marks)

2 a) Define the term **disproportionation** and explain why the reaction below is *not* an example of a disproportionation reaction. (2)

$$MnO_2 + 2MnO_4^- + 2H_2O \rightarrow$$
$$3MnO_4^{2-} + 4H^+$$

b) Calculate the oxidation numbers of chlorine in:
  i) ClO^- ions
  ii) ClO_2^- ions
  iii) ClO_3^- ions (3)

c) When $81.6\,cm^3$ of chlorine gas was bubbled into hot aqueous sodium hydroxide a disproportionation reaction took place forming Cl^- ions, ClO_x^- ions and water. The chloride ions were reacted with excess Ag^+ ions and the precipitate of AgCl weighed $0.813\,g$.

Calculate the value of x and write the ionic equation for the disproportionation reaction. You must show all your working. (7)

(The molar volume of gas under the conditions of the experiment is $24.0\,dm^3\,mol^{-1}$.)

d) In acid solution ClO^- ions will oxidise Fe^{2+} ions to Fe^{3+} and be reduced to Cl^- ions.
  i) Write the ionic half-equations for the reduction of ClO^- ions and the oxidation of Fe^{2+} ions. (2)
  ii) Use your answers to i) to write the overall equation. (1)
  (Total 15 marks)

6 The periodic table: group 2 (Topic 4)

The *s*-block consists of the elements in groups 1 and 2. The group 1 elements (lithium, sodium, potassium, rubidium, caesium and francium) are called the **alkali metals**. They form cations with a 1+ charge.

The elements in group 2 are the **alkaline earth metals**. They have a valency of 2, form cations with a charge of 2+ and have an oxidation number of +2 in their compounds. The elements in group 2 are:

- beryllium, Be
- magnesium, Mg
- calcium, Ca
- strontium, Sr
- barium, Ba
- radium, Ra

Radium is a rare, radioactive metal.

Trends in group 2

Some properties of the elements in group 2 are listed in Table 6.1.

Table 6.1 Properties of the group 2 elements

Element	Be	Mg	Ca	Sr	Ba
Atomic number, Z	4	12	20	38	56
Relative atomic mass, A_r	9	24	40	88	137
Electron configuration	[He] $2s^2$	[Ne] $3s^2$	[Ar] $4s^2$	[Kr] $5s^2$	[Xe] $6s^2$
Melting temperature/°C	1278	649	839	769	725
Atomic radius/nm	0.11	0.16	0.20	0.21	0.22
Ionic radius/nm	0.031	0.065	0.099	0.11	0.14
First ionisation energy/kJ mol^{-1}	900	736	590	548	502
First + second ionisation energy/ kJ mol^{-1}	2660	2196	1740	1608	1468
Electronegativity	1.5	1.2	1.0	1.0	0.9

Ionisation energy

The first ionisation energy is the energy required to remove one electron from each of a mole of gaseous atoms. For calcium it is the energy for the process:

$$Ca(g) \rightarrow Ca^+(g) + e^-$$

The second ionisation energy for calcium is the energy change for:

$$Ca^+(g) \rightarrow Ca^{2+}(g) + e^-$$

The energy change for the removal of both *s* electrons is the sum of the first and second ionisation energies.

The values for the group 2 elements are shown in Table 6.1.

The trend is for less energy being required to remove the electrons as the group is descended. The extra number of protons is compensated for by the equivalent number of extra inner shielding electrons, but the outer *s* electrons become further from the nucleus, making it easier to remove them. From magnesium to calcium, the nuclear charge increases by eight but the number of inner shielding electrons also increases by eight. The difference is that the electron being removed in calcium is a 4*s*-electron, which is further from the nucleus than the 3*s*-electron removed when magnesium is ionised.

In the same period, the first ionisation energy of the group 2 metal is larger than that of the equivalent group 1 metal. This is because the group 2 atom has a smaller radius than the group 1 atom (Table 6.2).

Table 6.2 Comparison of a group 1 and a group 2 element in the same period

	Sodium	Magnesium
Nuclear charge	11	12
Number of inner shielding electrons	10	10
Atomic radius/nm	0.19	0.16
First ionisation energy/kJ mol^{-1}	494	736

This causes both the group 1 and group 2 elements (except beryllium) to have the physical and chemical properties of metals. The reactivity *increases* down the group, but the reactivity of a group 2 element is less than that of the group 1 element in the same period.

Reactions of the group 2 metals

- In all their compounds, the group 2 metals are in the +2 oxidation state.
- Apart from beryllium, they are all metals and react to form positive ions of charge 2+. Their reactivity increases down the group because the sum of the first and second ionisation energies decreases down the group, making it easier to remove the two outer electrons.

Reaction with oxygen

All the group 2 metals burn in air. They react with the oxygen and form ionic oxides of formula, MO. For example, with calcium:

$$2Ca + O_2 \rightarrow 2CaO$$

The metal is oxidised. Each atom loses two electrons:

$$Ca \rightarrow Ca^{2+} + 2e^-$$

Reaction with chlorine

All the group 2 elements react when heated in chlorine. For example:

$$Ca + Cl_2 \rightarrow CaCl_2$$

They form ionic chlorides of formula MCl_2 which dissolve in water, producing solutions that contain hydrated cations of formula $[M(H_2O)_6]^{2+}$. For example:

$$MgCl_2(s) + aq \rightarrow [Mg(H_2O)_6]^{2+}(aq) + 2Cl^-(aq)$$

The hexaaquamagnesium ion (Figure 6.1) is partially deprotonated by solvent water molecules and the solution becomes slightly acidic:

$$[Mg(H_2O)_6]^{2+}(aq) + H_2O(l) \rightleftharpoons [Mg(H_2O)_5(OH)]^+(aq) + H_3O^+(aq)$$

The solution becomes acidic because H_3O^+ ions are formed.

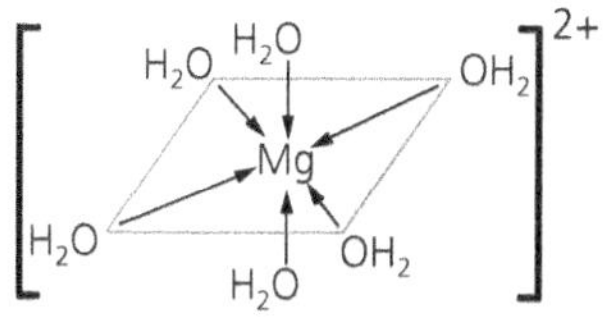

Reaction with water

- Magnesium reacts slowly with cold water to produce an alkaline suspension of magnesium hydroxide and hydrogen gas:

$$Mg + 2H_2O(l) \rightarrow Mg(OH)_2 + H_2$$

When heated in steam, magnesium burns, producing magnesium oxide and hydrogen:

$$Mg + H_2O(g) \rightarrow MgO + H_2$$

- Calcium, strontium and barium react rapidly with cold water to produce alkaline solutions of the metal hydroxide and bubbles of hydrogen gas — for example:

$$Ca(s) + 2H_2O(l) \rightarrow Ca(OH)_2(aq) + H_2(g)$$

Figure 6.1 The hexaaquamagnesium ion

Test yourself

1 Write the equations for the following reactions:

a) magnesium and oxygen   b) barium and water   c) magnesium and chlorine

---

Group 2 oxides and hydroxides

Group 2 oxides and hydroxides are bases. The general formulae are MO and $M(OH)_2$.

Reaction of the oxides with water

- Magnesium oxide reacts slowly to form a slightly alkaline suspension of magnesium hydroxide:

$$MgO(s) + H_2O(l) \rightarrow Mg(OH)_2(s)$$

- Calcium oxide is called quicklime. It reacts very exothermically with water to form an alkaline suspension of calcium hydroxide:

$$CaO(s) + H_2O(l) \rightarrow Ca(OH)_2(s) \rightleftharpoons Ca^{2+}(aq) + 2OH^-(aq)$$

Solid calcium hydroxide is called slaked lime and solutions of it are called limewater.
- Strontium and barium oxides react with water to form alkaline solutions of the hydroxide:

$$BaO(s) + H_2O(l) \rightarrow Ba^{2+}(aq) + 2OH^-(aq)$$

Reaction with acids

The oxides and hydroxides of the group 2 metals are bases. Therefore, they react with acids to form salts and water:

$$MO(s) + 2H^+(aq) \rightarrow M^{2+}(aq) + H_2O(l)$$

$$M(OH)_2(s) + 2H^+(aq) \rightarrow M^{2+}(aq) + 2H_2O(l)$$

- Magnesium oxide reacts with dilute sulfuric acid to form magnesium sulfate and water:

$$MgO(s) + H_2SO_4(aq) \rightarrow MgSO_4(aq) + H_2O(l)$$

- Calcium hydroxide reacts with nitric acid solution to form calcium nitrate and water. The ionic equation is:

$$Ca(OH)_2(s) + 2H^+(aq) \rightarrow Ca^{2+}(aq) + 2H_2O(l)$$

- Note that beryllium oxide is amphoteric. This means that it reacts both as a base and as an acid:

$$BeO(s) + 2H^+(aq) \rightarrow Be^{2+}(aq) + H_2O(l)$$
$$BeO(s) + 2OH^-(aq) + H_2O(l) \rightarrow Be(OH)_4^{2-}(aq)$$

Group 1 hydroxides react with acids in the same way to form salts. All the group 1 hydroxides are water-soluble and form alkaline solutions with a high pH. Aqueous sodium hydroxide reacts with dilute sulfuric acid, according to the equation:

$$2NaOH(aq) + H_2SO_4(aq) \rightarrow Na_2SO_4(aq) + 2H_2O(l)$$

Reaction of limewater with carbon dioxide

Carbon dioxide is an acidic oxide. It reacts with the base calcium hydroxide to form the salt, calcium carbonate, and water. Calcium carbonate is insoluble and appears as a milky precipitate. This reaction is the test for carbon dioxide:

$$Ca(OH)_2(aq) + CO_2(g) \rightarrow CaCO_3(s) + H_2O(l)$$

If carbon dioxide is passed into a suspension of calcium carbonate, the milkiness slowly clears as the soluble acid salt, calcium hydrogencarbonate, is formed:

$$CaCO_3(s) + H_2O(l) + CO_2(g) \rightarrow Ca(HCO_3)_2(aq)$$

Calcium hydrogencarbonate is soluble in water, whereas calcium carbonate is insoluble. This is the basis of a test to distinguish between a carbonate and a hydrogencarbonate of a group 1 metal. A solution of the test substance is added to a solution of calcium chloride. If the substance is a carbonate, a white precipitate of calcium carbonate is seen. If the test substance is a hydrogencarbonate, no precipitate forms until the mixture is heated. The hydrogencarbonate ions decompose, forming carbonate ions, carbon dioxide and water:

$$2HCO_3^{2-}(aq) \rightarrow CO_3^{2-}(aq) + CO_2(g) + H_2O(l)$$

The carbonate ions then react with the calcium ions to form a precipitate of insoluble calcium carbonate:

$$CO_3^{2-}(aq) + Ca^{2+}(aq) \rightarrow CaCO_3(s)$$

Test yourself

2 Write ionic equations for the reactions of solid barium oxide and:

a) nitric acid   b) water

Solubility of group 2 hydroxides and sulfates

The solubility of group 2 hydroxides *increases* down the group (Table 6.3):

- Magnesium hydroxide is very slightly soluble.
- Calcium hydroxide is slightly soluble.
- Strontium and barium hydroxides are more soluble.

Table 6.3 Solubility of group 2 hydroxides

	$Mg(OH)_2$	$Ca(OH)_2$	$Sr(OH)_2$	$Ba(OH)_2$
Solubility/mol dm^{-3}	0.0002	0.015	0.083	0.15
pH of saturated solution	10.6	12.5	13.2	13.5

The solubility of the sulfates *decreases* down the group:

- Magnesium sulfate is very soluble.
- Calcium sulfate is slightly soluble.
- Strontium sulfate is very slightly soluble.
- Barium sulfate is insoluble.

Barium ions in solution are highly poisonous; however, barium sulfate is so insoluble that it passes unaffected through the alimentary canal. This has led to its use in hospitals. A paste of barium sulfate is eaten ('barium meal') and, at various times, the patient is X-rayed. The progress of the barium sulfate through the digestive tract is observed and any obstructions seen. Barium compounds are opaque to X-rays because barium has a very high nuclear charge.

On adding a solution of sodium sulfate (or any solution containing sulfate ions, such as dilute sulfuric acid) to a solution of calcium, strontium and barium compounds, a white precipitate of an insoluble sulfate is produced.

The ionic equation for the reaction of barium chloride solution with sodium sulfate solution is:

$$Ba^{2+}(aq) + SO_4^{2-}(aq) \rightarrow BaSO_4(s)$$

This reaction is used as a test for sulfates. Dilute hydrochloric acid and then barium chloride solution are added to the unknown solution. A white precipitate confirms the presence of sulfate ions in the solution.

Tip

Barium carbonate is also very insoluble, but it cannot be used as a 'barium meal', because it would react with the hydrochloric acid in the stomach and release poisonous soluble barium ions.

Tip

Barium sulfate is so insoluble that when dilute sulfuric acid is added to a piece of barium metal, the reaction stops almost at once. The initial reaction causes a layer of insoluble barium sulfate to form on the surface of the metal. This layer prevents further acid from reaching the unreacted metal.

Thermal stability of group 1 and group 2 nitrates and carbonates

Thermal stability depends upon the polarising power of the cation, which is determined by its charge density. The larger the charge and the smaller the radius, the greater is the charge density (Table 6.4). Compounds containing cations that strongly polarise the anion are more easily decomposed than those with less polarising cations.

Table 6.4 Polarising power of group 1 and group 2 cations

Ion	Ionic radius/nm	Ion	Ionic radius/nm	
Li⁺	0.074			↓
Na⁺	0.102	Mg²⁺	0.072	Polarising
K⁺	0.138	Ca²⁺	0.100	power
		Sr²⁺	0.113	decreases

Polarising power increases →

This means that, in both groups 1 and 2, the ease of decomposition decreases down the group. This is because the ionic radius increases down the group, reducing the polarising power of the cation.

The ions of the group 2 elements have a charge of 2+, compared with a charge of 1+ for the group 1 elements. The group 2 ions also have a smaller ionic radius than the group 1 ions. Therefore, group 2 cations are considerably more polarising than group 1 cations and so group 2 compounds are less stable to heat and decompose more easily.

Nitrates

Thermal stability of group 1 nitrates

All group 1 nitrates decompose on strong heating. However, lithium nitrate decomposes in a different way from the other nitrates. The products are lithium oxide, nitrogen dioxide and oxygen. The nitrogen dioxide is visible as a brown gas:

$$4LiNO_3 \rightarrow 2Li_2O + 4NO_2 + O_2$$

- The small radius of the lithium ion causes it to have a high charge density, which polarises the O−N bonds in the nitrate ion sufficiently to break them and form an O^{2-} ion.
- The other group 1 cations are too large to polarise to this extent. Therefore, on heating, their nitrates do not decompose to give an oxide. Very strong heating causes them to melt, giving off oxygen and leaving a molten nitrite that contains the NO_2^- ion, for example:

$$2NaNO_3 \rightarrow 2NaNO_2 + O_2$$

Thermal stability of group 2 nitrates

The nitrate ion in a group 2 nitrate is sufficiently polarised by the 2+ cation to result in thermal decomposition by the same pathway as lithium nitrate.

On heating, group 2 nitrates decompose to the metal oxide, nitrogen dioxide and oxygen. The temperature at which thermal decomposition occurs is lowest for beryllium nitrate and highest for barium nitrate, which requires very strong heating before brown fumes of nitrogen dioxide are seen. The equation for the decomposition of magnesium nitrate is:

$$2Mg(NO_3)_2 \rightarrow 2MgO + 4NO_2 + O_2$$

Carbonates

Thermal stability of group 1 carbonates

Only lithium carbonate decomposes when heated. This is because the Li^+ cation is very small and polarises the $O-C$ bond in the CO_3^{2-} ion sufficiently for it to break and form an O^{2-} ion:

$$Li_2CO_3 \rightarrow Li_2O + CO_2$$

The other group 1 cations have larger radii. Therefore, their polarising power is not sufficient to cause decomposition of the *anhydrous* carbonates.

Thermal stability of group 2 carbonates

All the group 2 carbonates decompose on heating. The ease of decomposition decreases from Mg to Ba. The equation for the decomposition of calcium carbonate, for example, is:

$$CaCO_3 \rightarrow CaO + CO_2$$

Barium carbonate requires very strong heating before it is decomposed.

Test yourself

3 a) Place the following ions in order of decreasing polarising power:
Na$^+$, Mg^{2+}, Ca^{2+}

  b) Which of the nitrates of these ions will be the easiest to decompose?

Experiments to study thermal decomposition

The relative ease of decomposition of group 2 carbonates or nitrates can be studied by the following experiment:

- Place the same amount of each carbonate (or nitrate) in a series of hard glass test tubes.
- Fix a delivery tube to the test tube and clamp in a stand, as in Figure 6.2.
- Light the Bunsen and measure the time taken for the gas evolved to reach the mark on the test tube in the water bath.
- Repeat with the same amount (in moles) of the remaining carbonates. You must make sure that the Bunsen flame is the same and that the distance between the Bunsen and the hard glass test tube is the same in all experiments.

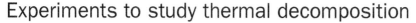

As a control, a test tube can be heated. The air in it will expand and some gas will be collected over the water bath.

Figure 6.2 Heating group 2 carbonates (Hazard: suck back is possible)

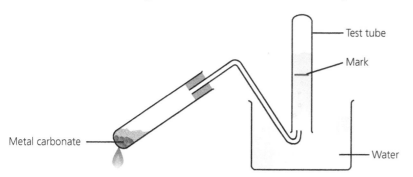

The group 2 carbonate that, on heating, fills the test tube the fastest is the one that is the easiest to decompose.

Tests for group 1 and group 2 cations

All compounds of the group 1 elements are soluble in water, as are many compounds of group 2 elements. Therefore, the identity of the cation cannot usually be detected by a precipitation reaction. However, apart from magnesium, they all colour a Bunsen flame.

The flame test

First the compound has to be converted into a chloride because chlorides are more volatile than other types of compound. The procedure is as follows:

- Take a platinum or nichrome wire or a specially marketed flame test rod. Do *not* use a spatula or a wooden splint.
- Check that it is clean by dipping the wire in some concentrated hydrochloric acid on a watch glass and then placing it in the hottest part of a Bunsen flame. The flame should not be coloured. If it is, repeat the treatment until the flame is not coloured.
- Once again, dip the wire in concentrated hydrochloric acid and then into some of the solid under test.
- Place this in the hottest part of the flame and observe the colour of the flame.

The colour of the flame identifies the cation present (Figure 6.3).

> **Tip**
>
> Magnesium salts do not give a colour to a flame.

Cation
Lithium

Flame colour:
Crimson

Cation
Calcium

Flame colour:
Yellow-red (brick-red)

Cation
Sodium

Flame colour:
Yellow

Cation
Strontium

Flame colour:
Red

Cation
Potassium

Flame colour:
Lilac

Cation
Barium

Flame colour:
Pale green (apple-green)

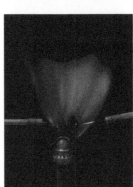

Figure 6.3 Flame test colours (Hazard: concentrated hydrochloric acid is harmful)

Explanation of flame colour

The flame colour is the result of the *emission* of coloured light.

The heat energy of the flame is absorbed and promotes an electron into an excited state. This means that the electron is not in the lowest available orbital, but in a higher one. This excited state is not stable, so the electron drops down to the ground state (the lowest available energy level). The energy released is given off in the form of visible light (Figure 6.4). The gaps between the energy levels in different cations are not the same, so the amount of energy, and hence the colour of the light emitted, varies from element to element.

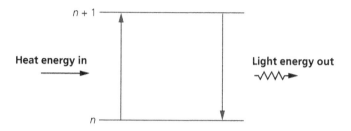

Figure 6.4 Electronic transitions on heating in a flame

Test yourself

4 A white solid gave a lilac colour in a flame test and gave off a colourless gas that ignited a glowing splint when strongly heated. Identify the solid and write the equation for its decomposition.

Summary tasks

Make sure that you can explain why:

- the sum of the first and second ionisation energies of the elements decreases down group 2
- the reactivity of the elements increases down group 2

Check that you can write equations for the reactions of:

- the group 2 metals with oxygen, with water and with chlorine
- the group 2 oxides and hydroxides with water and with acids

Make sure that you can:

- state how the solubility of the group 2 hydroxides and sulfates changes down the group
- state and explain the changes of thermal stability of their nitrates and carbonates
- describe how a flame test is carried out and explain the origin of the colour

Questions

1 Define the term **first ionisation energy**. Write an equation that represents the first ionisation of calcium.

2 Explain why the first ionisation energies decrease down group 2 from beryllium to barium.

3 Explain why the first ionisation energy of calcium is greater than that of potassium.

4 Explain why there is a big jump between the second and third ionisation energies for magnesium.

5 State and explain the trend in the thermal stability of the group 1 nitrates.

6 The composition by mass of a barium compound is: barium 81.1%; oxygen 18.9%.
   a) Calculate the empirical formula of this compound.
   b) The molar mass of this compound is $169.3\,g\,mol^{-1}$. Calculate its molecular formula.

7 a) State what is observed when strontium nitrate is heated.
   b) Write the equation for the thermal decomposition of strontium nitrate.
   c) Calculate the volume of gas produced when 2.12 g of strontium nitrate is heated. Assume that, under the conditions of the experiment, 1 mol of gas occupies $24.0\,dm^3$.

8 Explain why magnesium carbonate decomposes at a lower temperature than calcium carbonate.

9 Explain why calcium and strontium compounds give different colours to a flame.

Exam practice questions

1 a) The most polarising of the ions below is:

    A Mg^{2+} **C** Sr^{2+}

    B Ca^{2+} **D** Ba^{2+} (1)

  b) i) Write the equation for the decomposition of barium nitrate. (2)

    ii) Explain why magnesium nitrate decomposes at a lower temperature than sodium nitrate. (2)

    iii) Which takes the longest to produce brown fumes on heating?

        A $Mg(NO_3)_2$ **C** $Sr(NO_3)_2$

        B $Ca(NO_3)_2$ **D** $Ba(NO_3)_2$ (1)

    iv) Which is the only group 1 nitrate that produces brown fumes when it is heated strongly?

        A $LiNO_3$ **C** KNO_3

        B $NaNO_3$ **D** $RbNO_3$ (1)

                (Total 7 marks)

2 a) Group 2 carbonates decompose when heated.

    i) Write the equation for the decomposition of calcium carbonate. (1)

    ii) Describe an experiment that would show the relative ease of decomposing the carbonates of the group 2 metals magnesium to barium. (3)

    iii) State and explain the trend in thermal stability of the group 2 carbonates from magnesium to barium. (3)

  b) i) Both calcium and strontium react with hydrochloric acid. Explain why calcium is less reactive than strontium. (2)

    ii) Metallic calcium and metallic strontium have the same face-centred cubic structure. Explain why the melting temperature of calcium is higher than that of strontium. (2)

             (Total 11 marks)

3 One of the ingredients of cement is belite, which is a mixture of calcium oxide and silicon dioxide.

  a) A sample of belite of mass 4.24 g was mixed with $50.0\,cm^3$ of a solution of hydrochloric acid of concentration $2.00\,mol\,dm^{-3}$ and left until the reaction was complete. The unreacted silicon dioxide was filtered off and the solution containing the excess hydrochloric acid and the washings were made up to $250\,cm^3$. The excess hydrochloric acid in $25.0\,cm^3$ portions was titrated against $0.100\,mol\,dm^{-3}$ sodium hydroxide solution. The mean titre was $21.3\,cm^3$.

    i) Write equations for the reactions of calcium oxide with hydrochloric acid and of sodium hydroxide with hydrochloric acid. (2)

    ii) Use your answers to i) and the data to calculate the percentage of calcium oxide in the sample of belite. (7)

  b) Explain why calcium and strontium compounds give different colours to a flame. (3)

             (Total 12 marks)

7 The periodic table: group 7 (Topic 4)

The halogens

The elements in group 7 are called the **halogens**. This word is derived from the Greek for salt maker — halogens react with metals to form salts.

The elements are:

- fluorine, F
- chlorine, Cl
- bromine, Br
- iodine, I
- astatine, At

Astatine is a radioactive element with a half-life of 8.3 hours.

Physical properties of halogens

At room temperature and pressure, fluorine and chlorine are gases, bromine is a volatile fuming liquid and iodine is a solid that sublimes on heating.

The melting and boiling temperatures of the halogens increase from fluorine to iodine. This is because the numbers of electrons in the molecules increase (Table 7.1) causing the strength of the London intermolecular forces to increase.

Table 7.1 Physical properties of the halogens

	Fluorine	Chlorine	Bromine	Iodine
Colour	Pale yellow gas 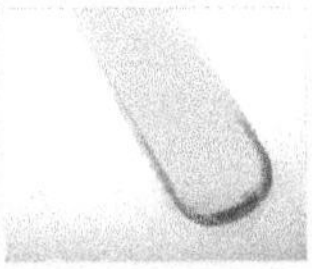	Greenish gas 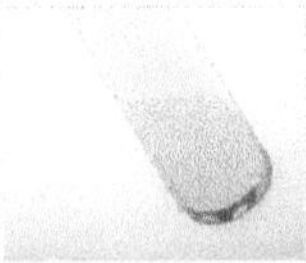	Brown liquid 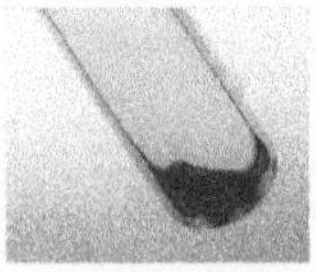	Dark grey-black solid which forms a violet vapour 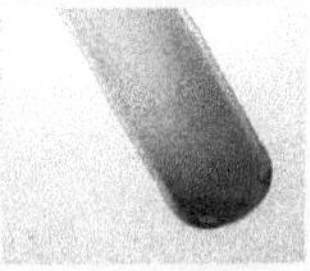
Electron configuration	[He] $2s^2\ 2p^5$	[Ne] $3s^2\ 3p^5$	[Ar] $3d^{10}\ 4s^2\ 4p^5$	[Kr] $4d^{10}\ 5s^2\ 5p^5$
Atomic radius/nm	0.07	0.10	0.11	0.13
Ionic radius/nm	0.14	0.18	0.20	0.22
First ionisation energy/kJ mol^{-1}	1680	1260	1140	1010
First electron affinity/kJ mol^{-1}	−348	−364	−342	−314
Electronegativity	4.0	3.0	2.8	2.5

> **Tip**
>
> Make sure that you know the colour and physical states of chlorine, bromine and iodine. They are often asked for.

Colour of solutions

- Chlorine and bromine are fairly soluble in water. Aqueous solutions of chlorine and bromine are called chlorine water and bromine water, respectively. Chlorine water is pale green and bromine water is orange.
- Iodine is only very slightly soluble in water. Solutions are pale brown, unless potassium iodide is present, in which case the solution is deep brown-red. This colour is due to the I_3^- ion:

$$I_2(aq) + I^-(aq) \rightarrow I_3^-(aq)$$

- All the halogens are more soluble in inert organic solvents such as trichloromethane or hexane than in water. This means that if hexane is added to an aqueous solution containing a halogen, the coloured halogen is concentrated in the organic layer. A solution of iodine in hexane is violet.

Trends in group 7

First ionisation energy

The first ionisation energy of the halogens decreases down the group. The nuclear charge increases, but the number of inner shielding electrons increases by the same amount. The effective nuclear charge therefore only alters slightly, but the major reason for the change is that the atomic radius increases as new shells are added, so the outermost electrons become less strongly held. This is why, from fluorine to iodine, the first ionisation energy decreases.

First electron affinity

Energy is released when a negative electron is brought from outside the atom towards the positive nucleus and into the outer orbit. The trend is a decrease in the exothermic electron affinity down the group. This is because the electron is not brought as close to the nucleus in large atoms as it is in smaller atoms. Therefore, less energy is released when a large atom gains an electron than when a smaller atom gains an electron.

Fluorine is an exception. This is because the atom is so small that the repulsion between the incoming electron and the seven electrons in the second shell reduces the energy liberated by the attraction between the incoming electron and the nucleus.

Electronegativity

Electronegativity decreases down the group as the atoms become larger and there is less attraction by the atom's nucleus for the bonding electrons. Fluorine is the most electronegative element in the periodic table.

Reactivity

All the elements have high values of electronegativity and so they readily accept electrons, forming negative ions. This gain of electrons is reduction and so the halogens are all oxidising agents.

$$X_2 + 2e^- \rightarrow 2X^-$$

where X represents a halogen.

The result of the decrease in electronegativity and increase in size makes the reactivity of the halogens as oxidising agents *decrease* down the group.

> **Key term**
>
> **Electronegativity** is defined as the ability of an element to draw a pair of bonding electrons towards itself.

Test yourself

1 a) Define the term **electronegativity**.

b) Which is the most electronegative of chlorine, bromine and iodine?

Bonding in compounds of halogens

Ionic bonding

All the halogens form anions with a 1− charge. This is because they all have high electronegativity values and, when a halogen atom accepts an electron, the electron configuration of a noble gas is achieved.

Bonding with group 1 and group 2 metals

Group 1 and group 2 metal halides are ionic. For example, the dot-and-cross diagram for calcium chloride is shown in Figure 7.1.

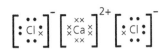

Figure 7.1

Bonding with aluminium (group 3)

Aluminium fluoride, AlF_3, is ionic, but anhydrous aluminium chloride is covalent.

Hydrated aluminium chloride, $AlCl_3.6H_2O$, is ionic.

Anhydrous aluminium chloride sublimes on heating, producing gaseous molecules of formula Al_2Cl_6 which, at higher temperatures, decompose to $AlCl_3$ molecules. In the dimer, the two $AlCl_3$ units are joined by two dative covalent bonds, each being from a chlorine atom in one $AlCl_3$ molecule to the aluminium atom in the other molecule. In this way, the outer orbit of both aluminium atoms contains an octet of electrons (Figure 7.2).

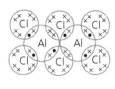

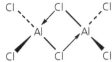

Figure 7.2

Tip

The aluminium atom in covalent $AlCl_3$ has only six electrons in its outer orbit (its own three plus one from each covalent bond). A lone pair from a chlorine atom in the other $AlCl_3$ molecule forms a dative covalent bond using an empty 3*p* orbital of the aluminium. As a result, the aluminium now has four pairs of electrons in its outer orbit. Therefore, the four chlorine atoms are arranged tetrahedrally around each aluminium. There are no bonds between the two aluminium atoms – drawing a bond here is a very common error in AS and A-level answers.

Covalent bonding

The halogens form polar covalent bonds with almost all non-metals.

- Fluorine is the most electronegative of all the elements and so is always in the −1 oxidation state in compounds.
- Chlorine is more electronegative than all other elements except for fluorine and oxygen. In compounds it is in the −1 oxidation state, apart from when it is bonded to fluorine or oxygen.

The halogens, other than fluorine, have empty *d* orbitals in the valence shell. For example, chlorine has five empty 3*d* orbitals. Therefore, one or more of the 3*p* electrons can be promoted into these energetically similar energy levels. This enables chlorine to form more than one covalent bond (Figure 7.3).

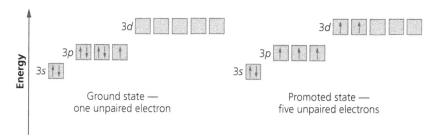

Figure 7.3 Electron promotion before bonding

This only happens when the extra bond energy released compensates for the energy required to promote the electrons, i.e. when it is bonded to a small electronegative atom such as oxygen:

- Chlorine forms chloric(I) acid (hypochlorous acid), HOCl, and chlorate(I) salts, which contain the ClO^- ion. In these ions, chlorine is in the +1 oxidation state.
- Chlorine also forms chlorate(v) salts, which contain the ClO_3^- ion. In these ions, the chlorine is in the +5 oxidation state. There are five covalent bonds between chlorine and the three oxygen atoms — two double bonds and one single bond (Figure 7.4).

Figure 7.4

Bromine and iodine form similar salts in which they are in the +1 and +5 oxidation states.

Reactions of the halogens

- The reactivity of the halogens decreases down the group. (Conversely, the reactivity of many of their compounds *increases* down the group.)
- The halogens are oxidising agents and can remove an electron from many substances.
- The ionic half-equation for chlorine acting as an oxidising agent is:

    $$Cl_2 + 2e^- \rightarrow 2Cl^-$$

- The oxidising power of the halogens decreases down the group.

Reactions with solutions of other halides

A halogen will displace a less reactive halogen from one of its salts:

- When chlorine is bubbled into a solution of potassium bromide, the chlorine oxidises the bromide ions. The solution turns orange as the bromine is liberated:

    $$Cl_2(g) + 2Br^-(aq) \rightarrow Br_2(aq) + 2Cl^-(aq)$$

    The chlorine molecule gains two electrons — one from each bromide ion. The process can be described using half-equations:

    $$2Br^-(aq) \rightarrow Br_2(aq) + 2e^-$$
    $$Cl_2(g) + 2e^- \rightarrow 2Cl^-(aq)$$

- Chlorine displaces iodine from iodides, forming a dark grey precipitate of iodine:

    $$Cl_2(g) + 2I^-(aq) \rightarrow I_2(s) + 2Cl^-(aq)$$

- Bromine also displaces iodine from iodides:

    $$Br_2(aq) + 2I^-(aq) \rightarrow I_2(s) + 2Br^-(aq)$$

Tip

The colour of the released halogen can be made more visible by adding an organic solvent such as hexane or trichloromethane. Halogens are more soluble in the organic solvent than in water and so the colour is concentrated in the solvent. Bromine forms a deep orange colour and iodine an intense violet colour.

These displacement reactions show the decreasing power as oxidising agents of chlorine to iodine. Chlorine displaces (oxidises) bromine from bromides, so is a stronger oxidising agent. Likewise, bromine oxidises iodide ions to iodine, so bromine is a more powerful oxidising agent than iodine. Iodine does not react with bromides; nor does bromine react with chlorides.

Reaction with metals

On heating, metals react with halogens to form halides in which the halogen is in the −1 oxidation state. For example, all the halogens react with the group 1 and 2 metals to form ionic halides:

$$Na + \tfrac{1}{2}Cl_2 \rightarrow NaCl$$

$$Mg + I_2 \rightarrow MgI_2$$

However, with metals with variable valency, such as iron, chlorine oxidises it to iron(III) chloride:

$$2Fe + 3Cl_2 \rightarrow 2FeCl_3$$

whereas the less powerful oxidising agent iodine oxidises it only to iron(II) iodide:

$$Fe + I_2 \rightarrow FeI_2$$

Reaction with water

- Chlorine reacts reversibly with water to form an acidic solution containing hydrochloric acid and the weak acid, chloric(I) acid. The solution is acidic because the hydrochloric acid is totally ionised into H^+ and Cl^- ions:

$$Cl_2(aq) + H_2O(l) \rightleftharpoons H^+(aq) + Cl^-(aq) + HOCl(aq)$$

Drinking water is treated with chlorine. This kills any bacteria that may be present and some chlorine remains in solution and so will kill any subsequent introduction of bacteria. Unsafe drinking water in undeveloped countries causes large loss of life, especially of children.

- Bromine reacts in a similar way, but the position of equilibrium lies more to the left:

$$Br_2(aq) + H_2O(l) \rightleftharpoons H^+(aq) + Br^-(aq) + HOBr(aq)$$

- Iodine does not react with water.

Reaction with alkali

With alkali at room temperature

Chlorine, bromine and iodine all react with *cold* aqueous sodium hydroxide by disproportionation reactions to produce a mixture of halide and halate(I) salts — for example, with chlorine:

$$Cl_2 + 2NaOH \rightarrow NaCl + NaOCl + H_2O$$
$$0 {-1} {+1}$$

The chlorine in the zero state is reduced to −1 in NaCl and oxidised to +1 in NaOCl (sodium chlorate(I)).

The ionic equation is:

$$Cl_2(aq) + 2OH^-(aq) \rightarrow Cl^-(aq) + OCl^-(aq) + H_2O(l)$$

> **Tip**
>
> This is an example of a disproportionation reaction. The chlorine (Cl_2) starts in the zero oxidation state and is reduced to −1 in the Cl^- ion and oxidised to +1 in chloric(I) acid, HOCl. A single species, chlorine, is simultaneously oxidised and reduced.

Fluorine reacts irreversibly with water to form hydrogen fluoride and oxygen.

If a solution containing chlorate(I) ions is heated, further disproportionation takes place and chlorate(V) ions are formed:

$$3OCl^-(aq) \rightarrow 2Cl^-(aq) + ClO_3^-(aq)$$
$$+1 -1 +5$$

The +1 chlorine in OCl^- is reduced to -1 in Cl^- and oxidised to +5 in ClO_3^-.

With hot alkali

This is also a disproportionation reaction. However, the halogen is oxidised to the +5 state in the chlorate(V) ion, ClO_3^-, rather than the +1 state, as is the case with cold alkali:

$$3Cl_2(aq) + 6OH^-(aq) \rightarrow 5Cl^-(aq) + ClO_3^-(aq) + 3H_2O(l)$$
$$0 -1 +5$$

Reaction with phosphorus

- In a limited supply of chlorine, phosphorus trichloride is formed:

$$2P + 3Cl_2 \rightarrow 2PCl_3$$

Phosphorus trichloride can then react with more chlorine to form phosphorus pentachloride:

$$PCl_3 + Cl_2 \rightarrow PCl_5$$

- In excess chlorine, phosphorus pentachloride is formed:

$$2P + 5Cl_2 \rightarrow 2PCl_5$$

- Iodine reacts with the red allotrope of phosphorus to form phosphorus triiodide:

$$2P + 3I_2 \rightarrow 2PI_3$$

If the mixture is damp, this then reacts with water to form hydrogen iodide gas:

$$PI_3 + 3H_2O \rightarrow 3HI + H_3PO_3$$

This is how gaseous hydrogen iodide is prepared.

Reactions with reducing agents

Iron(II) compounds are used here as examples of reducing agents.

Chlorine and bromine oxidise iron(II) ions to iron(III) ions. The two half-equations for oxidation by chlorine are:

$$Cl_2(aq) + 2e^- \rightarrow 2Cl^-(aq)$$

$$Fe^{2+}(aq) \rightarrow Fe^{3+}(aq) + e^-$$

The second half-equation has to be multiplied by 2 and then added to the first equation to give the overall equation:

$$Cl_2(aq) + 2Fe^{2+}(aq) \rightarrow 2Cl^-(aq) + 2Fe^{3+}(aq)$$

Iodine is too weak an oxidising agent to oxidise iron(II) to iron(III). The reverse happens. Iodide ions are oxidised by Fe^{3+} ions to iodine:

$$2I^-(aq) + 2Fe^{3+}(aq) \rightarrow I_2(s) + 2Fe^{2+}(aq)$$

The colourless solution containing iodide ions becomes a pale brown solution with a precipitate of iodine. Iodine can be tested for by the addition of starch. An intense blue, almost black, colour is obtained.

Tip

Note that the oxidation number of chlorine rises by 5, so there must be five chlorine atoms being reduced from 0 to -1 to balance the change in oxidation number of the chlorine from 0 to +5. There must be six OH^- ions on the left-hand side of the equation because there are six negative ions on the right and the equation must balance for charge.

Tip

White phosphorus is really P_4, but the symbol P is always used in equations at AS and A-level unless a volume of *gaseous* phosphorus is needed in an equation.

Note that the overall equation balances for charge. The charge on the left-hand side is 4+, as is the charge on the right-hand side: (2−) + (6+) = 4+.

Reaction with sodium thiosulfate

The oxidation number, y, of sulfur in sodium thiosulfate ($Na_2S_2O_3$) is given by:

$$2 \times (+1) + 2y + 3 \times (-2) = 0$$

$$2y = 6 - 2 = +4$$

The oxidation number of each sulfur atom $= y = +2$.

With chlorine and bromine

Chlorine and bromine oxidise the sulfur in thiosulfate to the +6 state in sulfate, SO_4^{2-}. The equation with the oxidation numbers underneath is:

$$4Cl_2(aq) + S_2O_3^{2-}(aq) + 5H_2O(l) \rightarrow 8Cl^-(aq) + 2SO_4^{2-}(aq) + 10H^+(aq)$$
$$0 \qquad\qquad 2 \times (+2) \qquad\qquad\qquad 8 \times (-1) \quad 2 \times (+6)$$

The total change in oxidation number of sulfur is from +4 to +12 (a change of +8), so eight chlorine atoms or four Cl_2 molecules are needed.

With iodine

Iodine oxidises thiosulfate ions to tetrathionate ions, $S_4O_6^{2-}$, in which the average oxidation state of sulfur is 2.5. This is a change of 0.5 per sulfur atom. The equation is:

$$I_2(aq) + 2S_2O_3^{2-}(aq) \rightarrow 2I^-(aq) + S_4O_6^{2-}(aq)$$

Tests for the halogens

Chlorine

Chlorine is a pale green gas. The tests for chlorine are as follows:

- Chlorine *rapidly* bleaches *damp* litmus paper.
- If chlorine gas is passed into a solution of potassium bromide, the colourless solution becomes orange.

A solution of chlorine can be tested in the same way. It is pale green. It rapidly bleaches litmus paper and also turns colourless potassium bromide solution brown.

Bromine

Bromine is a brown fuming liquid that bleaches *damp* litmus *slowly*.

The test for bromine is to add it to excess potassium iodide solution. The colourless solution goes deep red-brown. This is because iodine is liberated, and then reacts with excess I^- ions to form the red-brown I_3^- ion. Excess bromine would give a grey-black precipitate of iodine.

Iodine

Iodine is a grey-black solid. Solutions in aqueous potassium iodide are red-brown and aqueous solutions are pale brown.

The test for iodine is that it turns starch dark blue.

Hydrogen halides

Physical properties

The hydrogen halides are gases at standard temperature and pressure. Their boiling temperatures are given in Table 7.2 and graphically in Figure 7.5.

Hydrogen fluoride, HF, has an anomalous boiling temperature because it forms strong intermolecular hydrogen bonds. The hydrogen atom is δ^+ and the fluorine atom is both very small and is δ^-. Hydrogen chloride, HCl, does not form intermolecular hydrogen bonds because chlorine is less δ^- and the atom is too big.

All the hydrogen halides have instantaneous induced dipole forces (London forces) and dipole–dipole forces between the molecules. These forces are weaker than the hydrogen bonds in hydrogen fluoride. Therefore, less energy is needed to separate the molecules.

Trend for HCl to HI

The strength of the London forces increases from hydrogen chloride to hydrogen iodide as the number of electrons in the molecule increases. The increase in the strength of these forces is much greater than the decrease in the strength of the dipole–dipole forces. Therefore, from hydrogen chloride to hydrogen iodide, the total intermolecular force increases and the boiling temperatures increase.

Bonding

Anhydrous hydrogen halides are covalently bonded.

Hydrogen atoms have the electron configuration $1s^1$. Therefore, to reach the same configuration as the noble gas helium, one electron is needed. The outer electron configuration of the halogens is $ns^2\,np^5$. So, a halogen atom needs one electron to reach the configuration of a noble gas. Halogen halide molecules share two electrons, one from the halogen and one from hydrogen. The dot-and-cross diagram for hydrogen chloride is shown in Figure 7.6.

Chemical reactions

Hydrogen halides are acids. Hydrogen iodide, HI, is the strongest acid and hydrogen fluoride, HF, the weakest.

Table 7.2 Boiling temperatures of the hydrogen halides

	HF	HCl	HBr	HI
Boiling temperature/°C	+20	−85	−67	−35

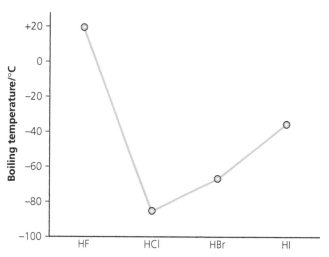

Figure 7.5 Boiling temperatures of the hydrogen halides

Tip

Make sure that you can explain why hydrogen fluoride has intermolecular hydrogen bonds and the other hydrogen halides do not. Remember to state and explain the trend in the boiling temperatures of the halides from hydrogen chloride to hydrogen iodide. Covalent bonds are *not* broken on boiling, so do not mention them in your answer.

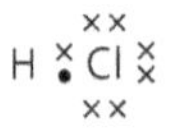

H $\overset{\times\times}{\underset{\times\times}{\overset{\times}{\bullet}}}$ Cl $\overset{\times}{\underset{\times}{}}$

Figure 7.6

Reaction with water

The hydrogen halides are all soluble in water. This is because they react with the water to form ions:

$$HCl(g) + H_2O(l) \rightarrow H_3O^+(aq) + Cl^-(aq)$$

The solutions are acidic because H_3O^+ ions are formed.

The H–halogen covalent bond is broken by the water. This bond breaking requires energy — it is endothermic. The energy is regained by the formation of the dative covalent bond between oxygen in a water molecule and a hydrogen ion, H^+, to form the H_3O^+ ion. Hydrogen iodide is the strongest acid of the hydrogen halides because the H–I bond is the weakest, so the removal of a hydrogen ion from hydrogen iodide by water is the most energetically favourable reaction:

$$HI(g) + H_2O(l) \rightarrow H_3O^+(aq) + I^-(aq)$$

$$HF(g) + H_2O(l) \rightleftharpoons H_3O^+(aq) + F^-(aq)$$

Reaction with ammonia

Ammonia is a base and, therefore, reacts with the hydrogen halides.

When gaseous hydrogen chloride reacts with gaseous ammonia, white fumes of solid ammonium chloride are formed:

$$HCl(g) + NH_3(g) \rightarrow NH_4Cl(s)$$

The same observation is made with the other hydrogen halides. This reaction is used as a test for gaseous HCl, HBr or HI, but it does not distinguish between them.

Halide salts

General properties

- Group 1 metals form ionic salts of formula MX, where X represents a halogen — for example, potassium iodide, KI, and sodium chloride, NaCl.
- Group 2 metals form ionic salts of formula MX_2 — for example, calcium bromide, $CaBr_2$.
- The d-block metals form salts of formula MX_2 or MX_3. When hydrated these salts are ionic — for example, copper(II) chloride, $CuCl_2$, and iron(III) chloride, $FeCl_3$. Silver forms halides of formula AgX.

Solubility

All halides are soluble in water, apart from silver halides and lead(II) halides.

If a solution of an ionic chloride such as sodium chloride is added to a solution of silver nitrate, a white precipitate of silver chloride is obtained:

$$Cl^-(aq) + Ag^+(aq) \rightarrow AgCl(s)$$

When a solution of an ionic bromide is added to a solution of silver nitrate, a cream precipitate of silver bromide is formed:

$$Br^-(aq) + Ag^+(aq) \rightarrow AgBr(s)$$

Tests for halides

Dilute nitric acid is added to a solution of the unknown halide, until the solution is *just* acidic. Silver nitrate solution is then added. Chlorides, bromides and iodides all produce a precipitate of the silver halide. The solubility of the silver halide precipitate in aqueous ammonia varies (Table 7.3).

Table 7.3 Tests for halides

	Colour of precipitate formed on addition of acidified silver nitrate	Solubility of precipitate in dilute aqueous ammonia	Solubility of precipitate in concentrated aqueous ammonia
Chlorides	White	Soluble	–
Bromides	Cream	Insoluble	Soluble
Iodides	Pale yellow	Insoluble	Insoluble

On addition of dilute nitric acid and silver nitrate solution:

- chlorides (including hydrochloric acid) give a white precipitate, which is soluble in dilute aqueous ammonia as a silver/ammonia complex ion is formed:

$$Ag^+(aq) + Cl^-(aq) \rightarrow AgCl(s)$$

then:

$$AgCl(s) + 2NH_3(aq) \rightarrow [Ag(NH_3)_2]^+(aq) + Cl^-(aq)$$

- bromides give a cream precipitate, which is insoluble in dilute aqueous ammonia but soluble in concentrated aqueous ammonia
- iodides give a pale yellow precipitate, which is insoluble in both dilute and concentrated aqueous ammonia

Tip

The second equation will only be required in the second year of the A-level course, as it is a typical reaction of transition metal ions.

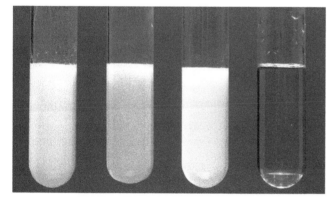

Silver halide precipitates. From left to right: silver iodide, silver bromide, silver chloride and a solution of silver fluoride

The dilute nitric acid has to be added to prevent the precipitation of other ions (e.g. carbonate) by the silver ions in the silver nitrate.

Chemical reactions of halides

Halide ions as reducing agents

The strength of halide salts as reducing agents *increases* from Cl^- to I^-.

The half-equation for the reduction of a halide ion X^- is:

$$2X^- \rightarrow X_2 + 2e^-$$

- Chloride ions are very difficult to oxidise. They are only oxidised by very strong oxidising agents such as ClO^- ions or potassium manganate(VII) in dilute sulfuric acid.
- Bromide ions are more easily oxidised. Chlorine, potassium dichromate(VI) in dilute sulfuric acid and potassium manganate(VII) in dilute sulfuric acid all oxidise bromide ions.

Tip

The second ionic half-equation has to be multiplied by two, so that the number of electrons on the left-hand side in the reduction half-equation (Fe^{3+} to Fe^{2+}) is the same as the number of electrons on the right-hand side in the oxidation half-equation (I^- to I_2).

- Iodide ions are strong reducing agents and are oxidised by many substances. For example, Fe^{3+} ions are reduced to Fe^{2+} ions by iodide ions in solution. The two ionic half-equations are:

$$2I^-(aq) \rightarrow I_2(s) + 2e^-$$

$$Fe^{3+}(aq) + e^- \rightarrow Fe^{2+}(aq)$$

Thus the overall equation is:

$$2Fe^{3+}(aq) + 2I^-(aq) \rightarrow 2Fe^{2+}(aq) + I_2(s)$$

Reaction of halide salts with concentrated sulfuric acid

When concentrated sulfuric acid is added to solid halides, the hydrogen halide is formed first — for example, with a sodium halide, NaX:

$$NaX + H_2SO_4 \rightarrow NaHSO_4 + HX$$

The hydrogen halide produced might then reduce the concentrated acid.

With chlorides, steamy fumes of hydrogen chloride are produced:

$$NaCl + H_2SO_4 \rightarrow NaHSO_4 + HCl$$

These fumes turn blue litmus red and give white fumes with gaseous ammonia. The hydrogen chloride is not further oxidised by the concentrated sulfuric acid.

With bromides, steamy fumes of hydrogen bromide are produced together with some orange gaseous bromine. Sulfur dioxide is also produced but it is not visible because it is a colourless gas. The equations for the reaction with potassium bromide are:

$$KBr + H_2SO_4 \rightarrow HBr + KHSO_4$$

$$2HBr + H_2SO_4 \rightarrow Br_2 + SO_2 + 2H_2O$$

With iodides, some steamy fumes of hydrogen iodide are formed, but the most obvious observation is a cloud of violet iodine vapour, mixed with some yellow sulfur. There is a smell of rotten eggs because hydrogen sulfide is also produced:

$$KI + H_2SO_4 \rightarrow HI + KHSO_4$$

then:

$$6HI + H_2SO_4 \rightarrow 3I_2 + S + 4H_2O$$

and:

$$8HI + H_2SO_4 \rightarrow 4I_2 + H_2S + 4H_2O$$

The results and observations are given in Table 7.4.

Table 7.4 Reaction of halide salts with concentrated sulfuric acid

Halide	Reduction of sulfuric acid	Observations
Fluoride	None	Steamy fumes (HF)
Chloride	None	Steamy fumes (HCl)
Bromide	Reduces sulfuric acid to gaseous sulfur dioxide	Steamy fumes (HBr) and brown gas (Br_2)
Iodide	Reduces sulfuric acid to solid sulfur and gaseous hydrogen sulfide	Clouds of violet gas (I_2), smell of bad eggs (H_2S) and yellow solid (S)

Progress of the reaction of potassium bromide with concentrated sulfuric acid

Test yourself

3 A white solid a) gave a yellow flame colour, b) gave off a gas that formed white smoke with ammonia when concentrated sulfuric acid was added and c) gave a white precipitate when silver nitrate solution was added. Identify the solid and write equations for the reactions in b) and c).

Analysis of inorganic compounds

Cations

Groups 1 and 2

These are identified by a flame test (see page 100).

Ammonium ion

Heat the solid or solution with aqueous sodium hydroxide and test the gas evolved:

$$NH_4^+ + OH^- \rightarrow NH_3 + H_2O$$

- *damp* red litmus turns blue in the ammonia gas given off
- when a glass rod is dipped in concentrated hydrochloric acid and held in the gas, white smoke of ammonium chloride observed:

$$NH_3(g) + HCl(g) \rightarrow NH_4Cl(s)$$

Anions

Halides

Add dilute nitric acid followed by aqueous silver nitrate to a solution of the suspected halide (see page 113).

- Chlorides give a white precipitate (of silver chloride), which is soluble in dilute ammonia:

$$Cl^-(aq) + Ag^+(aq) \rightarrow AgCl(s)$$

then

$$AgCl(s) + 4NH_3(aq) \rightarrow [Ag(NH_3)_4]^+(aq) + Cl^-(aq)$$

- Bromides give a cream precipitate (of silver bromide), which is insoluble in dilute ammonia but soluble in concentrated ammonia.
- Iodides give a pale yellow precipitate (of silver iodide), which is insoluble in both dilute and concentrated ammonia.

Carbonates and hydrogencarbonates

Add dilute hydrochloric acid to the solid (or to the solution). Both give off a gas that turns lime water milky:

$$2H^+ + CO_3^{2-} \rightarrow H_2O + CO_2$$

$$H^+ + HCO_3^- \rightarrow H_2O + CO_2$$

Sulfates

To a solution of the suspected sulfate add dilute hydrochloric acid followed by barium chloride solution. Sulfates give a white precipitate of barium sulfate:

$$SO_4^{2-}(aq) + Ba^{2+}(aq) \rightarrow BaSO_4(s)$$

Summary tasks

Make sure you can:

- describe the colours of the pure halogens and when in aqueous solution
- draw dot-and-cross diagrams of ionic and molecular compounds of the halogens
- explain why all, except fluorine, can form more than one covalent bond

Check that you can write equations for the reactions of the halogens with:

- metals and with non-metals such as phosphorus
- water and with alkalis

Make sure that you know:

- why HF has a higher boiling temperature than the other hydrogen halides
- the observations of adding concentrated sulfuric acid to solid halides and be able to explain them
- the tests for each halogen and each halide (except fluorine)
- the tests for groups 1 and 2 cations and the ammonium ions
- the tests for carbonates and hydrogencarbonates and for sulfates

Questions

1 Write the equations for the reaction of concentrated sulfuric acid with calcium chloride, and state *one* observation that could be made.

2 What would you observe when concentrated sulfuric acid is added to solid aluminium bromide? Identify the gases produced in this reaction.

3 Describe the chemical test for bromine.

4 Bromine reacts with hydrogen to form hydrogen bromide.
   a) Name the type of bonding in gaseous hydrogen bromide.
   b) Explain why hydrogen bromide is soluble in water and why the solution is acidic.
   c) Write an equation for the reaction of hydrogen bromide solution with sodium carbonate.

5 Potassium iodate, KIO_3, reacts in acid solution with potassium iodide according to the equation:

$$KIO_3 + 5KI + 6HCl \rightarrow 3I_2 + 6KCl + 3H_2O$$

   a) Deduce the oxidation numbers of iodine in KIO_3, KI and I_2.
   b) Use your answers from a) to explain which substance in the reaction is a reducing agent.
   c) Describe how you would test the solution to show the presence of iodine.

6 Explain why the first electron affinity of bromine is greater than that of iodine.

7 A white solid is known to be calcium chloride, calcium bromide or calcium iodide. Describe the tests to identify the salt. The answer should include all observations.

8 a) Write ionic half-equations for the following processes:
   i)   the oxidation of ClO^- ions to ClO_3^- ions
   ii) the reduction of ClO^- ions to Cl^- ions
   b) Using your answers to ai) and aii), write the overall equation for the disproportionation reaction of ClO^- ions.

9 Which of chlorine and iodine is the stronger oxidising agent? Describe *two* reactions that show this.

10 a) A compound X has the following composition by mass: lithium 7.75%; chlorine 39.25%; oxygen 53.0%. Calculate its empirical formula.
   b) The molecular formula of compound X is the same as the empirical formula. When a sample of X was heated, it decomposed into lithium chloride and oxygen gas. The volume of oxygen was found to be $1.77\,dm^3$. (The molar volume of oxygen under the conditions of the experiment is $24.0\,dm^3\,mol^{-1}$.) Write the equation for the decomposition of compound X and calculate the mass of X that decomposed.

11 A substance, Z, containing one cation and one anion, gave a pale green flame in a flame test.

A sample of Z was dissolved in water and the solution was divided into two portions:
   • Dilute sulfuric acid was added to one portion. A white precipitate was observed.
   • Dilute nitric acid followed by silver nitrate solution was added to the second portion. A pale yellow precipitate was obtained, which was insoluble in concentrated aqueous ammonia.

Identify the unknown compound Z. Justify your answer.

Exam practice questions

1 a) Chlorine reacts at room temperature with aqueous potassium hydroxide.
   i) Write the ionic equation for this reaction. (2)
   ii) State the type of reaction that takes place. (1)
b) The reaction $OCl^- + Cl^- + 2H^+ \rightarrow Cl_2 + H_2O$ is:
   A disproportionation   **C** redox
   B acid–base   **D** synthesis (1)
c) Chlorine oxidises sodium thiosulfate, $Na_2S_2O_3$, to sulfate, Na_2SO_4, but iodine oxidises it to sodium tetrathionate, $Na_2S_4O_6$.
   i) Write the equation for the reaction of chlorine with aqueous sodium thiosulfate. (2)
   ii) The oxidation number of sulfur in $Na_2S_4O_6$ is:
   A +2   **C** +6
   B +2.5   **D** +1 (1)
d) Which statement about the halogens and their compounds is **not** true?
   A Chlorine oxidises bromide ions to bromine.
   B Hydrogen iodide is more polar than hydrogen bromide.
   C Astatide ions, At^-, reduce Fe^{3+} ions to Fe^{2+} ions.
   D Silver chloride is soluble in concentrated aqueous ammonia. (1)
   (Total 8 marks)

2 This question is about chlorine and its compounds.
a) Domestic bleach is a solution containing sodium chlorate(I) and sodium chloride. When acidified the bleach releases chlorine, which remains dissolved. Write the ionic equation for this reaction. (1)
b) Chlorine reacts with potassium iodide solution.
   i) Write the ionic equation for this reaction. (1)
   ii) What colour change would be seen? (1)
c) An archaeologist discovered a silver ingot and gave it to a chemist to find out its purity. The chemist removed 1.23 g of the ingot and dissolved it in nitric acid. Excess sodium chloride solution was then added and a precipitate of silver chloride was formed. This was filtered, washed and dried and then weighed. It had a mass of 1.56 g.
   i) Explain why the precipitate was washed. (1)
   ii) Write the ionic equation, with state symbols, for the reaction between the silver ions and sodium chloride solution. (2)
   iii) Calculate the percentage by mass of silver in the ingot. (3)
   (Total 9 marks)

3 a) The structures of the thiosulfate ion and the tetrathionate ion are shown below.

Thiosulfate ion   Tetrathionate ion

Calculate the oxidation numbers of each of the sulfur atoms in:
   i) the thiosulfate ion
   ii) the tetrathionate ion (4)
   iii) Hence calculate the mean oxidation number of sulfur in the tetrathionate ion. (1)
b) Iodide ions react with iron(III) ions whereas chloride reacts with iron(II) ions.
   i) Write ionic equations for these reactions. (2)
   ii) Suggest why iodide does not react with iron(II) ions and why chloride ions do not react with iron(III) ions. (2)
c) When concentrated sulfuric acid is carefully added to solid sodium chloride in a test tube, steamy fumes are given off.
   i) Name the gas produced in this reaction and explain how the steamy fumes are formed. (2)
   ii) When the stopper of a concentrated ammonia bottle is held near the steamy fumes a white smoke is formed. Write the equation for the formation of the white smoke. (1)
   (Total 12 marks)

8 Formulae, equations and moles (Topic 5)

The ability to write correct chemical formulae is essential. Without this skill, equations and calculations become impossible.

- Many substances in AS and A-level are either ionically bonded or are organic compounds. This chapter should help with working out the formulae of ionic compounds and Chapter 10 should help with organic compounds.
- Chemical equations are internationally understood and are central to the understanding of chemical reactions.
- Substances react in simple whole number ratios by moles. Therefore, the ability to convert masses and volumes into moles is an essential part of quantitative chemistry. Calculations involving moles occur in all exams, so it is vital to be confident and skilled in this area.

In chemistry, the **amount of substance** is always measured in moles.

Formulae

Molecular formula

The molecular formula of a compound shows the number of atoms of each element in one molecule of the substance.

The molecular formula of glucose is $C_6H_{12}O_6$. One molecule of glucose contains six carbon atoms, 12 hydrogen atoms and six oxygen atoms.

Molar mass, *M*

Molar mass is the mass of 1 mol of the substance. The units are $g\,mol^{-1}$.

The value of the molar mass is found by adding the relative atomic masses of all the atoms present in the formula. The relative atomic masses can be found in the periodic table (page 314).

To calculate the molar mass of a substance (e.g. glucose, $C_6H_{12}O_6$), first use the periodic table to find the relative atomic masses. Here, the values needed are carbon = 12.0, hydrogen = 1.0, oxygen = 16.0.

$$\text{molar mass of glucose, } C_6H_{12}O_6 = (6 \times 12.0) + (12 \times 1.0) + (6 \times 16.0)$$
$$= 180.0\,g\,mol^{-1}$$

Empirical formula

The empirical formula of a substance is the simplest whole number ratio of the atoms of each element in the substance.

The empirical formula of glucose is CH_2O.

Calculation from percentage composition

Experiments can be carried out to determine the mass of each element in a given mass of a substance. The absolute values are then converted to percentage by mass. The percentage values are used to determine the empirical formula.

This calculation is usually carried out in two steps:

1 Divide each percentage by the relative atomic mass of the element, giving the answer to two decimal places. This gives the number of moles of each element in 100 g of the compound.

2 Divide the results of step 1 by the smallest value obtained in step 1. This gives a simple ratio by moles of each element. It is usually a whole number ratio.

If the values obtained in step 2 are not integers or very close to integers, one more step must be carried out:

3 Multiply the values obtained in step 2 by 2 so that they become integers. If this fails, multiply the values from step 2 by 3.

Tip

Do not round values ending in .5, or .67 or .33 to the nearest whole number as they become whole numbers when multiplied by 2 or 3. Values such as 3.9 may be rounded up to 4.0.

Tip

You will not be asked to calculate the empirical formulae of compounds containing a large number of atoms. If you obtain a ratio such as 1:2:53, you have made a mistake. First check that you used atomic masses and not atomic numbers in step 1. Then check your arithmetic. It is easy to enter a wrong number into a calculator.

....
This is best done in the form of a table.

Worked example

A compound contained 34.3% sodium, 17.9% carbon and 47.8% oxygen by mass. Calculate its empirical formula.

Answer

Element	%	Divide by r.a.m.	Divide by the smallest	Ratio
Sodium	34.3	34.3/23.0 = 1.49	1.49/1.49 = 1	1
Carbon	17.9	17.9/12.0 = 1.49	1.49/1.49 = 1	1
Oxygen	47.8	47.8/16.0 = 2.99	2.99/1.49 = 2.01 = 2	2

The empirical formula is $NaCO_2$.

Test yourself

1 A compound of rubidium and oxygen contains 72.6% rubidium by mass. Calculate its empirical formula.

Calculation from masses on combustion

The masses of carbon dioxide and water produced when a known mass of a substance is burnt are measured. The mass of carbon in the carbon dioxide is calculated as mass of $CO_2 \times 12/44$. The mass of hydrogen is mass of water $\times 2/18$. The percentage of carbon and hydrogen are calculated and any oxygen in the compound is found by subtraction. The empirical formula is then worked out as in previous examples.

Worked example

2.22 g of an organic compound X containing carbon, hydrogen and oxygen only was burnt in excess air and 3.26 g of carbon dioxide and 1.33 g of water were obtained. Calculate the empirical formula of compound X.

Answer

mass of carbon = $3.26 \times 12/44 = 0.889$ g

mass of hydrogen = $1.33 \times 2/18 = 0.148$ g

mass of oxygen = $2.22 - 0.889 - 0.148 = 1.18$ g

% carbon = $0.889 \times 100/2.22 = 40.0\%$

% hydrogen = $0.148 \times 100/2.22 = 6.67\%$

% oxygen = $1.18 \times 100/2.22 = 53.2\%$

Element	%	Divide by r.a.m.	Divide by the smallest	Ratio
C	40	40/12 = 3.3	3.3/3.3	1
H	6.67	6.67/1 = 6.67	6.67/3.3	2
O	53.2	53.2/16 = 3.3	3.3/3.3	1

The empirical formula of X is CH_2O.

Test yourself

2 An organic compound Z of mass 3.33 g containing carbon, hydrogen and oxygen only was burnt in excess air. 7.33 g of carbon dioxide and 4.00 g of water were obtained. Calculate the empirical formula of compound Z.

Molecular formula from empirical formula

If the molar mass (or relative molecular mass) is known, the molecular formula can be derived from the empirical formula.

- First, the empirical mass is worked out. If this is the same numerical value as the molar mass, the molecular and empirical formulae are the same.
- If the empirical mass and molar mass are not the same, they will be in a simple ratio to each other. To find this ratio, divide the molar mass by the empirical mass. If the answer is 2, then the molecular formula is twice the empirical formula. If the answer is 3, the molecular formula is three times the empirical formula.

In the worked example above, the empirical mass of CH_2O is $12 + 2 + 16 = 30$.

Given that the molar mass of compound X is $60.0 \, \text{g mol}^{-1}$, the molecular formula can be derived:

$$\frac{\text{molar mass}}{\text{empirical mass}} = \frac{60}{30} = 2$$

Hence, the molecular formula = $2 \times CH_2O = C_2H_4O_2$.

Worked example

A compound contains 38.7% calcium, 20.0% phosphorus and 41.3% oxygen by mass. The molar mass of the compound is $310\,\mathrm{g\,mol^{-1}}$. Calculate:

a) its empirical formula

b) its molecular formula

Answer

a)

Element	Divide by r.a.m.	Divide by the smallest	Multiply by 2 to find the whole number ratio
Calcium	38.7/40.1 = 0.97	0.97/0.65 = 1.5	1.5 × 2 = 3
Phosphorus	20.0/31.0 = 0.65	0.65/0.65 = 1	1 × 2 = 2
Oxygen	41.3/16.0 = 2.58	2.58/0.65 = 4	4 × 2 = 8

The empirical formula is $Ca_3P_2O_8$.

b) empirical mass = $(3 \times 40.1) + (2 \times 31.0) + (8 \times 16.0) = 310.3$

This is numerically the same as the molar mass. Therefore, the molecular formula is $Ca_3P_2O_8$.

> **Tip**
>
> In exams you must show your working. In this case, you must make it clear that because the molar and empirical masses are the same, the two formulae are the same.

Calculation of molar mass

The molar mass of organic compounds can be found from mass spectra by measuring the m/z value of the molecular ion peak.

The molar mass of volatile liquids and gases can also be calculated using the ideal gas equation:

$$pV = nRT$$

where p = the pressure in Pa (which is the same as $\mathrm{N\,m^{-2}}$), V = the volume in $\mathrm{m^3}$, n = the number of moles, R is the gas constant = $8.31\,\mathrm{J\,K^{-1}\,mol^{-1}}$ = $8.31\,\mathrm{N\,m\,K^{-1}\,mol^{-1}}$ and T is the kelvin temperature ($x°\mathrm{C} = (273 + x)\,\mathrm{K}$).

A sample of the unknown is weighed accurately and then vaporised at a known temperature. Its volume and the pressure are measured. The values are substituted into the ideal gas equation and the number of moles calculated. The molar mass can then be calculated using moles = mass/molar mass.

> **Tip**
>
> $1\,\mathrm{cm^3} = 1 \times 10^{-6}\,\mathrm{m^3}$ and $1\,\mathrm{dm^3} = 1 \times 10^{-3}\,\mathrm{m^3}$
>
> $100\,\mathrm{kPa} = 100\,000\,\mathrm{Pa} = 100\,000\,\mathrm{N\,m^{-2}}$

Worked example 1

a) 1.23 g of a hydrocarbon was burnt in excess oxygen. The water produced was adsorbed in silica gel and the carbon dioxide adsorbed by calcium oxide. The mass of water produced was 1.58 g and the mass of carbon dioxide was 3.87 g. Calculate its empirical formula.

b) 0.284 g of the same liquid hydrocarbon was injected into a gas syringe. This was then placed in an oven at 150°C where it fully vaporised. Its volume was 84.3 cm³ and the pressure was 106 kPa. Calculate the molar mass of the hydrocarbon and, using the answer to a), evaluate its molecular formula.

Answer

a) *Either:* mass of C = 3.87 × 12/44 = 1.055 g

%C = 1.055 × 100/1.23 = 85.8%   %H = 100 − 85.8 = 14.2%

or: mass of H = 1.58 × 2/18 = 0.1756 g

%H = 0.1756 × 100/1.23 = 14.3%   %C = 100 − 14.3 = 85.7%

Element	%	% + A_r	+ smallest
C 85.8	7.15	7.15/7.15	= 1
H 14.2	14.2	14.2/7.15	= 1.99 = 2

The empirical formula is CH_2.

b) $p = 106\,kPa = 106\,000\,Pa\ (= 106\,000\,N\,m^{-2})$

$V = 84.3\,cm^3 = 8.43 \times 10^{-5}\,m^3$

$T = 150 + 273 = 423\,K$

$R = 8.31\,J\,K^{-1}\,mol^{-1} = 8.31\,N\,m\,K^{-1}\,mol^{-1}$

$$n = \frac{pV}{RT} = \frac{106\,000 \times 8.43 \times 10^{-5}}{8.31 \times 423} = 0.00254\,mol$$

$$\text{molar mass} = \frac{\text{mass}}{\text{moles}} = \frac{0.284\,g}{0.00254\,mol} = 112\,g\,mol^{-1}$$

$$\frac{\text{molar mass}}{\text{empirical mass}} = \frac{112}{14} = 8$$

The molecular formula is C_8H_{16}.

Tip

The pressure must be converted to Pa. The volume must be converted to m³.

The units of pV/RT are $N\,m^{-2} \times m^3 / N\,m\,K^{-1}\,mol^{-1} \times K = mol$

Worked example 2

An acid prepared from rhubarb leaves contains 2.2% hydrogen, 26.7% carbon and 71.1% oxygen by mass.

a) Calculate its empirical formula.

b) The molecular ion peak in the mass spectrum of this acid had a *m/z* value of 90. Calculate its molecular formula.

Answer

a)

Element	Divide by r.a.m.	Divide by the smallest
Hydrogen	2.2/1 = 2.2	2.2/2.2 = 1
Carbon	26.7/12 = 2.2	2.2/2.2 = 1
Oxygen	71.1/16 = 4.4	4.4/2.2 = 2

The empirical formula is HCO_2.

b) empirical mass = 12 + 1 + (2 × 16) = 45

molecular mass = *m/z* value = 90

This is twice the empirical mass, so the molecular formula is $H_2C_2O_4$.

Ionic compounds

- Ionic compounds are made up of cations and anions.
- Aqueous solutions of metal compounds are ionic.

Cations

A cation is a positive ion formed by the loss of one or more electrons from an atom. Metals form cations.

The charges on some cations are shown in Table 8.1. The roman numerals in parentheses give the value of the positive charge on the cation in a compound. This is needed if the metal forms ions of more than one charge. For example, iron can lose two electrons and form Fe^{2+} ions or it can lose three electrons and form Fe^{3+} ions. Compounds containing Fe^{2+} ions are called iron(II) compounds; those containing Fe^{3+} ions are called iron(III) compounds.

Table 8.1 Cations and their charges

	1+ ions	2+ ions	3+ ions
Group 1	Li^+, Na^+, Rb^+, Cs^+		
Group 2		Be^{2+}, Mg^{2+}, Ca^{2+}, Sr^{2+}, Ba^{2+}	
Group 3			Al^{3+}
d-block	Ag^+	Zn^{2+}	Cr^{3+} in chromium(III) compounds
	Cu^+ in copper(I) compounds	Mn^{2+} in manganese(II) compounds	Fe^{3+} in iron(III) compounds
		Fe^{2+} in iron(II) compounds	
		Cu^{2+} in copper(II) compounds	
Ammonium	NH_4^+		

NH_4^+ is a polyatomic ion as it contains more than one atom.

Anions

- An anion is a negative ion that has been formed by the gain of one or more electrons.
- Some non-metals form anions.
- **Polyatomic anions** contain more than one element. One of the elements is usually oxygen. For example, carbonates contain the CO_3^{2-} anion.

The anions that you need to know in the first A-level year are shown, with their charges, in Table 8.2.

How to work out the formula of an ionic compound

Ionic compounds consist of positive and negative ions held together in the solid by the attraction between their opposite charges. In solution, these ions are separated by water molecules.

The formula of an ionic compound shows the *ratio* of cations to anions. In sodium chloride, NaCl, there is one Na^+ ion for every Cl^- ion. In calcium chloride, $CaCl_2$, there are two Cl^- ions for every Ca^{2+} ion.

Table 8.2 Anions and their charges

	Name	1– ions	2– ions	3– ions
Group 7	Fluoride	F^-		
	Chloride	Cl^-		
	Bromide	Br^-		
	Iodide	I^-		
Group 6	Oxide		O^{2-}	
	Sulfide		S^{2-}	
Group 5	Nitride			N^{3-}
Polyatomic ions	Hydroxide	OH^-		
	Nitrate	NO_3^-		
	Hydrogencarbonate	HCO_3^-		
	Manganate(VII)	MnO_4^-		
	Chlorate(I)	OCl^-		
	Chlorate(V)	ClO_3^-		
	Cyanide	CN^-		
	Superoxide	O_2^-		
	Peroxide		O_2^{2-}	
	Carbonate		CO_3^{2-}	
	Sulfate		SO_4^{2-}	
	Sulfite		SO_3^{2-}	
	Chromate(VI)		CrO_4^{2-}	
	Dichromate(VI)		$Cr_2O_7^{2-}$	
	Thiosulfate		$S_2O_3^{2-}$	
	Phosphate			PO_4^{3-}

The ratio of ions in a particular compound is worked out, based on the fact that the compound is neutral.

Rule 1: If the numerical charge on the ions is the same, the ratio is one cation to one anion.

Worked example

What is the formula of sodium hydroxide?

Answer

The ions are Na^+ and OH^-. They have the same numerical charge.

The formula of sodium hydroxide is NaOH.

Rule 2: If the numerical charges are not the same, the numbers of each ion have to be worked out so that the total positive charge equals the total negative charge.

- Write down the formulae of the ions, including their charges.
- Find the lowest common multiple of the two charges. This equals the charge on the ion multiplied by the numbers of that ion in the formula.
- Work out how many of each ion is needed to give this total charge.

Some examples of the application of rule 2 are shown below.

Worked example 1

Work out the formula of aluminium oxide.

Answer

The ions are Al^{3+} and O^{2-}. The lowest common multiple of 3 and 2 is 6.

For a charge of +6, two Al^{3+} ions are needed; for a charge of −6, three O^{2-} ions are needed.

The formula of aluminium oxide is Al_2O_3.

Tip

Parentheses are placed round the polyatomic HCO_3. This *must* be done if there is more than one of that polyatomic ion in the formula:

- calcium hydroxide is $Ca(OH)_2$, *not* $CaOH_2$
- iron(III) sulfate is $Fe_2(SO_4)_3$
- ammonium carbonate is $(NH_4)_2CO_3$

Worked example 2

Work out the formula of calcium hydrogencarbonate.

Answer

The ions are Ca^{2+} and HCO_3^-. The lowest common multiple of 2 and 1 is 2.

For a charge of +2, one Ca^{2+} ion is needed; for a charge of −2, two HCO_3^- ions are needed.

The formula of calcium hydrogencarbonate is $Ca(HCO_3)_2$.

An alternative way to work out formulae using rule 2 is the 'swapping-over' method. If the charges are not the same, the number of cations is equal to the value of the charge on the anion and the number of anions is equal to the value of the charge on the cation. Some examples of the swapping-over method are shown below.

Worked example 1

What is the formula of sodium carbonate?

Answer

The ions are Na^+ and CO_3^{2-}.

Sodium is 1^+, so there must be one carbonate ion. The carbonate ion is 2^-, so there must be two sodium ions.

$$Na^{1+} \quad CO_3^{2-}$$

The formula of sodium carbonate is Na_2CO_3.

Tip

You must not use the swapping-over method if the values of the charges are the same. It only applies when the values are different.

Worked example 2

What is the formula of aluminium sulfate?

Answer

The ions are Al^{3+} and SO_4^{2-}.

Aluminium is 3^+, so there must be three sulfate ions. The sulfate ion is 2^-, so there must be two aluminium ions.

The formula of aluminium sulfate is $Al_2(SO_4)_3$.

Tip

The ionic charges are usually left out when writing the formula of an ionic substance.

Test yourself

3 Write the formulae of the following ionic compounds:

a) calcium chloride   c) copper(ɪɪ) phosphate

b) silver nitrate   d) aluminium oxide

Hydrated ionic compounds

Many solid ionic compounds contain water of crystallisation. The number of water molecules in the formula of a hydrated compound is given by a full stop followed by the number of molecules of water. For instance, a formula unit of solid hydrated sodium carbonate contains ten molecules of water of crystallisation, so its formula is $Na_2CO_3.10H_2O$.

Molar masses of ionic compounds

Molar masses of ionic compounds are calculated in the same way as molar masses of molecular substances. For example:

molar mass of barium chloride, $BaCl_2 = 137.3 + (2 \times 35.5)$

$$= 208.3 \, g \, mol^{-1}$$

If an ionic compound contains water of crystallisation, the mass of water must also be taken into account. For example:

molar mass of hydrated copper(ɪɪ) sulfate, $CuSO_4.5H_2O$

$= 63.5 + 32.1 + (4 \times 16.0) + (5 \times 18.0)$

$= 249.6 \, g \, mol^{-1}$

or $250 \, g \, mol^{-1}$ to three significant figures

Note that the molar mass of water is $18 \, g \, mol^{-1}$.

Test yourself

4 Calculate the molar mass of ethanedioic acid, $H_2C_2O_4.2H_2O$.

Dissolving ionic substances

Many ionic compounds are soluble in water. This is because of the strong forces of attraction between the positive cation and the slightly negative oxygen atom in a water molecule, and between the negative anion and the slightly positive hydrogen atom in a water molecule.

Equations representing the dissolving of ionic compounds have the formula of the ionic compound on the left and the *separate* ions on the right. State symbols must be included (see page 130).

The equation for dissolving sodium chloride in water is:

$$NaCl(s) + aq \rightarrow Na^+(aq) + Cl^-(aq)$$

The equation for dissolving iron(III) sulfate in water is:

$$Fe_2(SO_4)_3(s) + aq \rightarrow 2Fe^{3+}(aq) + 3SO_4^{2-}(aq)$$

The symbol 'aq' stands for an unspecified number of water molecules. It comes from *aqua*, the Latin for water.

Chemical equations

- Chemical equations show the formulae of the reactants on the left-hand side and the formulae of the products on the right-hand side.
- The number of atoms of each element must be the same on the left as on the right.

Copper(II) oxide reacts with dilute hydrochloric acid to form copper(II) chloride and water. Therefore, in the equation, CuO and HCl are on the left and $CuCl_2$ and H_2O are on the right:

$$CuO + HCl \rightarrow CuCl_2 + H_2O$$

However, this equation does not balance. There is only one chlorine atom on the left, but two on the right. It also does not balance for hydrogen. To balance the equation a '2' must be put in front of the formula HCl.

The balanced equation is:

$$CuO + 2HCl \rightarrow CuCl_2 + H_2O$$

The equation means that 1 mol of copper(II) oxide reacts with 2 mol of hydrochloric acid to form 1 mol of copper(II) chloride and 1 mol of water.

The quantitative relationship in moles of the reactants and products is called the **stoichiometry** of the reaction.

Tip

Remember that a chemical equation not only identifies the products that are formed in the reaction, but also the molar ratio of the reactants and the products.

Balancing equations

Some equations do not need balancing. For example, the equations for the combustion of sulfur and the reaction between magnesium oxide and sulfuric acid are already balanced:

$$S + O_2 \rightarrow SO_2$$
$$MgO + H_2SO_4 \rightarrow MgSO_4 + H_2O$$

For equations that do need balancing, adopt the following strategy:

- Select the element that appears in the fewest number of species in the equation and balance it first.

Tip

Equations must always balance. *Never* write word equations. They will not score any marks.

- If there are two of these, start with the one with the least number of atoms in the formula.
- Then balance the next element, until all are balanced.
- Count groups such as sulfate, SO_4, and nitrate, NO_3, as entities rather than counting separate sulfur and oxygen atoms or nitrogen and oxygen atoms.

Tip

Never balance an equation by altering any formulae. Only the numbers in front of formulae may be altered.

Worked example 1

Consider the combustion of propane, C_3H_8, which burns in excess air to form carbon dioxide and water. The unbalanced equation is:

$$C_3H_8 + O_2 \rightarrow CO_2 + H_2O$$

- Carbon and hydrogen both appear in only two species, but oxygen appears in three.
- There are fewer carbon atoms than hydrogen atoms in propane, so start by balancing carbon. There are three carbon atoms on the left, so put a '3' in front of CO_2 to balance the carbon atoms.

$$C_3H_8 + O_2 \rightarrow 3CO_2 + H_2O$$

- Now balance for hydrogen. There are eight hydrogen atoms on the left, so there needs to be $4H_2O$ to get eight hydrogen atoms on the right.

$$C_3H_8 + O_2 \rightarrow 3CO_2 + 4H_2O$$

- Last, balance for oxygen. There are six oxygen atoms in $3CO_2$ and four oxygen atoms in $4H_2O$, so there has to be ten oxygen atoms or $5O_2$ on the left.

The balanced equation is:

$$C_3H_8 + 5O_2 \rightarrow 3CO_2 + 4H_2O$$

Worked example 2

A more difficult example is the combustion of ethane, C_2H_6, to form carbon dioxide and water. The unbalanced equation is:

$$C_2H_6 + O_2 \rightarrow CO_2 + H_2O$$

- Start with carbon. Put '2' as the coefficient of CO_2, then balance for hydrogen by putting '3' in front of H_2O.
- The number of oxygen atoms on the right is four (in $2CO_2$) plus three (in $3H_2O$), which is seven. Unfortunately, oxygen is diatomic. You have a choice:
  - Obtain seven oxygen atoms by having $3\frac{1}{2}O_2$ on the left. This is acceptable, as the molar ratio of ethane to oxygen would be $1:3\frac{1}{2}$. The half means half a mole, not half a molecule. The equation is:

$$C_2H_6 + 3\frac{1}{2}O_2 \rightarrow 2CO_2 + 3H_2O$$

  - Solve the problem of the odd number of oxygen atoms needed on the left by doubling the equation, which then becomes:

$$2C_2H_6 + 7O_2 \rightarrow 4CO_2 + 6H_2O$$

The ratios in the two equations are the same: $1:3\frac{1}{2}$ is the same ratio as 2:7.

Full equations have the full formulae for both molecular and ionic substances. The equations in the worked examples above are full equations.

State symbols

State symbols show the physical state of the substances in an equation. They are listed in Table 8.3.

Table 8.3 State symbols

Physical state	Solid	Liquid	Gas	Aqueous solution
State symbol	(s)	(l)	(g)	(aq)

Unless the question states that they are not required, state symbols should always be added to an equation:

- when a gas is produced from a solution or from a liquid
- when a precipitate is formed
- if it is a thermochemical equation (see Chapter 13)
- if it is an ionic equation

For example, the equation for the reaction of solid calcium carbonate with dilute nitric acid to give calcium nitrate, carbon dioxide and water is:

$$CaCO_3(s) + 2HNO_3(aq) \rightarrow Ca(NO_3)_2(aq) + CO_2(g) + H_2O(l)$$

The equation for the precipitation of copper(II) hydroxide from solutions of copper(II) sulfate and sodium hydroxide is:

$$CuSO_4(aq) + 2NaOH(aq) \rightarrow Cu(OH)_2(s) + Na_2SO_4(aq)$$

All nitrates are soluble in water.

All sodium salts are soluble.

Solubility of ionic solids

Knowledge of the solubility and insolubility of ionic compounds makes writing ionic equations much more straightforward.

Many ionic solids are soluble in water:

- All group 1 metal compounds are soluble.
- All ammonium compounds are soluble.
- All nitrates are soluble.
- All chlorides are soluble, apart from silver chloride and lead(II) chloride.
- All sulfates are soluble in water, apart from strontium sulfate, barium sulfate and lead(II) sulfate. Calcium sulfate is only very slightly soluble.

Some types of ionic compound are mostly insoluble in water:

- All carbonates are insoluble, apart from group 1 carbonates and ammonium carbonate.
- All hydroxides are insoluble, apart from group 1 hydroxides, ammonium hydroxide and barium hydroxide. Calcium and strontium hydroxides are slightly soluble.

Ionic equations

The essential character of a precipitation reaction, such as that between copper(II) sulfate and sodium hydroxide to form a precipitate of copper(II) hydroxide in a solution of sodium sulfate, becomes clear when a **net ionic equation** is written.

The rules for writing ionic equations are as follows:

Rule 1: Write the full equation and balance it. Then write another equation using rules 2, 3 and 4.

Rule 2: For dissolved ionic substances, write the ions separately.

Rule 3: For all solids (whether ionic or not), all liquids and all gases, write the full formula.

Rule 4: Cross out all the 'spectator' ions, i.e. those that appear separately on both sides of the equation.

Using the example of the reaction between copper(II) sulfate and sodium hydroxide, rule 1 gives:

$$CuSO_4(aq) + 2NaOH(aq) \rightarrow Cu(OH)_2(s) + Na_2SO_4(aq)$$

From this full equation, the application of rules 2 and 3 results in:

$$Cu^{2+}(aq) + \textbf{SO}_4{}^{2-}\textbf{(aq)} + \textbf{2Na}^+\textbf{(aq)} + 2OH^-(aq) \rightarrow$$
$$Cu(OH)_2(s) + \textbf{2Na}^+\textbf{(aq)} + \textbf{SO}_4{}^{2-}\textbf{(aq)}$$

The spectator ions are in bold type. Apply rule 4 by crossing out the $SO_4{}^{2-}$ ion on the left with the $SO_4{}^{2-}$ ion on the right and the $2Na^+$ ions on the left with the $2Na^+$ ions on the right. The net ionic equation is:

$$Cu^{2+}(aq) + 2OH^-(aq) \rightarrow Cu(OH)_2(s)$$

Thinking about what happens in a reaction can speed up the process of writing ionic equations. Copper(II) hydroxide is precipitated, so copper ions must have reacted with hydroxide ions. Therefore, the ionic equation must be:

$$Cu^{2+}(aq) + 2OH^-(aq) \rightarrow Cu(OH)_2(s)$$

Similarly, when solutions of silver nitrate and sodium chloride are mixed, a precipitate of silver chloride is formed. This means that silver ions must have joined with chloride ions to form insoluble silver chloride. Therefore, the ionic equation is:

$$Ag^+(aq) + Cl^-(aq) \rightarrow AgCl(s)$$

The nitrate and sodium ions are the **spectator ions**.

Strong acids, such as hydrochloric (HCl), sulfuric (H_2SO_4) and nitric (HNO_3), are fully ionised in solution. They are acidic because of the $H^+(aq)$ ions in the solution. When an acid reacts with a base, it is the $H^+(aq)$ ions that react.

> **Tip**
>
> You should practise ionic equations because they are frequently asked for.

Worked example

Write the ionic equation for the reaction of magnesium with dilute hydrochloric acid. The general reaction is:

acid + metal → salt + hydrogen

Answer

The 'long way' of doing this is to follow the rules above.

Rule 1:

$$Mg(s) + HCl(aq) \rightarrow MgCl_2(aq) + H_2(g)$$

Balance the equation:

$$Mg(s) + 2HCl(aq) \rightarrow MgCl_2(aq) + H_2(g)$$

Rules 2 and 3: split dissolved ionic substances into separate ions:

$$Mg(s) + 2H^+(aq) + \mathbf{2Cl^-(aq)} \rightarrow Mg^{2+}(aq) + \mathbf{2Cl^-(aq)} + H_2(g)$$

Rule 4: cancel the spectator ions (in bold), which are the $2Cl^-$ ions on each side, to give:

$$Mg(s) + 2H^+(aq) \rightarrow Mg^{2+}(aq) + H_2(g)$$

The 'short way' is to understand that the reactions of acids involve H^+ ions. Therefore, the reaction is between magnesium atoms and hydrogen ions. As salts are ionic compounds containing metal ions, the ionic equation is:

$$Mg(s) + 2H^+(aq) \rightarrow Mg^{2+}(aq) + H_2(g)$$

The type of reaction between solid aluminium oxide, which is a base, and dilute sulfuric acid is:

acid + base → salt + water

The reaction is essentially between Al_2O_3 and H^+ ions. Therefore, the ionic equation is:

$$Al_2O_3(s) + 6H^+(aq) \rightarrow 2Al^{3+}(aq) + 3H_2O(l)$$

This is a much simpler equation than the full equation:

$$Al_2O_3(s) + 3H_2SO_4(aq) \rightarrow Al_2(SO_4)_3(aq) + 3H_2O(l)$$

> You must check that ionic equations balance for charge as well as for atoms.

Equations based on test tube reactions

Displacement reactions

- Metals react with solutions containing ions of a metal below them in the reactivity series. Zinc reacts with copper sulfate solution. The blue solution goes colourless and a red solid is produced.

  Full equation: $Zn(s) + CuSO_4(aq) \rightarrow ZnSO_4(aq) + Cu(s)$

  Ionic equation: $Zn(s) + Cu^{2+}(aq) \rightarrow Zn^{2+}(aq) + Cu(s)$

- Halogens react with a solution containing the ions of a less reactive halogen. Chlorine reacts with potassium iodide solution to give a red-brown solution.

  Full equation: $Cl_2(g) + 2KI(aq) \rightarrow I_2(aq) + 2KCl(aq)$

  Ionic equation: $Cl_2(g) + 2I^-(aq) \rightarrow I_2(aq) + 2Cl^-(aq)$

Reaction of acids

- Acids react with many metals to give bubbles of hydrogen and a salt. Zinc reacts with sulfuric acid:

  Full equation: $Zn(s) + H_2SO_4(aq) \rightarrow H_2(g) + ZnSO_4(aq)$

  Ionic equation: $Zn(s) + 2H^+(aq) \rightarrow H_2(g) + Zn^{2+}(aq)$

- Acids react with bases to form a salt and water. Calcium oxide reacts with hydrochloric acid:

  Full equation: $CaO(s) + 2HCl(aq) \rightarrow CaCl_2(aq) + H_2O(l)$

  Ionic equation: $CaO(s) + 2H^+(aq) \rightarrow Ca^{2+}(aq) + H_2O(l)$

- Acids react with carbonates to give a salt, bubbles of carbon dioxide and water. A solution of sodium carbonate reacts with nitric acid:

  Full equation: $Na_2CO_3(aq) + 2HNO_3(aq) \rightarrow$
  $$2NaNO_3(aq) + CO_2(g) + H_2O(l)$$

  Ionic equation: $CO_3{}^{2-}(aq) + 2H^+(aq) \rightarrow CO_2(g) + H_2O(l)$

Precipitation reactions

- Insoluble salts can be prepared by adding solutions containing their constituent ions. For example, barium sulfate can be made by adding solutions of barium chloride to dilute sulfuric acid (or any sulfate):

  Full equation: $BaCl_2(aq) + H_2SO_4(aq) \rightarrow BaSO_4(s) + 2HCl(aq)$

  Ionic equation: $Ba^{2+}(aq) + SO_4{}^{2-}(aq) \rightarrow BaSO_4(s)$

Mole calculations

The mole

In chemistry, the **amount of substance** is always measured in moles.

The Avogadro constant, L or N_A, is equal to the number of carbon atoms in exactly 12 g of the carbon-12 isotope.

1 mole of some substances

The value of the Avogadro constant, to three significant figures, is $6.02 \times 10^{23}\,\mathrm{mol}^{-1}$.

- 1 mol of sodium contains 6.02×10^{23} sodium atoms.
- 1 mol of water contains 6.02×10^{23} water molecules.
- 1 mol of sodium chloride, NaCl, contains 6.02×10^{23} pairs of Na^+ and Cl^- ions, which is 6.02×10^{23} sodium ions and 6.02×10^{23} chloride ions.
- 1 mol of calcium chloride, $CaCl_2$, contains 6.02×10^{23} calcium ions and $2 \times 6.02 \times 10^{23} = 1.204 \times 10^{24}$ chloride ions.

The symbol for the mole is mol.

In most calculations it is simpler to use the following relationships:

1 mol of any substance equals the relative molecular mass measured in grams.

The molar mass of a substance is the mass of 1 mol of that substance and has units of $g\,mol^{-1}$.

The molar mass can be calculated from the relative atomic, molecular or formula mass.

The term formula mass and not molecular mass should be used for ionic substances.

- Sodium has a relative atomic mass of 23.0, so its molar mass is $23.0\,\mathrm{g\,mol^{-1}}$.
- Water has a relative molecular mass of $(1.0 + 1.0 + 16.0) = 18.0$, so its molar mass is $18.0\,\mathrm{g\,mol^{-1}}$.
- Sodium chloride has a formula mass of $23.0 + 35.5 = 58.5$, so its molar mass is $58.5\,\mathrm{g\,mol^{-1}}$.

Conversions

Conversions involving moles and mass are crucial to many calculations in A-level chemistry.

This is commonly expressed as $\text{moles} = \dfrac{\text{mass}}{\text{molar mass}}$

$$\text{amount of substance (moles)} = \frac{\text{mass of substance}}{\text{molar mass of substance}}$$

Some students like to use the 'mole triangle' (Figure 8.1) to help with this sort of calculation.

- The top (mass) = the two factors at the base (moles and molar mass) multiplied together.
- Either factor at the base (moles or molar mass) = the top divided by the other factor at the base.

Therefore:

$$\text{mass} = \text{moles} \times \text{molar mass}$$

$$\text{moles} = \frac{\text{mass}}{\text{molar mass}}$$

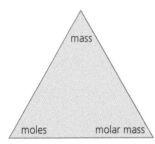

Figure 8.1 The mole triangle

$$\text{molar mass} = \frac{\text{mass}}{\text{moles}}$$

Calculations become easier and more reliable if the units for all quantities are put into the calculation. Some people find this a burden at first, but with practice it becomes second nature.

Tip

Practise putting units into all your calculations, both in your homework and in examinations. It is an important check to see if you are doing the calculation correctly.

Mass to mole

Worked example 1

Calculate the amount (in moles) of iron in 1.23 g.

Answer

$$\text{amount of iron} = \frac{\text{mass}}{\text{molar mass}} = \frac{1.23\,\text{g}}{55.8\,\text{g mol}^{-1}} = 0.0220\,\text{mol}$$

Worked example 2

Calculate the amount (in moles) of water in 4.56 g.

Answer

$$\text{amount of water} = \frac{\text{mass}}{\text{molar mass}} = \frac{4.56\,\text{g}}{18.0\,\text{g mol}^{-1}} = 0.253\,\text{mol}$$

Tip

Note that the identity of the chemical (iron or water) is stated in each calculation. In all but the simplest calculations, phrases such as 'moles = 0.0710' can be misleading.

Tip

Note that the unit g cancels leaving mol^{-1} on the bottom, which is the same as mol on the top. This is a check that you have the calculation the right way up. Had you thought that amount (in moles) = molar mass/mass, the calculation would have been:

$$\text{amount} = \frac{55.8\,\text{g mol}^{-1}}{1.23\,\text{g}} = 45.4\,\text{mol}^{-1}$$

This answer has the wrong unit for amount of substance, so your 'formula' must have been wrong.

Mole to mass

Worked example 1

Calculate the mass of 0.0222 mol of sodium hydroxide, NaOH (molar mass 40.0 g mol^{-1}).

Answer

mass = molar mass × amount of substance (moles)

mass of sodium hydroxide = $40.0\,\text{g mol}^{-1} \times 0.0222\,\text{mol} = 0.888\,\text{g}$

Worked example 2

Calculate the mass of 0.0333 mol of sulfuric acid, H_2SO_4.

Answer

molar mass of sulfuric acid = $(2 \times 1.0) + 32.1 + (4 \times 16.0) = 98.1\,\text{g mol}^{-1}$

mass of sulfuric acid = molar mass × amount (moles) = $98.1\,\text{g mol}^{-1} \times 0.0333\,\text{mol} = 3.27\,\text{g}$

Tip

Note that the mol^{-1} cancels out the mol, leaving the unit g, which is the correct unit for mass. Had you thought that mass = molar mass/moles, the calculation would have been:

$$\text{amount} = \frac{40.0\,\text{g mol}^{-1}}{0.0222\,\text{mol}} = 1802\,\text{g mol}^{-2}$$

This answer has an absurd unit and an unlikely large mass. Do think about the magnitude of your answer — examiners see many examples of students leaving ridiculous answers.

Mass and moles to molar mass

Worked example 1

0.0222 mol of an oxide of sulfur has a mass of 1.42 g. Calculate its molar mass.

Answer

$$\text{molar mass of the sulfur oxide} = \frac{\text{mass}}{\text{moles}} = \frac{1.42\,\text{g}}{0.0222\,\text{mol}} = 64.0\,\text{g mol}^{-1}$$

Analysis of the units in the calculation gives the correct unit of g mol^{-1} in the answer.

Worked example 2

0.0500 mol of an organic acid had a mass of 3.00 g. Calculate the molar mass of the acid.

Answer

$$\text{molar mass of the sulfur oxide} = \frac{\text{mass}}{\text{moles}} = \frac{3.00\,\text{g}}{0.0500\,\text{mol}} = 60.0\,\text{g mol}^{-1}$$

Test yourself

7 Calculate:

   a) the amount of substance (moles) in 4.44 g of sodium sulfate, Na_2SO_4

   b) the mass of 0.022 moles of magnesium chloride, $MgCl_2$

   c) the molar mass of a substance where 0.00575 moles has a mass of 0.2645 g

---

Volume and pressure of gas to molar mass
The ideal gas law is:

$$pV = nRT$$

or

$$pV = \frac{mRT}{M}$$

where p is the pressure in Pa, V is the volume in m³, n is the number of moles, m is the mass in g, M *is* the molar mass in g mol^{-1}, and T is the temperature in kelvin. The gas constant $R = 8.31\,\text{J K}^{-1}\text{mol}^{-1}$.

If a gas is produced from a solution, the mass of the solution lost equals the mass of gas produced.

Worked example

25 cm³ of a 0.75 mol dm⁻³ solution of sodium nitrite was placed in a conical flask and weighed. Using a pipette, 25 cm³ of a 1.0 mol dm⁻³ solution of ammonium chloride was added and the flask quickly connected to a gas syringe and placed on an electric heater and gently warmed. The two solutions reacted, giving off a gas. When all bubbles had ceased, the flask was weighed. The laboratory temperature and pressure were measured.

- mass of flask + sodium nitrite = 143.65 g
- mass of ammonium chloride solution = 25.00 g
- mass of flask after reaction = 168.60 g
- volume of gas evolved = 45 cm^3 = 4.5×10^{-5} m^3
- room temperature = 18.5°C = 291.5 K
- room pressure = 101 kPa = 101 000 Pa

Given that the gas constant, R, = 8.31 J K^{-1} mol^{-1} calculate the molar mass of the gas and hence suggest its identity.

Tip

All measurements of the gas must be in the basic SI units, i.e. pressure in Pa, volume in m^3 and temperature in K.

Answer

mass of flask + solutions before reaction = 143.65 + 25.00 = 168.65 g

mass lost in flask = 168.65 − 168.60 = 0.05 g = mass of gas produced

moles of gas, n, = $\dfrac{pV}{RT}$ = $(101\,000 \times 4.5 \times 10^{-5})/(8.31 \times 291.5)$ = 0.00188 mol

molar mass = $\dfrac{\text{mass}}{\text{moles}}$ = 0.05/0.00188 = 27 g mol^{-1}

The gas is likely to be nitrogen or an oxide of nitrogen. The one that most closely fits is nitrogen, molar mass 28 g mol^{-1}.

Molar mass of a volatile liquid

A two-necked flask of volume 250 cm^3 was weighed and then placed in a thermostatic tank and allowed to reach equilibrium. A gas syringe was attached and a small amount of volatile liquid was injected through a self-sealing cap and the volume of air displaced into the syringe was measured. The flask was then taken from the tank and allowed to cool. It was then reweighed, now containing air and the condensed volatile liquid.

mass of volatile liquid in the flask = mass at end − mass at beginning

The values for temperature, pressure, volume and mass were then substituted as in the worked example above and the molar mass calculated in the same way.

Neither of these methods is accurate, but a reasonable value enables the molecular formula to be accurately calculated from the empirical formula.

Worked example

A volatile liquid was found, by the method above, to have a molar mass = 94 g mol^{-1}. Its empirical formula is CH_2Cl. Calculate its molecular formula.

Answer

empirical mass = 12 + 2 + 35.5 = 49.5 g mol^{-1}

$\dfrac{\text{molar mass}}{\text{empirical mass}} = \dfrac{94}{49.5} = 1.90$

This must be a whole number, so the molar mass is twice the empirical mass and the molecular formula is twice the empirical formula = $C_2H_4Cl_2$.

Moles and mass to identity

The identity of a substance or one of its ions can be worked out from mass and amount of substance data.

Worked example 1

An alkene has the empirical formula CH_2. 0.075 mol of the alkene has a mass of 2.1 g. Calculate its molar mass and hence its molecular formula.

Answer

$$\text{molar mass} = \frac{\text{mass}}{\text{moles}} = \frac{2.1\,g}{0.075\,mol} = 28\,g\,mol^{-1}$$

This is twice the empirical mass of 14.0, so the molecular formula is twice the empirical formula, or C_2H_4.

Worked example 2

0.100 mol of hydrated sodium carbonate, $Na_2CO_3.xH_2O$, has a mass of 28.6 g. Calculate its molar mass and hence the number of molecules of water of crystallisation.

Answer

First, use the mass of the hydrated salt and the number of moles given in the question to work out the molar mass of the hydrated salt. Then calculate the mass and hence the moles of water in 1 mol of the solid.

$$\text{molar mass of hydrated sodium carbonate} = \frac{\text{mass}}{\text{moles}}$$

$$= \frac{28.6\,g}{0.100\,mol} = 286\,g\,mol^{-1}$$

mass of $Na_2CO_3 = (2 \times 23.0) + 12.0 + (3 \times 16.0) = 106.0\,g$

mass of water $= 286\,g - 106\,g = 180\,g$

There are 180 g of water in 1 mol of the hydrated solid.

$$\text{amount (moles) of water} = \frac{180\,g}{18.0\,g\,mol^{-1}}$$

$$= 10.0\,mol \text{ in 1 mol of solid}$$

The number of molecules of water of crystallisation is 10.

> This number is the sum of the mass of Na_2CO_3 and the mass of the water in 1 mol of the hydrated salt.

Tip

If the data are produced by experiment, the amount of water might be calculated as a number very close to 10, say 9.98. You cannot have 9.98 molecules of water. The discrepancy is due to experimental error. In this type of calculation, you must round your answer to the nearest whole number.

Worked example 3

0.0250 mol of a group 2 sulfate has a mass of 4.60 g. Calculate the molar mass of the sulfate and hence identify the group 2 metal ion in the compound.

Answer

$$\text{molar mass} = \frac{\text{mass}}{\text{moles}} = \frac{4.60\,\text{g}}{0.0250\,\text{mol}} = 184\,\text{g mol}^{-1}$$

The formula of group 2 sulfates is of the form MSO_4, where M represents the group 2 metal. Of the 184 g mol^{-1}, $32.1 + (4 \times 16.0) = 96.1$ g comes from the SO_4 group. Therefore:

$$\text{molar mass of the group 2 metal} = 184\,\text{g mol}^{-1} - 96.1\,\text{g mol}^{-1}$$
$$= 87.9\,\text{g mol}^{-1}$$

From the periodic table, the group 2 metal that has a molar mass nearest to 87.9 g mol^{-1} is strontium, Sr.

The difference between the calculated value of 87.9 and the correct value of 87.6 is due to experimental errors.

Mole to number of particles

This type of calculation often causes confusion. The answer is always a fantastically large number of many billions.

- The calculation is based on the definitions of the mole and of the Avogadro constant (page 134).
- The unit of the Avogadro constant is mol^{-1}, so to get a number, which is dimensionless and so has no unit, this must be multiplied by mol.

number of molecules = amount of substance (moles) × Avogadro constant

Therefore:

$$\text{number of water molecules in 1.44 mol water} = 1.44\,\text{mol} \times 6.02 \times 10^{23}\,\text{mol}^{-1}$$
$$= 8.67 \times 10^{23}$$

Usually you will have to work out the amount (moles) first.

Worked example 1

Calculate the number of molecules in 3.33 g of methane, CH_4 (molar mass = 16.0 g mol^{-1}).

Answer

$$\text{amount of methane} = \frac{\text{mass}}{\text{molar mass}} = \frac{3.33\,\text{g}}{16.0\,\text{g mol}^{-1}} = 0.208\,\text{mol}$$

$$\text{number of molecules} = 0.208\,\text{mol} \times 6.02 \times 10^{23}\,\text{mol}^{-1} = 1.25 \times 10^{23}$$

Calculations of the number of ions require an extra step.

Worked example 2

Calculate the number of sodium ions in 2.22 g of sodium sulfate, Na_2SO_4 (molar mass = 142.1 g mol^{-1}).

Answer

$$\text{amount of sodium sulfate} = \frac{\text{mass}}{\text{molar mass}} = \frac{2.22\,\text{g}}{142.1\,\text{g mol}^{-1}} = 0.0156\,\text{mol}$$

number of ion groups = $0.0156\,\text{mol} \times 6.02 \times 10^{23}\,\text{mol}^{-1} = 9.39 \times 10^{21}$

number of Na^+ ions = $2 \times 9.39 \times 10^{21} = 1.88 \times 10^{22}$

Each Na_2SO_4 ion group contains two Na^+ ions and one SO_4^{2-} ion.

Test yourself

8 Calculate the number of:

 a) ions in 0.0123 mol of aluminium sulfate, $Al_2(SO_4)_3$

 b) carbon atoms in 1.23 g of ethanoic acid, CH_3COOH

 The Avogadro constant = 6.02×10^{23} mol^{-1}.

Summary tasks

Check that you can:

- calculate the empirical formula from % composition by mass
- use the ideal gas equation to calculate the molar mass of a gas or of a volatile liquid
- write the formulae of ionic compounds such as aluminium sulfate and sodium carbonate
- list three insoluble sulfates and two insoluble chlorides
- write ionic equations, including state symbols, for acids reacting, e.g. HCl(aq) + Na_2CO_3(aq), and precipitation reactions, e.g. $MgSO_4$(aq) + NaOH(aq)

Make sure that you can write the expression relating:

- moles with mass and molar mass
- molar mass with mass and moles
- mass with molar mass and moles
- the number of moles of a gas with its pressure, volume and temperature

Make sure that you know the relationship between moles and:

- mass and molar mass
- the number of atoms, molecules or ions

Questions

1 An organic compound contains the following by mass: carbon 17.8%, hydrogen 3.0%, bromine 79.2%. Calculate its empirical formula.

2 An organic compound contains the following by mass: carbon 36.4%, hydrogen 6.1%, fluorine 57.5%.
   a) Calculate its empirical formula.
   b) The molar mass of the compound is $66\,g\,mol^{-1}$. Deduce its molecular formula.

3 Deduce the charge on the cations in the following compounds:
   a) $MnCO_3$ b) $V_2(SO_4)_3$

4 Calculate the molar masses of the following compounds:
   a) $Ca(OH)_2$ c) $FeSO_4.7H_2O$
   b) $Al_2(SO_4)_3$

5 Balance the following equations:
   a) $Mg(NO_3)_2 \rightarrow MgO + NO_2 + O_2$
   b) $Fe^{3+} + I^- \rightarrow Fe^{2+} + I_2$
   c) $C_8H_{18} + O_2 \rightarrow CO_2 + H_2O$

6 Write ionic equations, with state symbols, for:
   a) The precipitation of copper(II) hydroxide, produced on mixing solutions of copper(II) sulfate and sodium hydroxide.
   b) The precipitation of barium sulfate, produced on mixing solutions of barium chloride and potassium sulfate.
   c) The neutralisation reaction between dilute sulfuric acid and sodium hydroxide solution.

7 Calculate the amount (in moles) of:
   a) 1.11 g of calcium carbonate, $CaCO_3$
   b) 2.22 g of hydrated barium hydroxide, $Ba(OH)_2.8H_2O$

8 Calculate the masses of:
   a) 0.0100 mol of sulfuric acid, H_2SO_4
   b) 100 mol of sodium metal

9 0.0185 mol of hydrated magnesium sulfate, $MgSO_4.xH_2O$, has a mass of 4.56 g. Calculate the number of molecules of water of crystallisation in the hydrated salt.

10 Calculate the number of molecules in 1.2 g of water.

11 Calculate the number of oxygen atoms in 0.0100 mol of carbon dioxide, CO_2.

12 Calculate the number of hydroxide ions in 10.0 g of barium hydroxide.

Exam practice questions

1 a) The formula of aluminium sulfate is:

    A $AlSO_4$ **C** $Al_3(SO_4)_2$

    B $Al(SO_4)_3$ **D** $Al_2(SO_4)_3$ (1)

b) i) The molar mass/$gmol^{-1}$ (to 2 significant figures) of calcium hydroxide, $Ca(OH)_2$, is:

    A 34   **C** 58

    B 57   **D** 74   (1)

  ii) Use your answer to b)i) to calculate the number of ions in 1.0 g of calcium hydroxide. (Avogadro constant = 6.02 $\times 10^{23}$ mol^{-1})   (1)

c) i) The molar mass/$gmol^{-1}$ of hydrated sodium carbonate, $Na_2CO_3.10H_2O$, is:

    A 124.0   **C** 232.0

    B 142.0   **D** 286.0   (1)

  ii) Use your answer to c)i) and the ideal gas equation to calculate the volume in cm^3 of carbon dioxide gas given off, measured at a temperature of 18°C and a pressure of 95 kPa, when 1.22 g of hydrated sodium carbonate is heated and decomposes according to the equation:

$$Na_2CO_3 10H_2O(s) \rightarrow$$
$$2NaOH(s) + CO_2(g) + 9H_2O(g)$$
$$(R = 8.31 JK^{-1}mol^{-1} = 8.31 NmK^{-1}mol^{-1})$$
   (6)

d) Which equation does **not** balance?

    A $3Ca^{2+}(aq) + 2PO_4^{3-}(aq) \rightarrow Ca_3(PO_4)_2(s)$

    B $2Pb(NO_3)_2 \rightarrow 2PbO + 4NO_2 + O_2$

    C $Fe^{3+} + Sn^{2+} \rightarrow Fe^{2+} + Sn^{4+}$

    D $C_2H_6 + 3\frac{1}{2}O_2 \rightarrow 2CO_2 + 3H_2O$ (1)

                              (Total 11 marks)

2 a) Write the equation, with state symbols, for the reaction of solutions of silver nitrate and the chloride of a group 2 metal, MCl_2.   (2)

b) When a solution containing 1.23 g of MCl_2 was mixed with excess silver nitrate, 2.22 g of silver chloride was produced.

  i) Calculate the amount (moles) of silver chloride produced and hence the moles of MCl_2 in the reaction.   (2)

  ii) Calculate the molar mass of MCl_2 and hence give the identity of the metal M.   (2)

c) Phosphorus forms two chlorides, PCl_3 and PCl_5. When 0.203 g of a phosphorus chloride was vapourised at 100°C and a pressure of 97 kPa, the volume of gas obtained was 47.3 cm^3.

  i) Calculate the number of moles of the gaseous phosphorus chloride.   (4)

     $(R = 8.31 JK^{-1}mol^{-1})$

  ii) Use your answer to i) to calculate the molar mass of the phosphorus chloride and hence deduce its formula.   (2)

  iii) The shape of a molecule of this phosphorus chloride is:

    A planar

    B pyramidal

    C tetrahedral

    D trigonal bipyramidal   (1)

                           (Total 13 marks)

8 Formulae, equations and moles (Topic 5)

9 Calculations from chemical equations (Topic 5)

Calculations from chemical equations depend upon the ability to convert masses and volumes into amount of substance (moles) and to use the stoichiometry of an equation.

Calculations must be well laid out, with words explaining what is being calculated at each step. A series of numbers is not sufficient.

It is advisable to include units in calculations, rather than just adding them at the end. This makes it clear that you have used 'formulae' such as 'moles = concentration × volume' correctly and that you have used comparable units, such as dm^3 and not cm^3 for the volume, when the concentration is in $mol\,dm^{-3}$. This method of adding units to the calculation is slower at first, but with practice becomes second nature and is more likely to avoid careless mistakes.

Significant figures

Answers to calculations should be given to an appropriate number of significant figures. The way to do this is to analyse the data:

- Count the number of significant figures in each quantity given in the question.
- Give the answer to the same number of significant figures as the data.

Work out the correct number of significant figures based on the following rules:

- For whole numbers and decimals of numbers greater than 1, all the figures, *including any zeros at the end*, are counted. For example:
  - the number 102 is written to three significant figures (3 s.f.)
  - the number 1.02 is also written to 3 s.f.
  - the number 1.020 is written to 4 s.f.
  - the number 10.20 is also written to 4 s.f.
  - the measurement $100\,cm^3$ is expressed to 3 s.f.

- For decimals in numbers less than 1, count all the numbers, except the zeros *before* and *immediately after* the decimal point. For example:
  - the number 0.102 is written to 3 s.f.
  - the number 0.1020 is written to 4 s.f.
  - the number 0.00102 is written to 3 s.f., not 5 s.f.
  - the number 0.01200 is written to 4 s.f.
- For values written in scientific notation, all the numbers before and after the decimal place are counted as significant figures. The power of 10 is not counted. For example:
  - the number 1.02×10^{-3} is written to 3 s.f.

Rounding numbers

Questions often ask for answers to be rounded to a certain number of significant figures. If you have to round a number to *three* significant figures, look at the *fourth* significant figure. If it is less than 5, do not alter the third significant figure. For example, 6.372 becomes 6.37, because the fourth significant figure, 2, is less than 5.

If the fourth significant figure is 5 or more, increase the third significant figure by 1. For example, 6.379 becomes 6.38, because the fourth significant figure, 9, is greater than 5. The number 2.365 is rounded up to 2.37, because the fourth significant figure is 5.

Do not round up in stages. For example, 6.3749 rounds to 6.37, because the *fourth* figure is 4, which is less than 5. Do not round 6.3749 to 6.375 and then to 6.38.

Test yourself

1 Round the following:
   a) 0.01202 to 3 s.f.   b) 1.3469 to 2 s.f.   c) 0.1004 to 3 s.f.

Mass and volume calculations

Mass-to-mass calculations

A typical question involving mass–to–mass calculation is to ask for the mass of a product that could be obtained from a given mass of one of the reactants. For example, calculate the mass of barium sulfate that is precipitated when a solution containing 5.55 g of barium chloride, $BaCl_2$, is reacted with excess magnesium sulfate. (Molar mass of barium chloride = $137.3 + (2 \times 35.5) = 208.3 \, \text{g mol}^{-1}$.)

After the equation has been written, the calculation should be done in three steps:

1 Calculate the amount (moles) of reactant. In this example, the reactant is barium chloride.

2 Use the stoichiometry of the equation to calculate the amount (moles) of product.

3 Convert the moles of product to mass.

The stoichiometry of an equation is the ratio of the numbers of each reactant and product in the balanced equation.

The equation is:

$$BaCl_2(aq) + MgSO_4(aq) \rightarrow BaSO_4(s) + MgCl_2(aq)$$

Step 1:

$$\text{amount of barium chloride} = \frac{\text{mass}}{\text{molar mass}} = \frac{5.55\,g}{208.3\,g\,mol^{-1}} = 0.02664\ mol$$

Step 2: ratio $BaSO_4$:$BaCl_2$ is 1:1, so:

amount of $BaSO_4$ produced = amount of $BaCl_2$ = 0.02664 mol

Step 3:

molar mass of $BaSO_4 = 137.3 + 32.1 + (4 \times 16.0) = 233.4\,g\,mol^{-1}$

mass of barium sulfate produced = mol × molar mass

$$= 0.02664\,mol \times 233.4\,g\,mol^{-1} = 6.22\,g$$

Tip

The answer must be given to three significant figures because the mass of barium chloride was given to three significant figures. Never round down to one or two significant figures in the middle of a calculation.

The method can be illustrated by a flow diagram. The calculation is to find the mass of substance B produced from (or reacting with) substance A:

Mass of A $\xrightarrow{\text{step 1}}$ Moles of A $\xrightarrow{\text{step 2}}$ Moles of B $\xrightarrow{\text{step 3}}$ Mass of B

Steps 1 and 3 involve mass to moles and moles to mass conversions (pages 134–35). Step 2 uses the stoichiometry of the equation.

When the ratio in the equation is not 1:1, care must be taken in step 2.

Worked example

Calculate the mass of sodium sulfate produced when 3.45 g of sodium hydroxide is neutralised by dilute sulfuric acid. The equation is:

$$2NaOH + H_2SO_4 \rightarrow Na_2SO_4 + 2H_2O$$

Answer

Step 1: molar mass of NaOH = 23.0 + 16.0 + 1.0 = 40.0 g mol^{-1}

$$\text{amount (moles) of sodium hydroxide} = \frac{\text{mass}}{\text{molar mass}} = \frac{3.45\,g}{40g\,mol^{-1}}$$

$$= 0.08625\ mol$$

Step 2: ratio of Na_2SO_4:NaOH is 1:2, so *fewer* moles of sodium sulfate are produced:

$$\text{amount of sodium sulfate} = \frac{1}{2} \times 0.08625\ mol = 0.04313\ mol$$

Step 3: molar mass of $Na_2SO_4 = (2 \times 23.0) + 32.1 + (4 \times 16.0) = 142.1\,g\,mol^{-1}$

mass of sodium sulfate produced = moles × molar mass

$$= 0.04313\,mol \times 142.1\,g\,mol^{-1} = 6.13\,g$$

Test yourself

2 Calculate the mass of calcium phosphate (molar mass 310.3 g mol^{-1}) precipitated when 1.23 g of calcium chloride (molar mass 111.1 g mol^{-1}) in a solution was reacted with excess sodium phosphate.

$$3CaCl_2(aq) + 2Na_3PO_4(aq) \rightarrow Ca_3(PO_4)_2(s) + 6NaCl(aq)$$

Volume of gas calculations

These are based on Avogadro's hypothesis, which states that the volume occupied by 1 mol of all gases at a given temperature and pressure is the same. This volume is called the molar volume.

Under typical laboratory conditions (100 kPa or 1 atm pressure and at 20°C), the molar volume is $24 \, dm^3 \, mol^{-1} = 24\,000 \, cm^3 \, mol^{-1}$.

The relationship between amount of gas (moles) and volume is given by:

$$\text{amount (moles) of gas} = \frac{\text{volume of gas}}{\text{molar volume}}$$

Make sure that the units of the two volumes are the same; both must be either dm^3 or cm^3.

Again a 'mole triangle' (Figure 9.1) can be used:

$$\text{volume of gas} = \text{moles} \times \text{molar volume}$$

$$\text{moles} = \frac{\text{volume of gas}}{\text{molar volume}}$$

Mass to volume of gas calculations

The route for this type of calculation is similar to that for mass-to-mass calculations:

$$\text{Mass of A} \xrightarrow{\text{step 1}} \text{Moles of A} \xrightarrow{\text{step 2}} \text{Moles of gas B} \xrightarrow{\text{step 3}} \text{Volume of B}$$

Steps 1 and 3 use the conversions mass to moles and moles to volume of gas.

Step 2 uses the stoichiometry of the equation.

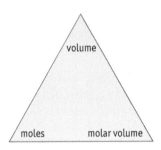

Figure 9.1

Worked example 1

Calculate the volume of carbon dioxide produced when 2.68 g of calcium carbonate is heated and decomposes according to the equation:

$$CaCO_3(s) \rightarrow CaO(s) + CO_2(g)$$

Under the conditions of the experiment, 1 mol of gas occupies $24\,000 \, cm^3$.

Answer

Step 1: molar mass of $CaCO_3 = 40.1 + 12.0 + (3 \times 16.0) = 100.1 \, g \, mol^{-1}$

$$\text{amount (moles) of calcium carbonate} = \frac{\text{mass}}{\text{molar mass}}$$

$$= \frac{2.68 \, g}{100.1 \, g \, mol^{-1}} = 0.0268 \, mol$$

Step 2: ratio of CO_2 to $CaCO_3$ is 1:1

amount (moles) of carbon dioxide = 0.0268 mol

Step 3: volume of carbon dioxide gas = moles × molar volume

$$= 0.0268 \, mol \times 24\,000 \, cm^3 \, mol^{-1} = 643 \, cm^3$$

The average family motorist uses about 1000 kg of petrol each year. Assume that the molecular formula of petrol is C_8H_{18} and that the equation for the reaction is:

$$C_8H_{18} + 12\tfrac{1}{2}O_2 \rightarrow 8CO_2 + 9H_2O$$

Calculate:

a) the yearly volume of carbon dioxide produced at room temperature and pressure

(The molar volume of gas at room temperature and pressure is 24 dm³ mol⁻¹.)

b) the mass of carbon dioxide (the carbon footprint) produced by the car in a year

Answer

a) Step 1: molar mass of C_8H_{18} is $(8 \times 12.0) + (18.0 \times 1.0) = 114.0\,\text{g mol}^{-1}$

$$\text{amount of petrol} = \frac{\text{mass}}{\text{molar mass}} = \frac{1\,000\,000\,\text{g}}{114.0\,\text{g mol}^{-1}} = 8772\,\text{mol}$$

Step 2: ratio of CO_2:C_8H_{18} = 8:1 (so more moles of CO_2 produced):

amount of CO_2 produced = $8 \times 8772\,\text{mol} = 7.02 \times 10^4\,\text{mol}$

Step 3: volume of carbon dioxide produced = $7.02 \times 10^4\,\text{mol} \times 24\,\text{dm}^3\,\text{mol}^{-1}$
$$= 1.68 \times 10^6\,\text{dm}^3$$

b) 1 mol of CO_2 has a mass of 44.0 g.

$7.02 \times 10^4\,\text{mol}$ of CO_2 has a mass of $7.02 \times 10^4 \times 44.0\,\text{g} = 3.09 \times 10^6\,\text{g} = 3.09\,\text{tonnes}$.

The family car has, on average, a carbon footprint of just over 3 tonnes.

Test yourself

3 Calculate the volume of oxygen produced when 3.60 g of hydrogen peroxide is decomposed according to the equation below [the molar volume of a gas under the conditions of the experiment was 24 dm³ mol⁻¹].

$$2H_2O_2(aq) \rightarrow 2H_2O(l) + O_2(g)$$

Volume of gas to volume of another gas calculation

There are two alternative methods for performing this type of calculation.

It can be done in three steps, similarly to mass-to-volume calculations:

Volume of gas A $\xrightarrow{\text{step 1}}$ Moles of gas A $\xrightarrow{\text{step 2}}$ Moles of gas B $\xrightarrow{\text{step 3}}$ Volume of B

Worked example

Calculate the volume of oxygen needed to react with 123 cm³ of gaseous methane, CH_4.

$$CH_4(g) + 2O_2(g) \rightarrow CO_2(g) + 2H_2O(l)$$

Tip

You may be given the molar volume for the gases. If not, assume that it is 24 000 $cm^3 mol^{-1}$ or give it a value of $V cm^3$. The value, V, will cancel.

Answer

Step 1: amount of methane

$$= \frac{\text{volume}}{\text{molar volume}} = \frac{123\,cm^3}{24000\,cm^3\,mol^{-1}} = 0.005125\,mol$$

Step 2: the ratio of oxygen to methane is 2:1:

amount of oxygen = 2 × 0.005125 mol = 0.01025 mol

Step 3: volume of oxygen = moles × molar volume

$= 0.01025\,mol \times 24\,000\,cm^3\,mol^{-1} = 246\,cm^3$

The alternative, and simpler method, is to use Avogadro's hypothesis:

Equal volumes of gases, measured at the same temperature and pressure, contain the same number of molecules.

This means that if there is twice the number of moles, the volume is doubled — as long as both substances are gases.

Tip

This method can only be used if, under the conditions of the experiment, both substances are gases. You do not need to know the value of the molar volume.

Worked example

Calculate the volume of oxygen gas needed to burn completely 200 cm^3 of gaseous butane.

$$2C_4H_{10}(g) + 13O_2(g) \rightarrow 8CO_2(g) + 10H_2O(l)$$

Answer

Both butane and oxygen are gases, therefore:

$$\frac{\text{volume of oxygen}}{\text{volume of butane}} = \frac{\text{moles of oxygen}}{\text{moles of butane}} = \frac{13}{2}$$

$$\text{volume of oxygen} = \frac{13}{2} \times \text{volume of butane} = \frac{13}{2} \times 200\,cm^3 = 1300\,cm^3$$

Test yourself

4 Calculate the volume of chlorine needed to react with 25.0 cm^3 of methane.

$$CH_4(g) + 4Cl_2(g) \rightarrow CCl_4(l) + 4HCl(g)$$

Percentage yield calculations

Many reactions do not produce the same amount of product as that calculated from the chemical equation. This is caused by the reaction being reversible (so equilibrium is reached) or because of competing reactions. This is especially true in organic chemistry.

Percentage yield is defined as:

$$\%\text{yield} = \frac{\text{actual yield}}{\text{theoretical yield}} \times 100$$

The actual yield is the measured mass of the product obtained in the experiment.

The theoretical yield is the mass that is calculated from the equation for the reaction, assuming that all the reactant is converted into the product.

Tip

The actual and theoretical yields are usually masses (grams), but *both* could be in moles.

Worked example

When 1000g of sulfur dioxide is reacted with excess oxygen, 1225g of sulfur trioxide is produced:

$$2SO_2 + O_2 \rightarrow 2SO_3$$

Calculate the percentage yield.

Answer

First, calculate the theoretical yield, using the method on page 145.

Step 1: molar mass of $SO_2 = 32.1 + (2 \times 16.0) = 64.1\,g\,mol^{-1}$

$$\text{amount of sulfur dioxide} = \frac{\text{mass}}{\text{molar mass}} = \frac{1000}{64.1} = 15.60\,mol$$

Step 2: ratio of SO_2:SO_3 is 2:2 = 1:1:

theoretical amount of sulfur trioxide produced = amount of SO_2 reacted = 15.60 mol

Step 3: molar mass of $SO_3 = 32.1 + (3 \times 16.0) = 80.1\,g\,mol^{-1}$

theoretical yield = moles × molar mass

$$= 15.60\,mol \times 80.1\,g\,mol^{-1} = 1250\,g$$

Second, use the theoretical yield to calculate the percentage yield:

$$\frac{\text{actual yield}}{\text{theoretical yield}} \times 100 = \frac{1225}{1250} \times 100 = 98.0\%$$

Tip

Do not calculate the percentage yield as:

$$\frac{\text{mass of product} \times 100}{\text{mass of reactant}}$$

Atom economy

Atom economy is defined as:

$$\textbf{atom economy} = \frac{\textbf{mass of the desired product in the equation}}{\textbf{sum of the masses of the products in the equation}} \times 100$$

Because of the law of conservation of mass, the atom economy is also:

$$\frac{\text{mass of the desired product in the equation}}{\text{sum of the masses of the reactants in the equation}} \times 100$$

The Haber process is an example of a process with a 100% atom economy as there is a single product:

$$N_2 + 3H_2 \rightleftharpoons 2NH_3$$

Tip

The yield of the reaction is not taken into account when calculating the atom economy.

Worked example

Calculate the atom economy for the reaction that produces the hydrogen for the Haber process:

$$CH_4(g) + 2H_2O(g) \rightleftharpoons CO_2(g) + 4H_2(g)$$

Answer

$$\text{atom economy} = \frac{4 \times \text{molecular mass of hydrogen}}{\text{molecular mass of carbon dioxide} + 4 \times \text{molecular mass of hydrogen}} \times 100$$

$$= (8/(44 + 8)) \times 100 = 15.4\%$$

For a reaction of the type A + B → C + D, two products are formed. If product C is the desired one, then D is considered a by-product. As it is a significant goal of green chemistry to maximise the efficiency of the reactants and minimise the production of waste, D must either be found to have a use or be as environmentally harmless as possible.

Test yourself

5 Sulfuric acid is manufactured from sulfur, oxygen and water. The overall equation is:

$$2S + 3O_2 + 2H_2O \rightarrow 2H_2SO_4$$

32 tonnes of sulfur produced 95 tonnes of sulfuric acid.

a) Calculate the percentage yield.

b) What is the atom economy of the process?

Percentage composition

Many salts contain water of crystallisation.

Worked example

The formula of hydrated copper(II) sulfate is $CuSO_4.5H_2O$. Calculate the percentage of water in this salt.

Answer

molar mass of the hydrated salt $= 63.5 + 32 + (4 \times 16) + 5(2 + 16) = 249.5\,\mathrm{g\,mol^{-1}}$

$$\% \text{ water} = \frac{5 \times (2 + 16)}{249.5} \times 100 = 36.1\%$$

Test yourself

6 Calculate the percentage by mass of carbon in 14.3 g of glucose, $C_6H_{12}O_6$.

Calculation of reaction stoichiometry

If the masses of both reactants (or of one reactant and one product) are known, the stoichiometry of the equation can be worked out. This is done by converting the masses to amounts and examining the ratio of these amounts.

Worked example

3.48 g of pure iron was placed in excess copper(II) sulfate solution and stirred until all reaction had ceased. The residue of copper was filtered off, washed and dried. It had a mass of 3.95 g. Use these data to work out which of the two reactions below took place.

$$Fe(s) + CuSO_4(aq) \rightarrow FeSO_4(aq) + Cu(s) \qquad \text{equation 1}$$
$$2Fe(s) + 3CuSO_4(aq) \rightarrow Fe_2(SO_4)_3(aq) + 3Cu(s) \qquad \text{equation 2}$$

Chemicals react in simple whole number ratios by moles. Therefore, 0.0624:0.0622 is a mole ratio of 1:1.

Test yourself

7 When heated, sodium hydrogencarbonate, $NaHCO_3$, decomposes leaving a solid residue. When 4.20 g of sodium hydrogencarbonate was heated until there was no further loss in mass, 2.65 g of solid was left.

Three equations have been suggested for this reaction:

$2NaHCO_3(s) \rightarrow Na_2O(s) + 2CO_2(g) + H_2O(g)$ equation 1

$2NaHCO_3(s) \rightarrow Na_2CO_3(s) + CO_2(g) + H_2O(g)$ equation 2

$NaHCO_3(s) \rightarrow NaOH(s) + CO_2(g)$ equation 3

Which of these equations is consistent with the experimental data?

Limiting reagent

When a reaction is carried out in the laboratory, the reactants are not always present in the exact stoichiometric ratio determined by the equation. As a result, one reactant is used completely; some of the other reactant is left over. The reagent left over is said to be in excess; the one used completely is said to be the limiting reagent.

An analogy is a factory producing sunglasses (*S*). Every frame (*F*) needs two lenses (*L*). The 'equation' for the process is:

$$F + 2L \rightarrow S$$

If the factory owner buys 144 frames and 280 lenses, the maximum number of sunglasses that can be produced is limited by the number of lenses. One hundred and forty-four frames need 288 lenses. There are only 280 lenses, so the lenses are the limiting factor and only 140 sunglasses can be made.

The lenses are the limiting 'reagent' and the frames are the 'reagent' in excess.

To identify the limiting reagent and hence calculate the theoretical yield, use the following method:

1 Calculate the amount (in moles) of one reagent and use the reaction stoichiometry to calculate the amount (in moles) of product that could be formed from this reagent.

2 Calculate the amount (in moles) of the second reagent and use the reaction stoichiometry to calculate the amount (in moles) of product that could be formed from this second reagent.

3 The reagent that produces the *least* amount (in moles) of product is the limiting reagent.

4 Calculate the theoretical yield of the product from the *least* amount (in moles) of product calculated in steps 1 and 2, i.e. from the limiting reagent.

Key term

A **limiting reagent** is the substance that determines the theoretical yield of product in a reaction.

Note the analogy to the mole here. The number of moles of a chemical is a measure of the (very large) number of molecules of that chemical.

In steps 1 and 2 you must be able to convert mass or volume of reactant into moles and then use the ratio of numbers of moles of reactant to product in the equation (the stoichiometry) to calculate the amount of product. Step 4 is the conversion of amount (moles) of product into mass or volume of product.

Worked example 1

Solutions containing 12.8g of sulfuric acid (molar mass $98.1\,g\,mol^{-1}$) and 10.0g of sodium hydroxide (molar mass $40.0\,g\,mol^{-1}$) are mixed and produce sodium sulfate and water according to the following equation:

$$2NaOH + H_2SO_4 \rightarrow Na_2SO_4 + 2H_2O$$

Calculate the mass of sodium sulfate (molar mass $142.1\,g\,mol^{-1}$) produced.

Answer

Step 1: amount of $NaOH = \dfrac{mass}{molar\ mass} = \dfrac{10.0\,g}{40.0\,g\,mol^{-1}} = 0.250\ mol$

ratio of Na_2SO_4 to $NaOH = 1:2$
theoretical amount of Na_2SO_4 that would be produced $= \dfrac{1}{2} \times 0.250$

$= 0.125\,mol$

Step 2: amount of $H_2SO_4 = \dfrac{mass}{molar\ mass} = \dfrac{12.8\,g}{98.1\,g\,mol^{-1}} = 0.130\ mol$

ratio Na_2SO_4 to $H_2SO_4 = 1:1$
theoretical amount of Na_2SO_4 that would be produced $= 0.130\,mol$

Step 3: the reagent that produces the least product (0.125 mol) is sodium hydroxide, so that is the limiting reagent.

Step 4: mass of Na_2SO_4 produced $=$ moles $\times$ molar mass
$= 0.125\,mol \times 142.1\,g\,mol^{-1} = 17.8\,g$

Even though there are more moles of sodium hydroxide, it is the limiting reagent. This is because of the stoichiometry of the equation where 2 moles of sodium hydroxide are required to react with 1 mole of sulfuric acid.

Worked example 2

7.95g of copper(II) oxide is mixed with a solution containing 7.35g of sulfuric acid. The equation for the reaction is:

$$CuO(s) + H_2SO_4(aq) \rightarrow CuSO_4(aq) + H_2O(l)$$

a) Determine which is the limiting reagent.

b) Hence, calculate the mass of $CuSO_4$ produced.

c) On evaporation of the solution, 16.3g of crystals of $CuSO_4.5H_2O$ were formed:

$$CuSO_4(aq) \rightarrow CuSO_4.5H_2O(s)$$

Calculate the percentage yield.

Answer

a) molar mass of $CuO = 63.5 + 16.0 = 79.5\,g\,mol^{-1}$

amount of $CuO = \dfrac{7.95\,g}{79.5\,g\,mol^{-1}} = 0.100\ mol$

The ratio $CuO:CuSO_4$ is 1:1, so 0.100 mol of $CuSO_4$ would be produced.

molar mass of $H_2SO_4 = (2 \times 1.0) + 32.1 + (4 \times 16.0) = 98.1\,g\,mol^{-1}$

amount of $H_2SO_4 = \dfrac{7.35\,g}{98.1\,g\,mol^{-1}} = 0.0750\ mol$

The ratio $H_2SO_4:CuSO_4$ is 1:1, so 0.0750 mol of $CuSO_4$ would be produced.

This is the smaller amount, so sulfuric acid is the limiting reagent.

b) amount of $CuSO_4$ produced = 0.0750 mol

molar mass of $CuSO_4$ = 63.5 + 32.1 + (4 × 16.0) = 159.5 g mol^{-1}

mass of $CuSO_4$ produced = 0.0750 mol × 159.6 g mol^{-1} = 12.0 g

c) 1 mol of $CuSO_4(aq)$ produces 1 mol $CuSO_4.5H_2O(s)$.

molar mass of $CuSO_4.5H_2O$ = 159.6 + (5 × 18.0) = 249.6 g mol^{-1}

theoretical yield = 0.0750 mol × 249.6 g mol^{-1} = 18.7 g

% yield = $\dfrac{\text{actual yield}}{\text{theoretical yield}}$ × 100 = $\dfrac{16.3}{18.7}$ × 100 = 87.2%

Concentration

A **solution** consists of a substance that is dissolved — the **solute** — and the substance that is doing the dissolving — the **solvent**. For example, when a salt is dissolved in water, the salt is the solute and the water is the solvent. Solutions may be coloured or colourless, but they are always clear and never cloudy.

Units of concentration

Solutions can contain different amounts of solute up to a maximum value, which is called the **solubility** of the solute. Therefore, the same volume of solutions of a solute can contain different amounts of that solute. To enable the amount or the mass of solute in a given volume to be determined, the concentration of the solution must be known.

- The most common unit of concentration is **mol dm^{-3}**.
- mol dm^{-3} is sometimes called molarity (symbol, M).
- To calculate a concentration in mol dm^{-3}, the amount (moles) of solute is divided by the volume of the solution in dm^3.

The volume is the volume of the solution, not of the solvent.

Conversions such as amount of solute to concentration can be performed using a version of the 'mole triangle' (Figure 9.2):

moles = concentration × volume

concentration = $\dfrac{\text{moles}}{\text{volume}}$

volume = $\dfrac{\text{moles}}{\text{concentration}}$

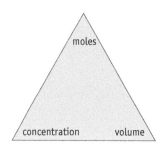

Figure 9.2

- Another unit of concentration that is sometimes used is **g dm^{-3}**. This is the mass of the solute divided by the volume (in dm^3) of the solution.
- The conversion of concentrations in mol dm^{-3} to g dm^{-3} is the same as converting mol to mass, which is to multiply by the molar mass of the solute.
- To convert concentrations in g dm^{-3} to mol dm^{-3}, divide by the molar mass of the solute.

Worked example 1

a) Calculate the concentration in $mol\,dm^{-3}$ of a solution made by dissolving 0.123 mol of sodium hydroxide in water and making up the solution to a total volume of $250\,cm^3$.

b) Calculate the concentration of this solution in $g\,dm^{-3}$.

Answer

a) volume of solution $= \dfrac{250}{1000} = 0.250\,dm^3$

concentration $= \dfrac{\text{moles of solute}}{\text{volume of solution}} = \dfrac{0.123\,mol}{0.250\,dm^3} = 0.492\,mol\,dm^{-3}$

b) molar mass of $NaOH = 23.0 + 16.0 + 1.0 = 40.0\,g\,mol^{-1}$

concentration of solution $= 0.492\,mol\,dm^{-3} \times 40.0\,g\,mol^{-1} = 19.7\,g\,dm^{-3}$

In b), mol cancels with mol^{-1}, leaving the final unit as $g\,dm^{-3}$. This is a useful check to make sure that you have carried out the conversion correctly.

Worked example 2

Calculate the mass of hydrated sodium carbonate, $Na_2CO_3.10H_2O$, that is required to make up $250\,cm^3$ of a $0.100\,mol\,dm^{-3}$ solution.

Answer

amount of sodium carbonate required = concentration × volume of solution

amount $= 0.100\,mol\,dm^{-3} \times \dfrac{250}{1000}\,dm^3 = 0.0250\,mol$

molar mass of $Na_2CO_3.10H_2O = (2 \times 23.0) + 12.0 + (3 \times 16.0) + (10 \times 18.0)$
$$= 286.0\,g\,mol^{-1}$$

mass required = moles × molar mass $= 0.0250\,mol \times 286.0\,g\,mol^{-1} = 7.15\,g$

In the question, the volume of the solution was given in cm^3. Therefore, it had to be converted to dm^3.

Worked example 3

Calculate the amount of sulfuric acid in $22.4\,cm^3$ of $0.0502\,mol\,dm^{-3}$ solution.

Answer

amount (in moles) of sulfuric acid = concentration × volume

amount $= 0.0502\,mol\,dm^{-3} \times \dfrac{22.4\,dm^3}{1000\,cm^3\,dm^{-3}} = 0.00112\,mol$

Test yourself

8 Calculate:

a) the number of moles of sodium hydroxide in $25.0\,cm^3$ of a solution of concentration $0.104\,mol\,dm^{-3}$

b) the volume of a $0.0500\,mol\,dm^{-3}$ solution of sulfuric acid that contains 0.0260 mol

Concentrations of very dilute solutions

There are two units used commonly:

- nanomoles per dm^3 ($nmol\,dm^{-3}$); $1\,nmol = 10^{-9}\,mol$
- parts per million (ppm)

'Parts per million' is normally the mass of a solute per million grams of solvent. (The assumption is made that the masses of the solvent and the solution are the same because the solution is very dilute.)

Tip

The concentration of a pollutant in a gaseous mixture is often stated in units of ppmV, which is the volume in cm^3 of pollutant per million cm^3 of gas.

Worked example 1

Aluminium sulfate is used as a coagulant in water treatment. Analysis of some water found that the aluminium ion concentration was $6.3\,nmol\,dm^{-3}$. Calculate the mass of aluminium ions in $1\,dm^3$ of the treated water.

Answer

$6.3\,nmol = 6.3 \times 10^{-9}\,mol$

molar mass of $Al^{3+} = 27.0\,g\,mol^{-1}$

mass of Al^{3+} ions in the water $= 6.3 \times 10^{-9}\,mol \times 27.0\,g\,mol^{-1}$

$= 1.70 \times 10^{-7}\,g \;(= 1.70 \times 10^{-4}\,mg = 170\,ng)$

Tip

The prefix *nano*, symbol n, means a multiple of 10^{-9}. The prefix *pico*, symbol p, is a multiple of 10^{-12}.

Worked example 2

A bottle of mineral water was labelled as containing $2.0\,ppm$ of sodium ions.

a) Calculate its concentration in $nmol\,dm^{-3}$.

b) Calculate the number of sodium ions in $1.0\,dm^3$ of the mineral water.

(Avogadro constant $= 6.02 \times 10^{23}\,mol^{-1}$)

Answer

a) $1\,000\,000\,g$ of water contain $2.0\,g$ of sodium ions.

$1000\,g$ of water has a volume of $1.0\,dm^3$ and contains $\dfrac{2.0}{1000} = 0.0020\,g$ of sodium ions.

amount (moles) of sodium ions $= \dfrac{0.0020g}{23.0\,g\,mol^{-1}}$

$= 8.7 \times 10^{-5}\,mol = 8.7 \times 10^4\,nmol$

The concentration of sodium ions is $8.7 \times 10^4\,nmol\,dm^{-3}$.

b) number of ions $=$ moles $\times$ Avogadro constant $= 8.7 \times 10^{-5}\,mol \times 6.02 \times 10^{23}\,mol^{-1}$

$= 5.2 \times 10^{19}$

$1\,mol = 1 \times 10^9\,nmol$, so $8.7 \times 10^{-5}\,mol$
$= 8.7 \times 10^{-5} \times 1 \times 10^9$
$= 8.7 \times 10^4\,nmol$.

Titrations

If the accurate concentration of one solution is known, a titration can be used to determine the concentration of another solution. The method involves having one solution in a burette and pipetting a known volume of the other solution into a conical flask. An indicator is then added to the solution in the conical flask and the solution is titrated from the burette until the indicator changes colour.

A left-handed student performing an acid-base titration

Acid–base titrations are described here. Other types will be met in the second year of the A level course, but the method and the method of calculation are the same.

Detailed method

- The burette is rinsed out with distilled water and then with a little of one of the solutions (solution B).
- The pipette is rinsed out with distilled water and then with a little of the other solution (solution P).
- A conical flask is rinsed out with distilled water.
- The burette is filled with solution B. The tap is opened and some of the solution is run out so that the stem below the tap does not contain any air bubbles. The burette is read to $0.05\,cm^3$ and the volume is recorded.
- Using a pipette filler, the pipette is filled with solution P so that the bottom of the meniscus is on the line.
- The contents of the pipette are discharged into the conical flask. A few drops of indicator are added.
- The solution from the burette solution is added, with constant swirling of the flask, until the indicator changes colour. The burette is read and the difference between the starting volume and the final volume is calculated. This is called the **titre**. This titre is approximate because the burette solution was added quickly and it is, therefore, likely that the end point was overshot.

- The conical flask is emptied and washed out thoroughly with water.
- The process is repeated, but this time solution B is added quickly until about $1\,cm^3$ or $2\,cm^3$ short of the approximate titre.
- Solution B is then added slowly — finally dropwise — swirling the flask constantly, until the indicator changes to the required colour. At this point, the burette reading is taken and the first accurate titre calculated.
- The titration is repeated until at least two concordant titres are obtained. Concordant means that the two titres are within $0.2\,cm^3$ of each other.
- The concordant titres are then averaged to give the mean (average) titre.

Indicators

The common acid–base indicators are **methyl orange** and **phenolphthalein**. Some indicators and their colours are given in Table 9.1.

Table 9.1 Some indicators and their colours

Indicator	Colour in acid	Colour in alkali	End-point colour
Methyl orange	Red	Yellow	Orange
Bromophenol blue	Yellow	Blue	Green
Methyl red	Red	Yellow	Orange
Bromothymol blue	Yellow	Blue	Green
Phenolphthalein	Colourless	Purple	Pale pink

Calculations

To find the concentration of one of the solutions

The concentration of one solution is known. This solution is called the **standard solution**. The reacting volumes are determined by titration.

The calculation is carried out in three steps.

1 Calculate the amount (in moles) of the reagent of known concentration using:

moles = concentration × volume

2 Calculate the amount (in moles) of the other reagent.

Use the stoichiometry of the equation.

3 Calculate the concentration of the other solution using:

$$\text{concentration} = \frac{\text{moles}}{\text{volume}}$$

Tip

The equation for the reaction is normally given in the question. If it is not, you must write it before starting the calculation.

Worked example 1

In a titration, neutralisation of 25.0 cm^3 of 0.100 mol dm^{-3} hydrochloric acid solution required 26.8 cm^3 of sodium hydroxide solution.

$$NaOH + HCl \rightarrow NaCl + H_2O$$

Calculate the concentration of the sodium hydroxide.

Answer

Step 1: amount of HCl = concentration × volume

$$= 0.100 \, \text{mol dm}^{-3} \times \frac{25.0}{1000} \, \text{dm}^3 = 0.00250 \, \text{mol}$$

Step 2: the ratio of HCl to NaOH is 1:1.

amount of NaOH = amount (moles) of HCl = 0.00250 mol

Step 3: concentration of sodium hydroxide solution = $\dfrac{\text{moles}}{\text{volume}}$

$$\text{concentration} = \frac{0.00250 \, \text{mol}}{(26.8/1000)} \, \text{dm}^3 = 0.0933 \, \text{mol dm}^{-3}$$

The volumes have to be changed from cm^3 to dm^3. This is done by dividing by 1000.

Tip

'Amount' in chemistry is measured in moles.

Worked example 2

25.0 cm^3 of a 0.0504 mol dm^{-3} solution of sulfuric acid was titrated with a solution of sodium hydroxide. The mean titre was 27.3 cm^3. The equation for the reaction is:

$$2NaOH + H_2SO_4 \rightarrow Na_2SO_4 + 2H_2O$$

Calculate the concentration of the sodium hydroxide solution.

Tip

Care must be taken if the stoichiometric ratio is not 1:1.

Answer

Step 1: amount of H$_2$SO$_4$ = concentration × volume

$$\text{amount} = 0.0504 \, \text{mol dm}^{-3} \times \frac{25.0}{1000} \, \text{dm}^3 = 0.00126 \, \text{mol}$$

Step 2: the ratio of NaOH to H$_2$SO$_4$ is 2:1.

amount of NaOH = 2 × amount of H$_2$SO$_4$

$$= 2 \times 0.00126 = 0.00252 \, \text{mol}$$

Step 3: concentration of sodium hydroxide solution $= \dfrac{\text{moles}}{\text{volume}}$

$$\text{concentration} = \dfrac{0.00252\,\text{mol}}{(27.3/1000)\,\text{dm}^3} = 0.0923\,\text{mol}\,\text{dm}^{-3}$$

Tip

Some students like to use the formula:
$$\dfrac{M_1 V_1}{n_1} = \dfrac{M_2 V_2}{n_2}$$
where n_1 is the number in front of the formula of substance 1 in the equation and n_2 is the number in front of the formula of substance 2 in the equation.

Test yourself

9 A solution of sodium hydroxide of volume $25.0\,\text{cm}^3$ required $23.75\,\text{cm}^3$ of a $0.0512\,\text{mol}\,\text{dm}^{-3}$ solution of ethanedioic acid for neutralisation.

$$2\text{NaOH} + \text{H}_2\text{C}_2\text{O}_4 \rightarrow \text{Na}_2\text{C}_2\text{O}_4 + 2\text{H}_2\text{O}$$

Calculate the concentration of the sodium hydroxide solution in $\text{mol}\,\text{dm}^{-3}$.

To find the volume needed

In this type of calculation, both concentrations are given in the question. The first two steps are the same as in calculations to find the concentration of a solution. The third step is to use the concentration of the second solution to work out the volume required:

$$\text{volume} = \dfrac{\text{moles}}{\text{concentration}}$$

Worked example

Calculate the volume of $0.100\,\text{mol}\,\text{dm}^{-3}$ hydrochloric acid solution required to neutralise $25.0\,\text{cm}^3$ of $0.0567\,\text{mol}\,\text{dm}^{-3}$ sodium carbonate solution. The equation for the reaction is:

$$2\text{HCl} + \text{Na}_2\text{CO}_3 \rightarrow 2\text{NaCl} + \text{H}_2\text{O} + \text{CO}_2$$

Answer

Step 1: amount of sodium carbonate = concentration × volume
$$\text{amount} = 0.0567\,\text{mol}\,\text{dm}^{-3} \times \dfrac{25.0}{1000}\,\text{dm}^3 = 0.001418\,\text{mol}$$

Step 2: the ratio of HCl to Na_2CO_3 is 2:1.
$$\text{amount of hydrochloric acid} = 2 \times 0.001418 = 0.002836\,\text{mol}$$

Step 3: volume of hydrochloric acid solution $= \dfrac{\text{moles}}{\text{concentration}}$

$$\text{volume} = \dfrac{0.002836\,\text{mol}}{0.100\,\text{mol}\,\text{dm}^{-3}} = 0.0284\,\text{dm}^3 = 28.4\,\text{cm}^3$$

Preparation of a primary standard solution

A primary standard solution is one of known and accurate concentration. To prepare one, the acid or base must:

1 be obtainable pure

2 not absorb moisture or carbon dioxide from the air

3 not lose water of crystallisation to the air

Points 1 and 2 stop sulfuric acid from being used.

Point 2 stops sodium hydroxide (and any other base) from being used.

Point 3 stops hydrated sodium carbonate from being used.

A suitable acid for the preparation of a standard solution is ethanedioic acid, $H_2C_2O_4$. It can be obtained as a pure solid and does not interact with the air.

The following method is used to prepare $250\,cm^3$ of a standard solution of the acid:

- Accurately weigh out about 1.1 g of ethanedioic acid.
- Pour it into a beaker and wash out the weighing bottle into the beaker.
- Add water and stir until all the solid has dissolved.
- Pour the solution through a funnel into a volumetric flask. Wash the stirring rod and beaker and finally the funnel with water so that the liquid goes into the volumetric flask.
- Make up the volume in the flask with distilled water until the level is on the mark. Shake the flask thoroughly.

$$\text{amount (in moles) of ethanedioic acid} = \frac{\text{mass}}{\text{molar mass}} = \frac{\text{mass}}{90}$$

$$\text{concentration of acid} = \frac{\text{moles}}{0.250\,dm^3}$$

This acid solution can then be used to find the concentration of a base such as sodium hydroxide, which can then be used as a (secondary) standard solution.

Worked example

Calculate the concentration of a solution of sodium hydroxide using the following data:

- Mass of weighing bottle empty = 28.20 g
- Mass of weighing bottle + ethanedioic acid = 29.34 g
- Volume of ethanedioic acid solution made up = $250\,cm^3$
- Volume of sodium hydroxide taken in each titration = $25.00\,cm^3$
- Mean titre = $23.45\,cm^3$

$$H_2C_2O_4 + 2NaOH \rightarrow Na_2C_2O_4 + 2H_2O$$

Answer

mass of ethanedioic acid = 29.34 − 28.20 = 1.14 g

$$\text{moles of ethanedioic acid} = \frac{1.14\,g}{90\,g\,mol^{-1}} = 0.012667$$

$$\text{concentration of ethanedioic acid solution} = \frac{0.012667}{0.250} = 0.0507\,mol\,dm^{-3}$$

$$\text{moles of ethanedioic acid in } 23.45 \, cm^3 = 0.0507 \times 0.02345 = 0.001188$$

$$\text{moles of sodium hydroxide} = 2 \times 0.001188 = 0.002376$$

$$\text{concentration of sodium hydroxide solution} = \frac{0.002376}{0.02500} = 0.0951 \, mol \, dm^{-3}$$

Back titrations

A back titration is used when the substance being investigated is either insoluble or, for some other reason, cannot be titrated directly.

The method is as follows:

- Weigh a sample of the substance being investigated.
- Add excess of a standard solution of a substance, usually an acid or a base.
- Either titrate the excess or make up the solution to $250 \, cm^3$ and titrate portions of the diluted solution that contain the excess.

An example is the determination of the purity of a sample of chalk, which is impure calcium carbonate. The procedure is as follows:

- Weigh a sample of impure chalk and place it in a beaker.
- Add $50 \, cm^3$ of $1.00 \, mol \, dm^{-3}$ hydrochloric acid solution. This amount of acid must be enough to react with all the calcium carbonate, with some acid in excess.
- Use a funnel to pour the solution obtained (which contains the excess acid) into a standard $250 \, cm^3$ flask. Wash the beaker and the funnel into the flask and make up to the mark with distilled water. Shake the standard flask thoroughly.
- Titrate $25.0 \, cm^3$ portions of this diluted solution against a solution of sodium hydroxide of known concentration.
- Repeat the titration until two consistent titres have been obtained.

The calculation starts with the sodium hydroxide needed in the titration:

1 mean titre $\rightarrow$ moles NaOH $\rightarrow$ moles of excess HCl in $25 \, cm^3$ portion $\rightarrow$ total moles of excess HCl

2 original volume of HCl $\rightarrow$ moles of HCl taken

3 (original moles of HCl) $-$ (total moles of excess HCl) = moles HCl reacted with $CaCO_3$ $\rightarrow$ moles $CaCO_3$ $\rightarrow$ mass of $CaCO_3$ in the chalk sample $\rightarrow$ % purity

> **Tip**
>
> If this type of calculation is asked for at AS, the question will be structured so that you are guided through the many steps.

> **Worked example**
>
> 1.41 g of a sample of chalk, which is mostly calcium carbonate with some inert impurities, was placed in a beaker and $50.0 \, cm^3$ of $1.00 \, mol \, dm^{-3}$ hydrochloric acid solution was slowly added. The equation for the reaction is:
>
> $$CaCO_3 + 2HCl \rightarrow CaCl_2 + H_2O + CO_2$$
>
> When the fizzing had ceased, the contents of the beaker were washed into a standard $250 \, cm^3$ volumetric flask, made up to the mark and thoroughly shaken.
>
> A pipette was used to transfer a $25.0 \, cm^3$ sample into a conical flask. The sample was titrated against $0.100 \, mol \, dm^{-3}$ sodium hydroxide solution. The equation is:
>
> $$HCl + NaOH \rightarrow NaCl + H_2O$$

The titration was repeated. The mean titre was $23.6\,cm^3$.

a) Calculate the amount of sodium hydroxide in the mean titre.

b) Calculate the total amount of hydrochloric acid in excess.

c) Calculate the amount of hydrochloric acid originally taken.

d) Use your answers to b) and c) to calculate the amount of hydrochloric acid that reacted with the chalk.

e) Hence, calculate the amount of calcium carbonate in the chalk sample.

f) Calculate the mass of calcium carbonate in the sample and hence the % purity.

Answer

a) amount of NaOH in mean titre = concentration × volume

$$amount = 0.100\,mol\,dm^{-3} \times \frac{23.6}{1000}\,dm^3 = 0.00236\,mol$$

b) The ratio of HCl to NaOH is 1:1.

amount of HCl in $25\,cm^3$ = 0.00236 mol

amount of HCl in $250\,cm^3$ = 10 × 0.00236 = 0.0236 mol = amount of excess HCl

c) amount of HCl taken = concentration × volume

$$amount = 1.00\,mol\,dm^{-3} \times \frac{50.0}{1000}\,dm^3 = 0.0500\,mol$$

d) amount HCl reacted with $CaCO_3$ = amount taken − amount of excess

amount = 0.0500 mol − 0.0236 mol = 0.0264 mol

e) The ratio of $CaCO_3$ to HCl = 1:2.

$$amount\ of\ CaCO_3\ in\ sample = \frac{1}{2} \times 0.0264 = 0.0132\,mol$$

f) molar mass of $CaCO_3$ = 40.0 + 12.0 + (3 × 16.0) = $100.0\,g\,mol^{-1}$

mass of $CaCO_3$ in sample = moles × molar mass

mass of $CaCO_3$ = 0.0132 mol × $100.0\,g\,mol^{-1}$ = 1.32 g

$$\%\ purity = \frac{1.32\,g}{1.41\,g} \times 100 = 93.6\%$$

To find the stoichiometry of a reaction

In questions that ask for the determination of the stoichiometry of a reaction, the concentrations and volumes of both solutions will be given. The calculation is performed in three steps:

1 Calculate the amount (moles) of one reagent.

2 Calculate the amount (moles) of the other reagent.

3 Find the whole number ratio of these amounts. This is the reactant ratio, which allows the equation to be written.

Worked example

$25.0\,cm^3$ of a $0.100\,mol\,dm^{-3}$ solution of sodium hydroxide required $25.8\,cm^3$ of a $0.0485\,mol\,dm^{-3}$ solution of phosphoric(III) acid, H_3PO_3. Work out the equation for this acid + base reaction.

Answer

Step 1: amount of sodium hydroxide = concentration × volume

$$\text{amount} = 0.100\,\text{mol}\,\text{dm}^{-3} \times \frac{25.0}{1000}\,\text{dm}^3 = 0.00250\,\text{mol}$$

Step 2: amount of phosphoric(III) acid = concentration × volume

$$\text{amount} = 0.0485\,\text{mol}\,\text{dm}^{-3} \times \frac{25.8}{1000}\,\text{dm}^3 = 0.001251\,\text{mol}$$

Step 3: molar ratio NaOH to $H_3PO_3 = \dfrac{0.00250}{0.001251} = 2:1$

2 mol of NaOH react with 1 mol of H_3PO_3, so the equation is:

$$2NaOH + H_3PO_3 \rightarrow Na_2HPO_3 + 2H_2O$$

Minimising errors in titrations

Errors because of the apparatus

Burettes and **pipettes** measure volumes to certain degrees of accuracy. In most cases, the error in each measurement is $\pm0.05\,\text{cm}^3$. This means that the maximum possible error when calculating the titre is $2 \times 0.05 = 0.1\,\text{cm}^3$. In a titre of $24.00\,\text{cm}^3$, this is a percentage error of $0.1 \times 100/24.00 = 0.42\%$. If the titre had been $12.00\,\text{cm}^3$, the error would be the same, but the percentage error would be $0.1 \times 100/12.00 = 0.83\%$, which is twice as large.

Beakers are very inaccurate for measuring volumes and should not be used to measure out solutions for titration. The use of a pipette involves a single measurement and so the error is $\pm0.05\,\text{cm}^3$ which for a standard pipette is $0.05 \times 100/25.00 = 0.20\%$.

Titrations are planned to give a titre between $20\,\text{cm}^3$ and $30\,\text{cm}^3$ in order to minimise apparatus error.

A **standard laboratory balance** reads to $0.01\,\text{g}$. The uncertainty of a reading is $\pm0.005\,\text{g}$ and so, as two readings always have to be taken, the uncertainty in a mass of a substance is $\pm 2 \times 0.005 = \pm0.01\,\text{g}$. For a solid weighing $1.34\,\text{g}$ this is a possible error of $0.01 \times 100/1.34 = 0.75\%$. A mass of less than $1\,\text{g}$ would have a percentage error of more than 1%.

The total error in a titration can be calculated as the sum of all the other apparatus errors.

Errors because of poor technique

Practice and care will reduce errors due to poor technique. Common mistakes include:

- not rinsing all the solid from the weighing bottle
- not rinsing the stirrer and funnel into the volumetric (graduated) flask
- not shaking the volumetric flask thoroughly after making up to $250\,\text{cm}^3$
- not rinsing out the burette and the pipette with the correct solutions
- not ensuring that there is no air below the tap in the burette
- getting air bubbles in the stem of the pipette
- running in the solution from the burette too quickly and overshooting the end point
- not swirling the flask after each addition of solution from the burette

Summary tasks

Check that you know the relationship between moles and:

- mass and molar mass
- volume and molar volume
- the concentration of a solution and its volume

Make sure that you can use the expressions above and the equation for the reaction to calculate:

- the mass or volume of a reactant needed or product produced given data
- the stoichiometry of a reaction given data about the masses or volumes of reactants and products
- which is the limiting reagent given masses of reactants and the equation for the reaction

Be sure you can calculate:

- the percentage yield in a reaction
- the atom economy of a reaction
- the concentration of a solution from titration data

Check that you can:

- describe the correct technique for making up a standard solution
- identify and evaluate errors in titrations

Questions

1 Calculate the mass of iron(III) hydroxide precipitated in the reaction between 12.7 g of iron(III) sulfate and excess sodium hydroxide solution.

$$Fe_2(SO_4)_3(aq) + 6NaOH(aq) \rightarrow$$
$$2Fe(OH)_3(s) + 3Na_2SO_4(aq)$$

2 Copper reacts with silver nitrate solution according to the equation:

$$Cu(s) + 2AgNO_3(aq) \rightarrow$$
$$Cu(NO_3)_2(aq) + 2Ag(s)$$

Calculate the mass of copper needed to react with a solution containing 12.6 g of silver nitrate.

3 Calculate the volume of oxygen produced when 33.3 g of sodium nitrate is heated. Sodium nitrate decomposes according to the equation:

$$2NaNO_3(s) \rightarrow 2NaNO_2(s) + O_2(g)$$

Under the conditions of the experiment, 1 mol of gas occupies a volume of 25.0 dm³.

4 When 60 dm³ of hydrogen is reacted with excess nitrogen under high pressure and temperature in the presence of an iron catalyst, 25 dm³ of ammonia was produced.

$$N_2 + 3H_2 \rightarrow 2NH_3$$

Calculate the theoretical yield and hence the percentage yield in the process.

5 Calculate the amount of sulfuric acid in $23.4\,cm^3$ of a $0.0545\,mol\,dm^{-3}$ solution of the acid.

6 Calculate the volume of a $0.106\,mol\,dm^{-3}$ solution of sodium hydroxide, which contains $0.00164\,mol$.

7 Calculate the mass of ethanedioic acid, $H_2C_2O_4.2H_2O$, that is needed to make $250\,cm^3$ of a $0.0500\,mol\,dm^{-3}$ solution.

8 $4.50\,g$ of iron powder was added to $50.0\,cm^3$ of $2.00\,mol\,dm^{-3}$ copper(II) sulfate solution. The equation for the reaction is:

$$Fe(s) + CuSO_4(aq) \rightarrow Cu(s) + FeSO_4(aq)$$

a) Calculate which reagent is limiting.
b) Calculate the mass of copper produced.
c) What observation would tell you that you were correct in identifying the limiting reagent?

9 $21.5\,g$ of sodium hydroxide was added carefully to $500.0\,cm^3$ of $1.00\,mol\,dm^{-3}$ sulfuric acid solution.
a) Write the equation for the reaction.
b) Calculate which reagent is limiting.
c) Calculate the mass of sodium sulfate produced.
d) What would be observed if pieces of red and blue litmus paper were added to the solution after the reaction?

10 The limit of carbon monoxide in the air as set by the European Union is $3.13\,ppmV$. Calculate the maximum permitted mass of carbon monoxide in $1.00\,dm^3$ air.

11 Iron(II) sulfate contains water of crystallisation. Its formula can be written as $FeSO_4.xH_2O$.

When $5.46\,g$ of hydrated iron(II) sulfate was heated it lost water and the residue of anhydrous iron(II) sulfate weighed $2.98\,g$. Calculate the number of molecules of water of crystallisation in the formula.

12 Nanotechnology can involve the use of tiny amounts of chemicals. The junctions of nanofibre polymers hold a volume of approximately $4.0 \times 10^{-18}\,dm^3$. One such junction was saturated with a minute amount of a solution of glucose, $C_6H_{12}O_6$, with a concentration of $0.054\,g$ of glucose per dm^3. Calculate:
a) the number of moles of glucose at the nanofibre junction
b) the number of molecules of glucose in that junction

(The Avogadro constant is $6.0 \times 10^{23}\,mol^{-1}$.)

13 $1.55\,g$ of sodium carbonate monohydrate, $Na_2CO_3.H_2O$, was dissolved in $250\,cm^3$ of water in a beaker. A burette was filled with this solution and titrated against a solution of hydrochloric acid. The mean titre was $26.70\,cm^3$.

$$Na_2CO_3.H_2O(aq) + 2HCl(aq) \rightarrow$$
$$2NaCl(aq) + 2H_2O(l) + CO_2(g)$$

a) Point out two errors in the technique.
b) Calculate the concentration of the hydrochloric acid solution.

14 The skin of peaches can be loosened by standing them in a solution of potassium hydroxide. After a short time, the skins can be removed easily by machine. The skinned peaches are then washed to remove excess potassium hydroxide. The final washings are tested to see how much potassium hydroxide remains. $100\,cm^3$ of the final washings was titrated with $0.0050\,mol\,dm^{-3}$ hydrochloric acid. The mean titre was $7.55\,cm^3$. Calculate the concentration of potassium hydroxide in the final washings in parts per million.

Exam practice questions

1 Chalk is an impure form of calcium carbonate. It reacts with aqueous hydrochloric acid according to the equation:

$$CaCO_3(s) + 2HCl(aq) \rightarrow$$
$$CaCl_2(aq) + H_2O(l) + CO_2(g)$$

When excess dilute hydrochloric acid was added to 1.23 g of a sample of chalk, 289 cm^3 of carbon dioxide was collected.

a) Calculate the amount (in moles) of carbon dioxide released and hence the percentage purity of the chalk sample. (The molar volume of gas under the conditions of the experiment is 24.4 dm^3.) (4)

b) What is the minimum volume of a 2.00 mol dm^{-3} solution of hydrochloric acid required for complete reaction of the chalk? (2)

(Total 6 marks)

2 25 ibuprofen tablets were reacted with 50.0 cm^3 of 1.00 mol dm^{-3} sodium hydroxide solution. The reaction is:

$$C_{12}H_{17}COOH + NaOH \rightarrow$$
$$C_{12}H_{17}COONa + H_2O$$

When the reaction was over, the solution, containing excess sodium hydroxide, was made up to 250 cm^3 with distilled water. 25.0 cm^3 samples were titrated against 0.110 mol dm^{-3} hydrochloric acid solution:

$$NaOH + HCl \rightarrow NaCl + H_2O$$

The mean titre was 23.35 cm^3.

a) The colour change at the end point when acid is added from a burette to an alkali in the presence of a few drops of phenolphthalein is:
   A from purple to colourless
   B from purple to pale pink
   C from colourless to purple
   D from pale pink to purple (1)

b) If 12 tablets had been taken, the mean titre would have been 11.21 cm^3. The percentage error when using a burette that is accurate to ±0.05 cm^3 is:
   A 0.0045%   C 0.45%
   B 0.0089%   D 0.89% (1)

c) Calculate the amount (in moles) of hydrochloric acid used in the titration. (1)

d) Calculate the amount (in moles) of excess sodium hydroxide in a 25.0 cm^3 sample and hence calculate the amount (in moles) of total excess sodium hydroxide. (2)

e) Calculate the amount (in moles) of sodium hydroxide originally taken and use it and your answer to b) to calculate the amount (in moles) of sodium hydroxide that reacted with the 25 ibuprofen tablets. (2)

f) Hence, calculate the amount (in moles) of ibuprofen in 25 tablets and the mass, in mg, of ibuprofen in one tablet. (2)

(Total 9 marks)

3 a) State the relationship between moles and:
   i) mass and molar mass
   ii) volume of gas and molar volume
   iii) number of particles (3)

b) When chlorine reacts with 6.075 g of magnesium, the mass of product is:
   A 11.5 g   C 20.45 g
   B 18.95 g   D 23.825 g (1)

c) The number of ions in 8.55 g of Al$_2$(SO$_4$)$_3$ (molar mass 342.3 g mol^{-1}) is:
   A 0.025   C 1.5 × 10^{22}
   B 0.125   D 7.5 × 10^{22} (1)

   (Avogadro constant = 6.02 × 10^{23} mol^{-1})

d) When 8.55 g of rubidium metal was reacted with oxygen, 11.75 g of product was formed. Which equation is supported by these data?
   A $Rb + O_2 \rightarrow RbO_2$
   B $Rb + \frac{1}{2}O_2 \rightarrow RbO$
   C $2Rb + O_2 \rightarrow Rb_2O_2$
   D $2Rb + \frac{1}{2}O_2 \rightarrow Rb_2O$ (1)

e) When 7.95 g of copper(II) oxide, CuO, was reacted with sulfuric acid and the resulting solution filtered and allowed to crystallise, 23.0 g of hydrated copper sulfate, CuSO$_4$.5H$_2$O, was produced. The percentage yield is:
   A 109   C 69
   B 92   D 34 (1)

(Total 7 marks)

4 A student was required to make up a standard solution of hydrated sodium carbonate. The procedure that the student used was as follows:

- A weighing bottle was placed on a balance and the balance was tared.
- Some solid hydrated sodium carbonate was added and the balance read and recorded to 2 decimal places.
- The solid was tipped into a beaker and $25\,cm^3$ of water added. The mixture was stirred until all the solid had dissolved.
- The solution was poured into a standard flask and the volume made up to $250\,cm^3$.
- Samples of the solution were removed using a $25\,cm^3$ pipette and titrated against a solution of hydrochloric acid. The results are shown below.
- Mass of hydrated sodium carbonate, $Na_2CO_3.10H_2O = 7.03\,g$.

Titre	1	2	3	4
Initial volume/cm^3	2.25	0.00	4.35	2.70
Final volume/cm^3	27.30	25.35	30.00	28.10
Volume added/cm^3				
Equation	Na$_2$CO$_3$(aq) + 2HCl(aq) $\rightarrow$ 2NaCl(aq) + CO$_2$(g) + H$_2$O(l)			

a) State and explain three errors in technique that the student made. (6)

b) i) Complete the table above. (1)

    ii) Identify the concordant titres and use them to calculate the mean titre. (2)

    iii) Calculate the concentration of the hydrochloric acid solution in $mol\,dm^{-3}$. Give your answer to three significant figures. (4)

(Total 13 marks)

10 Introduction to organic chemistry (Topic 6)

Organic chemistry is the study of compounds containing carbon and hydrogen atoms. Some organic compounds contain other elements, such as oxygen, a halogen or nitrogen. A few contain sulfur. Carbon is unique in that, in compounds, it forms strong and stable bonds with other carbon atoms. Chains of several thousand carbon atoms are possible, giving rise to potentially millions of organic compounds.

Carbon has the electron configuration $1s^2\,2s^2\,2p_x^{\,1}\,2p_y^{\,1}\,2p_z^{\,0}$. It has only two unpaired electrons, so it might be thought that a carbon atom would only form two bonds. However, it is energetically favourable for one electron from the $2s$-orbital to be promoted into the empty $2p_z$-orbital, which results in four unpaired electrons. The energy required for this promotion is much less than the extra energy released when the atom forms four, rather than two, covalent bonds.

> Every carbon atom *must* have four bonds.

Bonding in organic chemistry

The four bonds around every carbon atom can be:
- four single bonds — four σ-bonds (Figure 10.1)
- two single bonds and one double bond — three σ-bonds and one π-bond (Figure 10.2)
- one single bond and one triple bond — two σ-bonds and two π-bonds (Figure 10.3)
- two double bonds — two σ-bonds and two π-bonds (Figure 10.4)
- three single bonds and one ionic bond (Figure 10.5)

> **Tip**
>
> Remember that all carbon atoms have a valency of four. This means that each carbon atom has four bonds. In the examples above, note that there are four lines (covalent bonds) coming off each carbon atom, apart from the last type where there are three lines and a charge. In A-level chemistry, you will mostly come across the first two types of bonding.

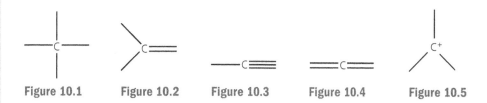

Figure 10.1   Figure 10.2   Figure 10.3   Figure 10.4   Figure 10.5

Four single bonds: four σ-bonds

The four pairs of bonding electrons around the carbon atom repel each other and, as there are no lone pairs, the resulting molecule is tetrahedral in shape with bond angles of 109.5°. The simplest example is methane, CH_4 (Figure 10.6).

> σ- and π-bonds are explained on page 46.

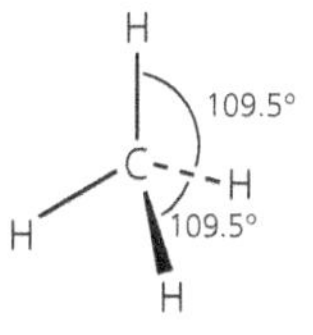

Two single and one double bond: three σ-bonds and one π-bond

A double bond consists of a σ-bond and a π-bond. The σ- and π-electrons in the double bond occur along the same axis. They repel the other two bonded pairs in the two single σ-bonds. Therefore, the three 'lots' of electrons take up a position of

Figure 10.6

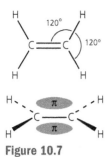

Figure 10.7

maximum separation, which is a planar arrangement with bond angles of 120°. The simplest example is ethene, $H_2C=CH_2$ (Figure 10.7).

The π-electrons are above and below the σ-bond between the two carbon atoms. If the two CH_2 groups were rotated, the π-bond would break and only reform after a rotation of 180°. This bond breaking would require a large amount of energy (about $250\,kJ\,mol^{-1}$) and so does not happen unless the substance is heated very strongly. Therefore, *at room temperature*, there is no rotation about a double bond.

Representing molecules

The **molecular formula** of a compound gives the numbers of atoms of each element present in one molecule of the substance. It does not indicate how the atoms are joined together. The molecular formula of ethanol is C_2H_6O and that of ethene is C_2H_4.

The **empirical formula** is the simplest whole number ratio of the atoms of each element in the compound. The empirical formula of ethanol is the same as its molecular formula; the empirical formula of ethene is CH_2.

Any formula that is used to represent a compound must be unambiguous. Molecules of ethanol and methoxymethane each have two carbon atoms, six hydrogen atoms and one oxygen atom. Therefore, the molecular formula C_2H_6O is ambiguous. The molecular formula of ethene is C_2H_4, which is unambiguous and so can be used to represent ethene in equations.

The use of structural formulae overcomes ambiguous molecular formulae. The **structural formula** of ethanol (molecular formula C_2H_6O) is CH_3CH_2OH and that of methoxymethane (also with molecular formula C_2H_6O) is CH_3OCH_3. The structural formula should include any double bonds that are present in the molecule; the structural formula of ethene is $H_2C=CH_2$.

> The CH_3CH_2 group is often written as C_2H_5 in structural formulae.

Figure 10.8

The **displayed** or **full structural formula** must show all the atoms separately and all the bonds between them. The displayed formula for ethene is shown in Figure 10.8.

In a **skeletal formula** the carbon atoms are not drawn. A straight line represents a single bond and a double line represents a double bond. A carbon atom is assumed to be at the end of these lines unless another atom, such as oxygen, is shown (see Figure 10.9). Hydrogen atoms that are bonded to carbon are also omitted, but those joined to an oxygen or nitrogen atom are included. However, remember that each carbon atom has enough hydrogen atoms joined to it to make a total of four bonds.

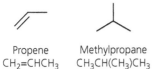

Propene
$CH_2=CHCH_3$

Methylpropane
$CH_3CH(CH_3)CH_3$

Propan-2-ol
$CH_3CH(OH)CH_3$

Cyclohexane
C_6H_{12}

Figure 10.9

Figure 10.9 shows examples of skeletal formulae.

The skeletal method is particularly useful when drawing the formulae of large molecules, such as cholesterol (Figure 10.10).

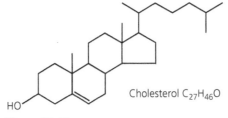

Cholesterol $C_{27}H_{46}O$

HO

Figure 10.10

> 'Omega-3' means that the first double bond is on the *third* carbon atom counting from the non-carboxylic end of the acid. (Omega is the last (end) letter in the Greek alphabet.)

The skeletal formula of an unsaturated fat containing an omega-3 acid (A), an omega-6 acid (B) and saturated stearic acid (C) is represented in Figure 10.11.

10 Introduction to organic chemistry (Topic 6)

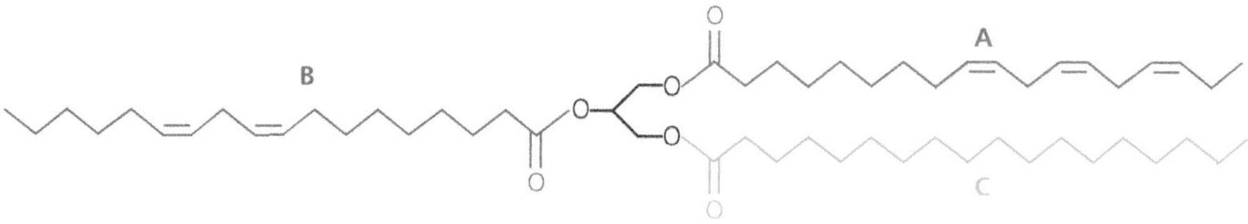

Figure 10.11

Figure 10.12 shows how the formula of this unsaturated fat is normally written.

$H_2COOCC_{17}H_{29}$
$HCOOCC_{17}H_{31}$
$H_2COOCC_{17}H_{35}$

Figure 10.12

Test yourself

1 Draw the skeletal formulae of:

a) pentane, C_5H_{12} b) butan-2-ol, $CH_3CH_2CH(OH)CH_3$

Families of organic compounds

As there are millions of organic compounds, order has to be brought out of chaos. Organic substances are divided into 'families' or **homologous series**. The members of a homologous series show a trend in physical properties, such as melting and boiling temperatures and solubility.

Key terms

A **homologous series** is a series of compounds that contain the same **functional group** and that have the same general formula. The formula of each member of the series differs from the next by CH_2.

A **functional group** is a small group of atoms or a single halogen atom that gives the compounds in the series particular chemical properties. The functional groups covered at AS are shown in Table 10.1.

Table 10.1 Functional groups

Functional group	Name of series	Suffix	General formula	First member
None	Alkanes	-ane	C_nH_{2n+2}	Methane, CH_4
C=C	Alkenes	-ene	C_nH_{2n}	Ethene, $H_2C{=}CH_2$
–X, where X is a halogen	Halogenoalkanes	-ane	$C_nH_{2n+1}X$	Chloromethane, CH_3Cl
–OH	Alcohols	-ol	$C_nH_{2n+1}OH$	Methanol, CH_3OH
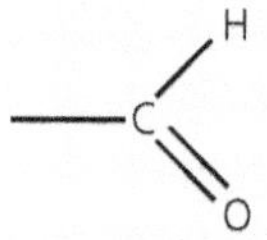	Aldehydes	-al	RCHO where R is an alkyl group or H	Methanal, HCHO
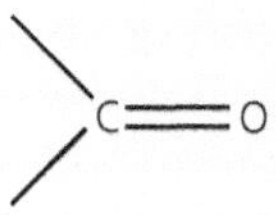	Ketones	-one	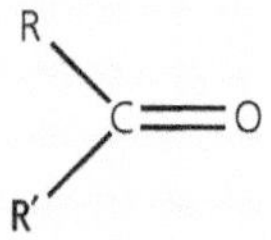 where R and R′ are alkyl groups	Propanone, CH_3COCH_3
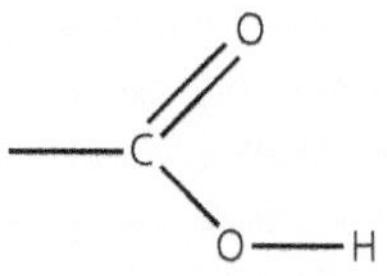	Carboxylic acids	-oic acid	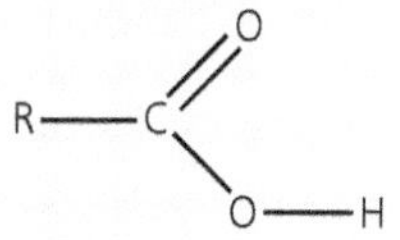 where R is an alkyl group or H	Methanoic acid, HCOOH

The functional group for an aldehyde must be written CHO and not COH to avoid confusion with alcohols.

Test yourself

2 Identify the functional groups in the following:

a) $CH_2OHCOCH(NH_2)COOH$

b) $CH_2{=}CHCH(OH)CHO$

Naming organic compounds

Organic compounds are named according to the IUPAC (International Union of Pure and Applied Chemistry) system.

Hydrocarbons

Alkanes

Key terms

Hydrocarbons are compounds that contain the elements carbon and hydrogen *only*.

An **alkane** is a saturated hydrocarbon in which all the bonds between carbon atoms are single.

- The alkanes are an example of a homologous series.
- The names of all alkanes end in the suffix *-ane*.
- They have the general formula C_nH_{2n+2}

The names of individual members of the homologous series of alkanes are found by using three rules.

Rule 1: identify the longest unbranched carbon chain to establish the stem name. The stem names for the alkanes are given in Table 10.2.

Table 10.2 Names of alkanes

Longest unbranched carbon chain	Alkane stem name	Alkane
1	Meth-	Methane
2	Eth-	Ethane
3	Prop-	Propane
4	But-	Butane
5	Pent-	Pentane
6	Hex-	Hexane
7	Hept-	Heptane
8	Oct-	Octane

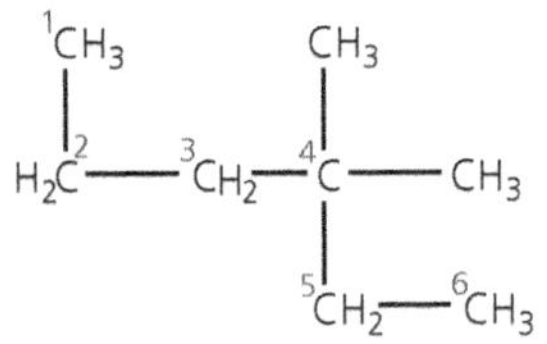

Figure 10.13

Formulae of alkanes are traditionally drawn with the carbon atoms in a straight line, but they are really a three-dimensional zigzag.

The compound in Figure 10.13 has a six-carbon chain. The six carbon atoms are numbered 1 to 6.

Rule 2: name any substituent groups that are bonded to a carbon atom (Table 10.3). If there are two or more substituents, they must be named in alphabetical order.

Table 10.3 Alkyl substituent groups

Substituent group	Formula
Methyl	CH_3
Ethyl	CH_3CH_2
Propyl	$CH_3CH_2CH_2$
Butyl	$CH_3CH_2CH_2CH_2$

Rule 3: identify the position of each substituent by a number.

- The numbering is done from the end of the carbon chain that gives the lowest number for the substituent group.
- If there are two identical groups on the *same* carbon atom, the number is repeated and the prefix *di-* is added to the name of the substituent group.
- If there are two or more identical groups on *different* carbon atoms, the substituent groups are numbered and the prefixes di-, tri- or tetra- (for two, three or four substituents) are used.

Worked example

Name the following compound:

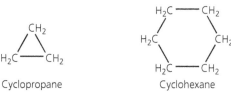

Answer

Rule 1: The longest unbranched carbon chain has five carbon atoms — pentane.

Rules 2 and 3: There are three methyl groups bonded to this chain — two on carbon atom number 2 and one on carbon atom number 4.

The name of the compound is 2,2,4-trimethylpentane.

2,2,4-trimethylpentane is used as a fuel in petrol-driven cars and has an octane number of 100.

Cycloalkanes

Cycloalkanes have the general formula C_nH_{2n}, which is the same as that of alkenes. The first member of the homologous series is cyclopropane, C_3H_6. The most stable is cyclohexane, C_6H_{12} (Figure 10.14).

Cyclopropane

Cyclohexane

Figure 10.14

Alkenes

Unsaturated compounds have one or more double or triple bonds between carbon atoms, so alkenes are a type of unsaturated compound.

The name of an alkene is derived by replacing the ending *-ane* in the corresponding alkane with the ending *-ene* and, if necessary, specifying the position of the double bond.

Alkenes include:

- ethene, $H_2C{=}CH_2$
- propene, $CH_2{=}CHCH_3$
- butene, C_4H_8

There are two positional isomers of butene, depending on where the double bond is in the chain. The number assigned is the lowest number, counting from the shorter end of the longest chain of carbon atoms.

- $H_2C{=}CHCH_2CH_3$ is but-1-ene
  1 2 3 4
- $H_3CCH{=}CHCH_3$ is but-2-ene
  1 **2** 3 4
- $CH_3CH_2CH{=}CHCH_3$ is pent-2-ene not pent-3-ene
  5 4 3 **2** 1

Naming other organic compounds

Tip

Be particularly careful when naming carboxylic acids. The carbon of the $-COOH$ group is part of the carbon chain. Therefore, CH_3CH_2COOH has a three-carbon atom chain and is called *propan*oic acid. The same applies to aldehydes and ketones. CH_3CHO is *ethan*al, and CH_3COCH_3 is *propan*one.

Rule 1: identify the series or class of organic compound to which the formula belongs and ascertain the longest unbranched carbon chain. The suffix of the series is added to the corresponding alkane name (minus the final *e*) of the longest carbon chain. For example, CH_3CH_2OH is ethanol, rather than ethaneol; $CH_3CH_2CH_2CHO$ is butanal, not butaneal.

Rule 2: name any substituent groups that are bonded to a carbon atom. If there are two or more substituents, they must be named in alphabetical order.

Rule 3: identify the position of each substituent by a number.

Worked example

Name the following compounds:

a)

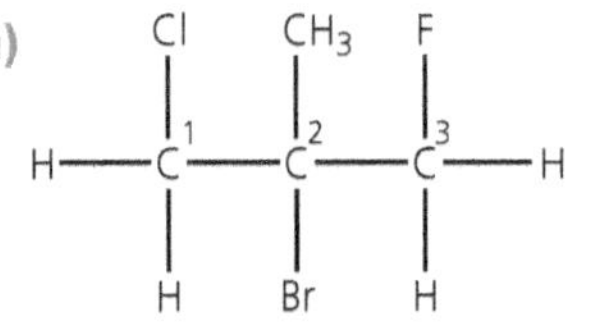

b)

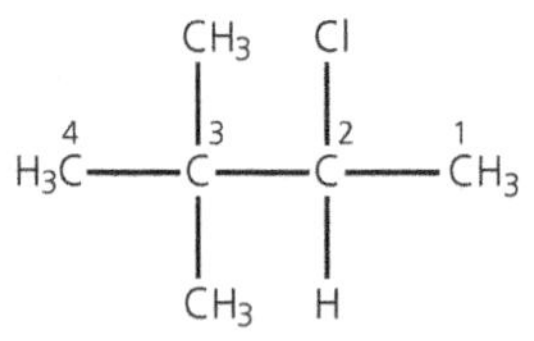

c)

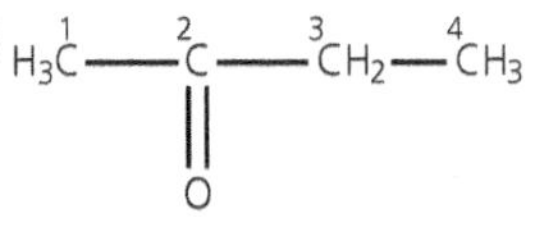

There is no need to state a number, as the =O must be on one of the inner carbon atoms.

Answers

a) Chain length three — propane; substituent groups named in alphabetical order: 2-bromo-1-chloro-3-fluoro-2-methylpropane

b) Chain length four — butane; substituent groups named in alphabetical order: 2-chloro-3,3-dimethylbutane

c) Compound is a ketone with a chain length of four: butanone

Isomerism

There are two main types of isomerism.

Structural isomerism

Structural isomers have the same molecular formula but different molecular structures. This means that the isomers have the same number of atoms of the same elements, but that these atoms are arranged differently.

Structural isomers can be divided into three categories: carbon–chain, positional and functional-group.

Key term

Isomers are compounds with the same molecular formula but different structural formulae.

Carbon-chain isomers

The only way in which these isomers differ is in the length of the carbon chain. For example, butane and methylpropane both have the molecular formula C_4H_{10}, but butane has a carbon chain of four atoms and methylpropane has a carbon chain of three atoms (Figure 10.15). The skeletal formulae of these two isomers are shown in Figure 10.16.

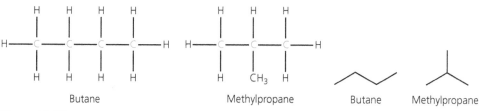

Butane   Methylpropane   Butane   Methylpropane

Figure 10.15   **Figure 10.16**

Positional isomers

Positional isomers have the same functional group in different locations on the carbon framework. A simple example is provided by the alcohols propan-1-ol and propan-2-ol. Both have the molecular formula C_3H_8O, but their structural formulae are $CH_3CH_2CH_2OH$ and $CH_3CH(OH)CH_3$ respectively. Their displayed formulae are shown in Figure 10.17.

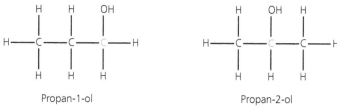

Propan-1-ol   Propan-2-ol

Figure 10.17

The carbon chains can also be different. Butan-1-ol and butan-2-ol are positional isomers, as are 2-methylpropan-2-ol and 2-methylpropan-1-ol. However, butan-1-ol and 2-methylpropan-1-ol are carbon–chain isomers, as are butan-2-ol and 2-methylpropan-2-ol. All four substances have the molecular formula $C_4H_{10}O$. Their displayed and skeletal formulae are shown in Figure 10.18.

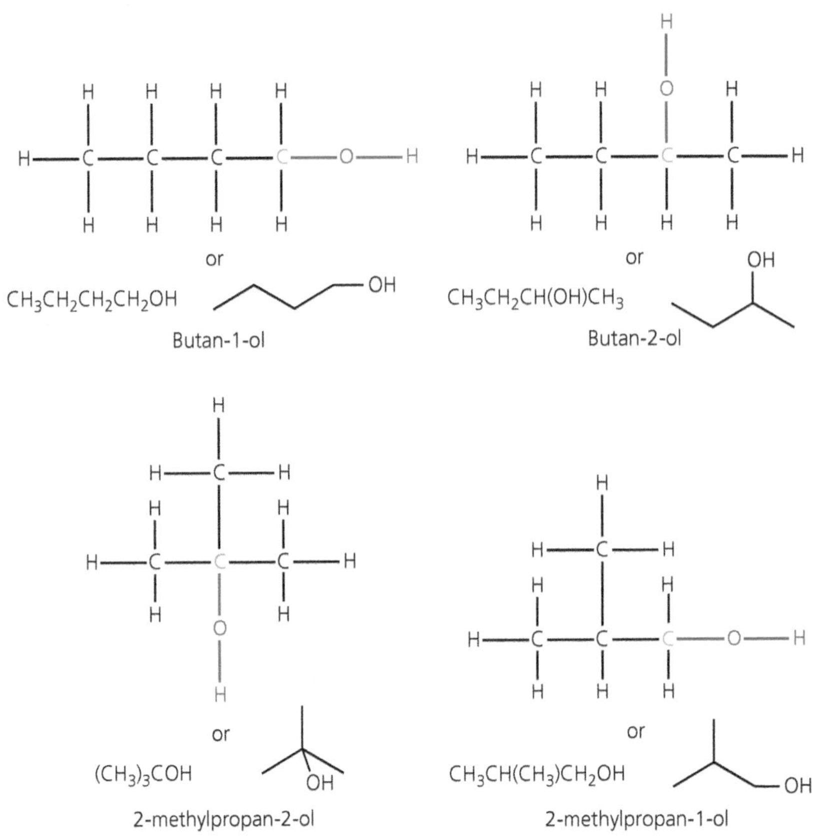

$CH_3CH_2CH_2CH_2OH$

Butan-1-ol

$CH_3CH_2CH(OH)CH_3$

Butan-2-ol

$(CH_3)_3COH$

2-methylpropan-2-ol

$CH_3CH(CH_3)CH_2OH$

2-methylpropan-1-ol

Figure 10.18

Test yourself

3 Draw and name all the structural isomers of:

a) C_4H_9OH b) C_4H_8

Functional-group isomers

Functional-group isomerism occurs when two compounds with the same molecular formula are members of different homologous series and have different functional groups. For example, the ester methyl methanoate, $HCOOCH_3$, is an isomer of ethanoic acid, CH_3COOH (Figure 10.19).

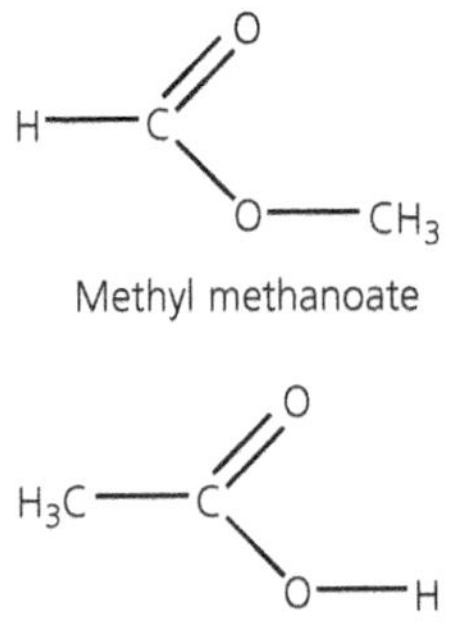

Another example is hex-1-ene and cyclohexane, both of which have the molecular formula C_6H_{12}. However, a molecule of hex-1-ene has a double bond whereas a cyclohexane molecule is cyclic with no double bond.

Stereoisomerism

There are two quite separate types of stereoisomer — geometric and optical. In both types, the carbon chain, the position of the groups on the chain and the nature of the functional groups are the same. However, the arrangement of the atoms in space is different.

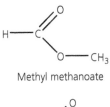

Methyl methanoate

Ethanoic acid

Figure 10.19

Geometric isomers

The most common way in which geometric isomerism occurs is when a molecule has a C=C group and both of these carbon atoms have two different groups or atoms joined to them. For example, but-2-ene exists as two geometric isomers. The two double-bonded carbon atoms and the four atoms joined to them all lie in a plane and can take up different spatial positions in that plane (Figure 10.20).

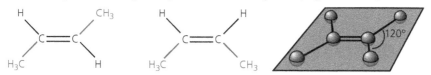

Figure 10.20 The isomers of but-2-ene

The geometry of the two isomers is different. In the left-hand isomer, the two $-CH_3$ groups are staggered at 180° to each other and are on opposite sides of the double bond. This compound is called the *trans or E* isomer. In the right-hand isomer, the two $-CH_3$ groups are on the same side of the double bond. This compound is called the *cis or Z* isomer.

Naming geometric isomers
There are two methods of naming geometric isomers:

- *cis/trans* — the *cis*-isomer has the same functional groups on the same side of the double bond and the *trans*-isomer has them on opposite sides, as shown in Figure 10.20.
- *E-/Z-* — in this method 'priorities' are assigned to the atoms attached to each of the C=C carbon atoms. The higher the atomic number, the higher is the priority assigned to that atom. An example is 1-bromo-2-chloro-2-iodoethene (Figure 10.21).

The left-hand carbon atom of the double bond has a bromine atom (atomic number 35) and a hydrogen atom (atomic number 1) attached. The bromine has the higher priority.

The right-hand carbon atom has an iodine atom (atomic number 53) and a chlorine atom (atomic number 17) attached. The iodine has the higher priority.

If the two higher priority atoms are on the opposite sides of the double bond, the isomer is labelled *E* (for *entgegen*, the German for opposite). If they are on the same side, the isomer is labelled *Z* (for *zusammen*, the German for together). The name of this isomer is *Z*-1-bromo-2-chloro-2-iodoethene.

The *cis/trans* method of naming geometric isomers breaks down if there are four different groups attached to the carbon atoms in the double bond. In 3-chloropent-2-ene shown in Figure 10.22, the $-CH_3$ group on the left is *cis* to the $-C_2H_5$ group on the right but *trans* to the chlorine atom on the right, so the *E-/Z-* method must be used.

The names and structural formulae of its two isomers of are shown in Figure 10.22. The higher-priority atoms are marked in red.

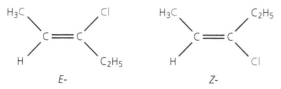

Figure 10.22 The geometric isomers of 3-chloro-pent-2-ene

Geometric isomers exist because there is restricted rotation around the double bond. Therefore, one isomer cannot spontaneously convert into the other unless sufficient energy is supplied (page 168).

But-1-ene does not have geometric isomers because one of the carbon atoms in the double bond has two hydrogen atoms attached to it:

Figure 10.21

A way to remember this is that *E* is a vowel and 'opposite' starts with a vowel. Similarly, *Z* is a consonant and 'same' starts with a consonant. (*Z* meanz on ze zame zide!)

Tip

Do not state that there is no rotation about the double bond; the rotation is restricted and does not occur at room temperature.

The exact shape of a molecule is often important in biochemistry. For example, vision in human beings depends upon the geometric isomerism of retinal, which is found bonded to the protein in the retina in the eye. When light hits a cell containing *cis*-retinal, the energy of the light breaks the π-bond. The molecule rotates and reforms as the *trans*-isomer. This shape change causes a signal to be sent, via the optic nerve, to the brain.

Tip

In *E*- and *Z*-notation, the *cis*-acids are called *Z*-acids.

Cis- and *trans*-fatty acids

Oils and fats are the esters of propane-1,2,3-triol and long-chain fatty acids, some of which are unsaturated. In natural oils and fats, the fatty acids are all *cis*-isomers, in which a hydrogen atom is attached to each carbon atom in each double bond. When an unsaturated fat is partially hydrogenated in the presence of a nickel catalyst, some of the double bonds are broken. Rotation occurs and the *trans*-isomer is formed. *Trans*-fatty acids are more harmful than the *cis*-acids and can cause heart disease.

The skeletal formula of a polyunsaturated fat in Figure 10.11 on page 169 shows that the omega-3 and the omega-6 fatty acids are *cis*- (or *Z*-) isomers.

Test yourself

4 Draw the skeletal formulae of the geometric isomers of pent-1,3-diene, $CH_2CHCHCHCH_3$.

Optical isomers

Optical isomers are molecules that have non-superimposable mirror images. Knowledge of optical isomers is only required in the second year of the A-level course and so is not covered in this book.

Types of reaction

Addition: a molecule with a double bond reacts with a different molecule to form a single molecule:

$$H_2C=CH_2 + HBr \rightarrow H_3C-CH_2Br$$

Elimination: a small molecule is lost from a single molecule, forming a double bond:

$$CH_3CH_2OH \rightarrow H_2C=CH_2 + H_2O$$

Substitution: an atom or small group in one molecule is replaced by a different atom or group:

$$CH_3CH_2Cl + OH^- \rightarrow CH_3CH_2OH + Cl^-$$

Oxidation: oxygen is added to a substance or hydrogen removed (or when electrons are removed):

$$CH_3CH_2OH + [O] \rightarrow CH_3CHO + H_2O$$

[O] and [H] represent oxidising and reducing agents, not oxygen and hydrogen gas.

Reduction: hydrogen is added or oxygen removed (or when electrons are added):

$$CH_3COOH + 4[H] \rightarrow CH_3CH_2OH + H_2O$$

Hydrolysis: water or H^+ ions or OH^- ions break a bond in a molecule splitting it into two parts. In the example below the O−C bond is broken:

$$CH_3COOC_2H_5 + OH^- \rightarrow CH_3COO^- + C_2H_5OH$$

Polymerisation: many molecules join together to form a single long-chain molecule:

$$nH_2C{=}CH_2 \rightarrow -CH_2{-}CH_2-_n$$
$$\text{ethene} \qquad\qquad \text{poly(ethene)}$$

Alkanes

> **Key term**
>
> **Alkanes** are saturated hydrocarbons that have the general formula C_nH_{2n+2}.

Physical properties

Boiling temperature

The first four members of the homologous series of alkanes are gases at room temperature. The remainder are liquids up to a value of about $n = 30$; subsequently they are waxy solids. A graph of boiling temperatures at 1 atm pressure is shown in Figure 10.23.

The boiling temperature rises because of the increasing number of electrons in the molecule. This causes stronger instantaneous induced dipole–induced dipole forces of attraction (London forces — page 63). Stronger intermolecular forces require more energy to separate the molecules, resulting in a higher boiling temperature.

Propane and butane can easily be liquefied at room temperature by increasing the pressure. The liquid in bottles of domestic gas and camping gas and in cigarette lighters is compressed butane and propane. LPG (liquefied petroleum gas or Autogas) is sold as an alternative fuel to petrol (gasoline) and is also a mixture of propane and butane. However, it produces about 25% less energy per litre than petrol.

'Saturated' means that the molecules do not have any double bonds, so they cannot react with hydrogen.

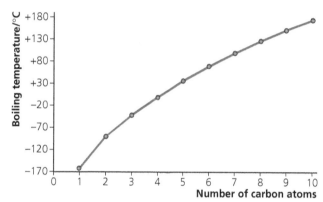

Figure 10.23 Boiling temperatures of the first ten unbranched alkanes

Branched alkanes have lower boiling temperatures than their straight-chain isomers. This is because there are fewer points of contact between adjacent molecules — they do not pack so well together (Table 10.4).

Table 10.4 Boiling temperatures of butane and pentane and their branched isomers

Name	Number of carbon atoms	Boiling temperature/°C
Butane	4	−0.5
Methylpropane	4	−12
Pentane	5	36
2-methylbutane	5	28
2,2-dimethylpropane	5	10

Solubility

Alkanes are insoluble in water, but dissolve readily in each other. Crude oil is a mixture of over 100 different alkanes dissolved in each other.

Density

Liquid alkanes are less dense than water. Their density increases as the molar mass of the alkane increases.

Occurrence

The major source of methane is natural gas. Crude oil is the source of many other alkanes. It is first fractionally distilled. The heavier fractions are either used as fuels or are **cracked** to give a mixture of alkenes and smaller alkanes. These alkanes, together with the gasoline and naphtha fractions, are **reformed** to give a fuel with a higher octane rating.

On heating with a suitable metal catalyst, the straight-chain alkanes turn into branched-chain isomers. These do not explode at the high pressures inside the cylinder of a car engine, until they are ignited with a spark. Therefore, they have higher octane ratings than unbranched alkanes. The gasoline and naphtha fractions are reformed to give a fuel with a higher octane rating.

Fractional distillation

The petroleum is pre-heated and then pumped into the fractionating tower, where it separates into fractions according to boiling temperatures. A typical breakdown of the products is shown in Table 10.5.

Table 10.5 Products of fractional distillation of crude oil

Type	% produced	Number of carbon atoms in molecule	Boiling temperature/°C	Use
Refinery gas	2–5	1–4	0–30	Bottled gas
Naphtha	20–40	5–12	30–150	Source for cracking (see below)
Kerosene (paraffin)	10–20	12–18	150–250	Fuel for jet engines
Gas oil	10–20	15 to 25	250–350	Diesel fuel
Fuel oil	15–20	>25	High	Fuel for power stations and ships
Residue	10–20	>30	Very high	Further treatment to give lubricating oils and bitumen (road surfacing)

Cracking

Cracking is the name given to breaking up large hydrocarbon molecules into smaller ones. This is achieved by using high pressures and temperatures without a catalyst, or lower temperatures and pressures in the presence of a catalyst.

The source of the large hydrocarbon molecules is often the naphtha fraction or the gas oil fraction from the fractional distillation of crude oil (petroleum). The hydrocarbon molecules are broken up in different ways to produce mixtures of smaller alkanes and alkenes. One possible reaction involving the hydrocarbon $C_{20}H_{42}$ is:

$$C_{20}H_{42} \rightarrow C_2H_4 + C_3H_6 + C_8H_{16} + C_7H_{16}$$

Modern cracking uses **zeolites** as the catalyst. The alkane is passed over the catalyst at a temperature of about 500°C and at moderately low pressures and produces a mixture of alkenes and a high percentage of hydrocarbons with between 5 and 10 carbon atoms.

Reforming

Petrol is a mixture of alkanes or cycloalkanes with 5–10 carbon atoms. For efficient combustion in the engine a significant number of the alkanes must be branched or be cycloalkanes. Reforming is the process in which hydrocarbon molecules are rearranged into other molecules. An example is the conversion of straight-chain alkanes, such as octane, into a variety of branched alkanes such as 2,2,4-trimethylpentane or hexane into cyclohexane and hydrogen (Figure 10.24).

Figure 10.24 The skeletal equation for the reforming of hexane

The equation for the reforming of octane is:

$$CH_3CH_2CH_2CH_2CH_2CH_2CH_2CH_2 \rightarrow CH_3CH(CH_3)CH_2C(CH_3)_2CH_3$$
octane   2,2,4-trimethylpentane

This is a very important process in the manufacture of petrol. It enables straight-chain alkanes to be converted into branched-chain alkanes and cyclohexanes, which increase the octane rating of petrol.

Chemical reactions

Alkanes are the least reactive of the organic compounds studied at A level.

Free radical substitution reaction with halogens

In the presence of bright white or ultraviolet light, alkanes react with chlorine and bromine. The reaction involves the replacement of the hydrogen atoms in the alkane by halogen atoms. There is normally a mixture of products as the hydrogen atoms are successively replaced:

$$CH_4 + Cl_2 \rightarrow HCl + CH_3Cl$$

$$CH_3Cl + Cl_2 \rightarrow HCl + CH_2Cl_2$$

and so on. The products are hydrogen chloride and a mixture of chloromethane, dichloromethane, trichloromethane and tetrachloromethane (carbon tetrachloride).

This is an example of a *free-radical substitution reaction*.

Reaction mechanism

The **reaction mechanism** of an organic reaction shows the pathway from the reactants, via the transition state or any intermediates, to the products. It also shows the movement of electrons during the reaction by the use of arrows.

A **half-headed** or **fishhook** arrow represents the movement of a *single* electron:

A half-headed arrow can start:

- from a covalent bond. In this case, there are two half-headed arrows going either to an atom (thus forming a radical) or to another radical (thus forming a covalent bond).
- from the single electron in a free radical. In this case, it goes to an atom in a molecule or to another radical (thus forming a covalent bond).

A free radical is represented by a *single* dot beside the symbol of the atom. For instance, Cl• represents a chlorine radical.

The free radical substitution reaction is made up of three steps:

- **initiation**
- **propagation**
- **termination**

In the **initiation** step light energy splits a chlorine molecule into chlorine radicals in a reaction called homolytic fission.

The light must be of a high enough frequency to cause the σ-bond to break. It does so homolytically with one of the bonding electrons going to each chlorine atom:

$$Cl{-}Cl \xrightarrow{\text{UV}} Cl\bullet + Cl\bullet$$

This process is called photolysis, because the bond is broken (-*lysis*) by light (*photo–*).

Chlorine radicals are very reactive. **Propagation** begins when a chlorine radical collides with a methane molecule with sufficient energy to remove a hydrogen atom, forming a methyl radical, •CH_3, and a molecule of hydrogen chloride:

$$CH_4 + Cl\bullet \rightarrow \bullet CH_3 + HCl$$

Methyl radicals are also very reactive and will remove a chlorine atom from a chlorine molecule, forming a chloromethane molecule and another chlorine radical:

$$\bullet CH_3 + Cl_2 \rightarrow CH_3Cl + Cl\bullet$$

The chlorine radical then removes a hydrogen atom from another methane molecule and so on. This type of reaction is called a **chain reaction** as a small amount of UV light results in many propagation reactions.

It has been estimated that, in the reaction of methane with chlorine, a single photon of light causes 10^6 propagation steps.

The chlorine radical cannot bond to the carbon atom until a hydrogen atom has been removed, so the propagation step is *not* $CH_4 + Cl\bullet \rightarrow CH_3Cl + H\bullet$. The energetics of this reaction are less favourable than for the reaction in which a chlorine radical removes a hydrogen atom.

As the concentration of CH_3Cl builds up, an alternative propagation step becomes increasingly likely — a chlorine radical collides with a CH_3Cl molecule and removes a hydrogen radical from it:

$$CH_3Cl + Cl\bullet \rightarrow \bullet CH_2Cl + HCl$$

The $\bullet CH_2Cl$ radical then removes a chlorine atom from a chlorine molecule, thus continuing the chain reaction:

$$\bullet CH_2Cl + Cl_2 \rightarrow CH_2Cl_2 + Cl\bullet$$

Termination (chain breaking) occurs when two radicals collide. As their concentration is low, the chance of the chain reaction being broken is slight. The second propagation step has the highest activation energy, so the $\bullet CH_3$ radicals have the longest life and are the most likely to be involved in chain breaking. Examples of chain-breaking reactions are:

$$\bullet CH_3 + \bullet CH_3 \rightarrow CH_3CH_3 \text{ (ethane)}$$

$$\bullet CH_3 + Cl\bullet \rightarrow CH_3Cl$$

$$Cl\bullet + Cl\bullet \rightarrow Cl_2$$

Any of these reactions breaks the chain and slows down the reaction.

When there are no radicals left, the reaction stops.

Products of the reaction

The reaction between methane and chlorine in the presence of UV light produces a mixture of mono- and poly-substituted chloromethanes, hydrogen chloride and some ethane. It is the presence of the ethane that provides conclusive evidence for the mechanism given above. The absence of any H_2 molecules in the product is evidence that no hydrogen radicals are formed in the propagation steps.

Evidence for the free-radical mechanism includes:

- the production of ethane as a minor by-product
- the need for high-frequency light to produce chlorine radicals from chlorine molecules; intense red light does not initiate the reaction

Test yourself

5 Write the equation for the reaction that produces butane when chlorine and ethane are mixed in the presence of diffused sunlight.

In focused sunlight or strong ultraviolet light, chlorine and methane react explosively.

The reaction of alkanes with bromine is much slower because the second propagation step has a very high activation energy (page 261). The reaction can be demonstrated in the laboratory by placing a few drops of hexane into each of two small conical flasks, very carefully adding two drops of liquid bromine and stoppering both flasks. One flask is placed on a windowsill and the other in a lightproof cupboard.

The next day, the contents of the flask in the cupboard will still show the brown colour of bromine but the contents of the flask on the windowsill will be colourless.

If this flask is carefully opened in a fume cupboard, steamy fumes of hydrogen bromide will be observed.

Combustion

Alkanes, like most organic compounds, burn when ignited in air. If the air is in excess, the products are water and carbon dioxide. Combustion is highly exothermic and is the source of energy in gas-fired power stations:

$$CH_4(g) + 2O_2(g) \rightarrow CO_2(g) + 2H_2O(g) \qquad \Delta H = -802\,\text{kJ mol}^{-1}$$

Combustion of gasoline provides the power in petrol-driven cars. The equation for the combustion of octane is:

$$C_8H_{18}(g) + 12\tfrac{1}{2}O_2(g) \rightarrow 8CO_2(g) + 9H_2O(g) \qquad \Delta H = -5074\,\text{kJ mol}^{-1}$$

Some of the nitrogen in the air reacts at the very high temperatures in the cylinder to produce nitric oxide. This is a pollutant and can cause photochemical smog as well as trigger asthma attacks.

$$N_2 + O_2 \rightarrow 2NO$$

It is also acidic and causes damage to human lungs, buildings and trees. It is the major constituent of acid rain.

Incomplete combustion takes place when alkanes burn in a limited amount of air. Carbon monoxide and even some carbon particulates may be produced as well as some cracked alkanes. The hydrogen in the alkanes is always oxidised to water.

Carbon monoxide is toxic as it reacts with haemoglobin in the blood, thus stopping it carrying oxygen around the body.

Crude oil also contains sulfur compounds. These can be found in heavy oils used on ships and power stations and they produce sulfur dioxide when burnt. This is acidic and causes damage to buildings and to the natural environment. Cruise ships using heavy oil are not permitted to go to Antarctica.

Test yourself

6 Write the equation for the complete combustion of hexane.

Sustainability and climate change

Alkanes are examples of fossil fuels. Over many millions of years, dead marine organisms have been converted to a mixture of hydrocarbons. Some of these became trapped underground as natural gas (mostly methane) and oil. However, these resources are limited.

Although new gas and oil fields are being discovered, eventually there will not be enough oil and gas in the world to satisfy demand. In addition, the combustion of fossil fuels releases carbon dioxide into the air. The increase in atmospheric carbon dioxide is a well-established fact. It is also known that carbon dioxide is a greenhouse gas and contributes to climate change.

A possible new source of methane is methane hydrate. This is found on the continental shelves of oceans at a depth of more than 300 feet and in permafrost (Figure 10.25).

The methane molecules are trapped in a cage of ice crystals. It has been estimated that the amount of methane hydrate on Earth is twice that of all previously known gas and oil reserves.

Methane is also found trapped in shale deposits. It can be extracted in a process called **fracking** which involves pumping water and sand under high pressure into the shale deposits that are deep underground. The sand opens up cracks in the shale and the water forces out the methane. This is being used so much in the USA that the country is no longer dependent on overseas sources of methane, and gas prices have fallen substantially.

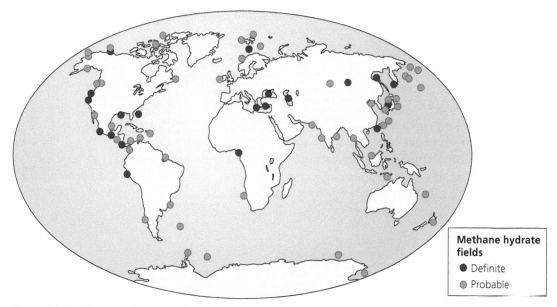

Figure 10.25 Known and suspected methane hydrate deposits

Carbon dioxide emissions could be reduced by a number of methods, for example:

- by using alternative sources of energy such as nuclear, solar, wind or wave power
- by using fuels with a higher hydrogen to carbon content, for example methane, CH_4, rather than octane, C_8H_{18}
- by pumping CO_2 from power stations into old oil and natural gas wells
- by conserving energy in the home and workplace. For example, recycling old aluminium cans requires much less energy than making new aluminium from bauxite ore.

Alkenes

Key terms

Alkenes are **unsaturated compounds** that have the general formula C_nH_{2n}.

An **unsaturated compound** is one that contains a carbon–carbon double bond and so will add hydrogen and become saturated.

Alkenes contain one C=C functional group. Compounds containing two such groups are called alkadienes. They react in the same way as alkenes.

Bonding

The two carbon atoms in the functional group are joined by a σ-bond and a π-bond. A σ-bond results from the head-on overlap of two atomic orbitals, one from each carbon atom, and the π-bond from a sideways overlap of two p-orbitals (see page 46). The overlapping of the p-orbitals in the π-bond is above and below the σ-bond electrons. Rotation of the molecule around the double bond would cause the π-bond to break. This requires a large amount of energy and so does not happen except at high temperatures. This lack of rotation can result in geometric isomerism (see page 174).

The bond angle around the carbon atoms in the double bond is 120° as there are three σ-bonds around each carbon atom and they repel each other to a position of least repulsion (maximum separation).

Manufacture

Alkenes do not occur naturally. They are made from alkanes by the process of **cracking**. The naphtha fraction from the primary distillation of crude oil is mixed with steam and rapidly heated to 900°C. The yield of ethene is about 30%, with a smaller amount of propene and about 25% high-grade petrol. A temperature of 700°C gives less ethene but more high-grade petrol. Alkenes can also be made by cracking propane and butane mixtures (LPG) and by the catalytic cracking of heavier fractions from the primary distillation of oil.

Physical properties

- Alkenes have lower melting and boiling temperatures than corresponding alkanes. This is because the rigidity of the double bond does not allow the molecules to pack together as efficiently as alkanes. This effect of molecules packing together is shown by the difference in the melting temperatures of fats and oils. Fats are saturated esters and pack well together, so they are soft solids at room temperature. Oils, such as corn or sunflower oil, are esters of unsaturated acids that are always geometric *cis*-isomers. These molecules do not pack well together and so are liquid. Fish oils are highly unsaturated and remain liquid even in the very cold temperatures of arctic waters. Unsaturated oils are metabolised more easily than saturated fats. Fish oils are particularly good at lowering cholesterol levels.
- Ethene, propene and all three butenes are gases at room temperature. The other alkenes are liquids or waxy solids.
- Alkenes are insoluble in water because they cannot form hydrogen bonds with water molecules (see page 64).

Chemical reactions

Key term

An **addition** reaction occurs when two substances react together to form a single substance.

- Alkenes are much more reactive than alkanes.
- Alkenes burn in air when ignited. However, as each alkene has a smaller percentage of hydrogen than the corresponding alkane, they need more oxygen per mole and so tend to burn with a smoky flame, producing carbon and water vapour.
- Most of the reactions of alkenes are addition reactions. The π-bond breaks, leaving a σ-bond between the two carbon atoms. Two atoms or groups add on — one to each of the carbon atoms (Figure 10.26).

Figure 10.26

A π-bond breaks and two new σ-bonds form. A π-bond is weaker than a σ-bond. Alkanes have no π-bond, so they are much less reactive than alkenes. Some bond strengths are given in Table 10.6.

Table 10.6 Strengths of carbon–carbon bonds

Bond type	Bond enthalpy/kJ mol^{-1}
σ-bond in C–C	348
σ-bond + π-bond in C=C	612
π-bond only (difference between C=C and C–C)	264

The reactions of the alkenes are illustrated below using ethene as the example. The other alkenes react similarly.

Combustion

Like almost all organic compounds, alkenes burn when ignited:

$$H_2C=CH_2 + 3O_2 \rightarrow 2CO_2 + 2H_2O$$

However, they are more useful as chemicals, so they are not used as fuels.

Free radical addition reactions

With hydrogen

When ethene is mixed with hydrogen and passed over a suitable catalyst, an addition reaction occurs. The product is ethane:

$$H_2C=CH_2 + H_2 \rightarrow H_3C-CH_3$$

The π-bond breaks, leaving the σ-bond between the two carbon atoms.

Reagent: hydrogen

Conditions: catalyst of nickel at 150°C

Product: ethane

Reaction type: free radical addition

The catalyst weakens the bonds between the hydrogen atoms, which then add on across the double bond.

This reaction is used in the hardening of polyunsaturated vegetable oils to form margarine (see below).

Worked example

0.747 g of an unsaturated hydrocarbon, C_6H_8, reacts with 448 cm^3 of hydrogen gas. Calculate the molar ratio of hydrogen to hydrocarbon and hence the number of carbon-to-carbon double bonds in the hydrocarbon, assuming that the product is saturated. Under the conditions of the experiment, the molar volume of gas is 24.0 dm^3 mol^{-1}.

Vegetable oils are esters of polyunsaturated long-chain carboxylic acids, such as $C_{17}H_{29}COOH$, and propan-1,2,3-triol and can be converted into a semi-liquid form, which is put into tubs and sold as spreading or low-fat margarine. One way of doing this is **partial hydrogenation** — a controlled amount of hydrogen is added to the oil in the presence of a catalyst (normally nickel). Some of the double bonds are saturated and a harder fat is produced.

Disadvantage: the C=C is weakened as it bonds to the active sites on the catalyst. On desorption, some of the molecules rotate around the remaining weakened double bonds and some *trans* isomers are formed. These are believed to increase cholesterol levels in the blood.

The altered oils are then mixed with untreated vegetable oils and with lipid-soluble additives such as vitamins, colouring agents and emulsifiers. This mixture is then blended with water-soluble additives such as milk whey, milk proteins and salt. The result is a spreadable margarine.

Electrophilic addition reactions

Alkenes react with reagents such as halogens and hydrogen halides by electrophilic addition.

The π-bond between the carbon atoms is an area of high electron density. The first step in electrophilic addition is the movement of these π-electrons towards the electrophile to make a new covalent σ-bond. This movement of a pair of electrons is shown by a full-headed curly arrow ($\curvearrowright$). A curly arrow must:

- start from a σ- or π-bond and go *towards* an atom forming a new bond
- start from a σ- or π-bond and go *to* an atom forming a negative ion
- start from an atom or ion with a *lone pair* of electrons and go towards another atom forming a new bond

In the examples of mechanisms below, the alkene is represented by the formula $RCH=CH_2$, where R can be a hydrogen atom (ethene) or a group, for example – CH_3 (propene). R can also represent much more complex groups in, for example, complex natural products such as limonene.

> **Key term**
>
> An **electrophile** is a species that bonds to an electron-rich site in a molecule. It accepts a pair of electrons from that site and forms a new covalent bond.

> **Tip**
>
> Never *start* a curly arrow from a hydrogen atom or an H^+ ion as neither has a lone pair of electrons.

Reaction with halogens

When ethene is passed into liquid bromine or bromine dissolved in an inert solvent such as tetrachloromethane, an addition reaction takes place. The π-bond breaks and a bromine atom adds on to each carbon atom:

$$H_2C=CH_2 + Br_2 \rightarrow H_2CBr-CH_2Br$$

Reagent: bromine

Conditions: mix at room temperature

Observation: the orange bromine goes colourless

Product: 1,2-dibromoethane

Reaction type: electrophilic addition

Bromine attacks the electron-rich π-bond in the ethene molecule and forms a σ-bond with one of the carbon atoms. This reaction is described as **electrophilic addition**.

Alkenes react in a similar way with chlorine, but do not react with iodine.

Mechanism of the addition of bromine (bromination)

Addition of bromine across a double bond is a two-step reaction. The Br_2 molecule is non-polar. However, on its approach to the high electron density of the π-bond, a δ^+ charge is induced in the nearer bromine. This atom is the electrophile. It attracts the π-electrons and forms a covalent bond with one of the carbon atoms. At the same time, the Br−Br σ-bond breaks heterolytically and a Br^- ion is formed.

Tip

In heterolytic fission both electrons in the broken bond go to the same atom.

Step 1: see Figure 10.27.

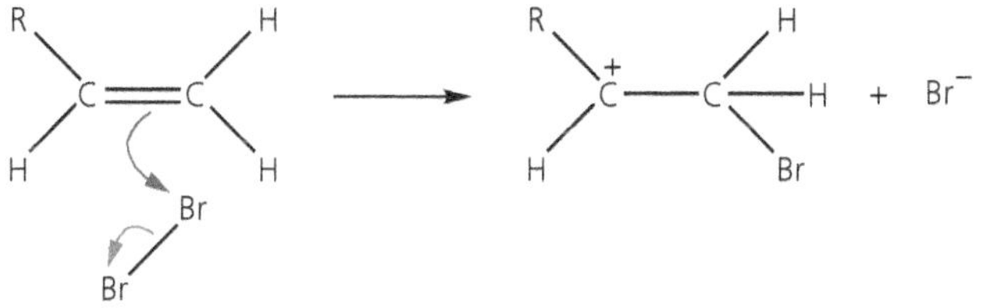

Figure 10.27

The red curly arrow shows the movement of the π-electrons and the blue curly arrow shows the movement of the Br−Br σ-electrons.

The molecule is planar, with a bond angle of 120°, around the positively charged carbon atom in the carbocation intermediate.

Step 2: see Figure 10.28.

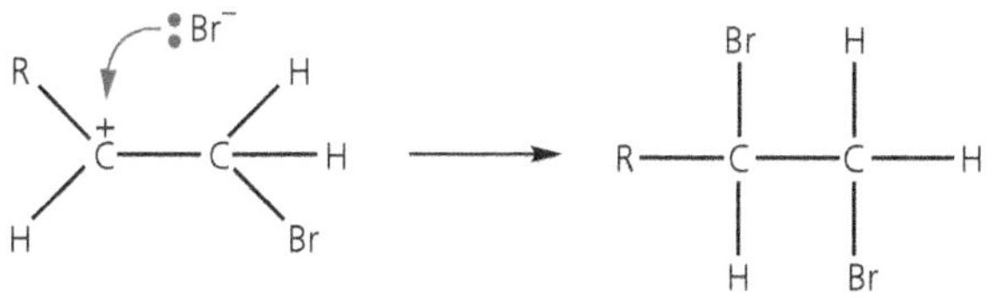

Figure 10.28

The red curly arrow shows the movement of the lone pair of electrons on the Br^- ion as it forms a covalent bond with the positively charged carbon atom.

The same mechanism occurs when an alkene reacts with chlorine.

Iodine is not a strong enough electrophile to undergo this reaction, unless the C=C group is activated by an oxygen atom on one of the carbon atoms.

Evidence for this mechanism is the formation of CH_2ClCH_2Br when ethene reacts with bromine in the presence of sodium chloride. Step 1 is the same, with the formation

The Br^- ion attacks from the side away from the bromine atom. This has stereochemical implications for alkenes such as RCH=CHR because stereoisomers are possible in the product.

The electrophile, Br^+, attaches to the carbon atom that has more hydrogen atoms bonded to it, thus forming the secondary carbocation. This is more stable than a primary carbocation.

of the intermediate carbocation $H_2C^+CH_2Br$. This can then be attacked by either a Br^- ion (thus forming CH_2BrCH_2Br) or by a Cl^- ion (thus forming CH_2ClCH_2Br).

The compound CH_2ClCH_2Cl does not form because there is no $δ^+$ chlorine atom in sodium chloride.

Addition with bromine water: the test for alkenes

If an alkene is shaken with bromine dissolved in water (bromine water), an addition reaction takes place and the brown colour of bromine disappears. This is a test for compounds containing one or more C=C bonds.

Reagent: bromine dissolved in water

Conditions: mix at room temperature

Observation: the orange bromine water forms a colourless solution

Reaction type: electrophilic addition

The reaction between $RCH=CH_2$ and bromine water produces $RCH(OH)CH_2Br$ as the major product, rather than $RCHBrCH_2Br$. This is because the intermediate, RC^+HCH_2Br, is more likely to collide and react with a water molecule than with a Br^- ion.

$$RCH=CH_2 + Br_2 \rightarrow RC^+H-CH_2Br + Br^-$$

$$RC^+H-CH_2Br + H_2O \rightarrow RCH(OH)CH_2Br + H^+$$

This reaction is used as a test for the presence of a carbon–carbon double bond. The decolourisation of brown bromine water to a colourless solution, without any precipitate being formed, is proof of the presence of a C=C group.

Reaction with hydrogen halides

When a gaseous hydrogen halide is mixed with ethene, an electrophilic addition reaction takes place:

$$H_2C=CH_2 + H-Br \rightarrow H_3C-CH_2Br$$

The reaction is fastest with hydrogen iodide and slowest with hydrogen chloride. This is because the H−I bond is weaker than the H−Br bond, which is weaker than the H−Cl bond.

Reagent: hydrogen bromide

Conditions: mix gases at room temperature

Product: bromoethane

Reaction type: electrophilic addition

Mechanism of addition of hydrogen bromide

Addition of hydrogen bromide across a double bond is a two-step reaction. The HBr molecule is polar (see page 57) with the hydrogen atom $δ^+$ and the more electronegative bromine $δ^-$. The $δ^+$ hydrogen is the electrophile. It attacks the electron-rich π-bond in the alkene and adds on to one of the carbon atoms by attracting the π-electrons from the double bond and forming a covalent bond. As this happens, the H−Br σ-bond breaks and the two electrons both go to the bromine atom, forming a Br^- ion. This uneven breaking of the H−Br bond is called **heterolytic fission**.

Step 1: see Figure 10.29.

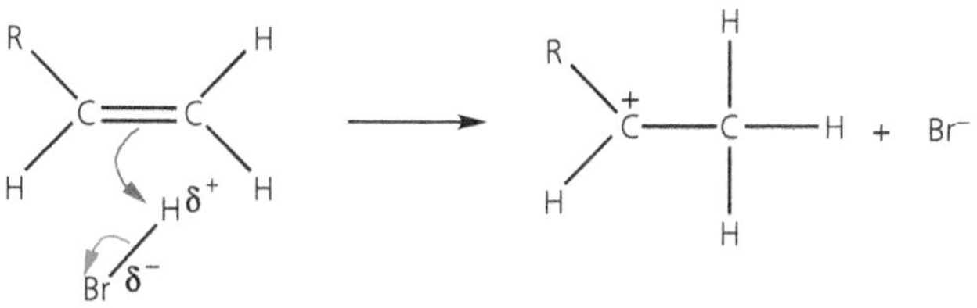

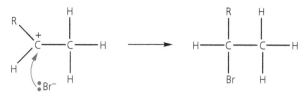

Figure 10.29

The red curly arrow shows the movement of the π-electrons and the blue curly arrow shows the movement of the H–Br σ-electrons.

Step 2: The Br^- ion then adds on to the positive carbon atom (Figure 10.30).

Figure 10.30

The red curly arrow shows the movement of the lone pair of electrons on the Br^- ion as it forms a covalent bond with the carbon atom.

Hydrogen chloride, HCl, and hydrogen iodide, HI, also undergo addition reactions with this type of mechanism. The rate of reaction is HI > HBr > HCl, because the HI bond is the weakest and HCl the strongest. This means that the reaction with HCl has a higher activation energy (see page 261).

Tip

Do not forget to include the positive charge on the carbon atom in the intermediate or the partial δ^+ and δ^- charges on the HBr.

Test yourself

7 Write the equation for the reaction between hydrogen iodide and 2-methylbut-2-ene.

Addition to asymmetrical alkenes: Markovnikoff's rule

If the alkene is asymmetrical, such as propene, two addition products are possible. For example, the reaction between propene, $CH_3CH{=}CH_2$, and hydrogen bromide can give two products:

$CH_3CH{=}CH_2 + HBr \rightarrow CH_3CHBrCH_3$ (2-bromopropane)

$CH_3CH{=}CH_2 + HBr \rightarrow CH_3CH_2CH_2Br$ (1-bromopropane)

The *major* product is 2-bromopropane. This is predicted, but *not* explained, by Markovnikoff's rule:

When HX adds to an asymmetrical alkene, the hydrogen atom goes to the carbon which already has more hydrogen atoms directly attached.

The explanation for this is that a secondary carbocation, $CH_3C^+HCH_3$, is formed preferentially to a primary carbocation, $CH_3CH_2C^+H_2$, or that a tertiary carbocation is more stable than a secondary carbocation.

A carbocation is an organic ion that has a positive charge on a carbon atom.

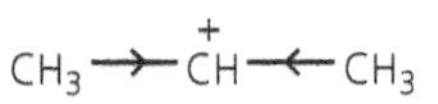

$$CH_3 \longrightarrow \overset{+}{C}H \longleftarrow CH_3$$

Figure 10.31

The secondary carbocation is stabilised by the electron-pushing effect of the CH_3 groups, whereas the primary carbocation is less stabilised (Figure 10.31).

An arrowhead in the middle of a σ-covalent bond represents a movement of the bonding electrons in the direction the arrowhead is pointing. In the above example, it is pointing towards the positively charged carbon atom in the intermediate carbocation, reducing its charge and hence stabilising the cation. A CH_2 group does not do this to the same extent as a CH_3 group, and a CH group does it even less. The reason is that carbon is more electronegative than hydrogen and so gets a δ^- charge from each hydrogen.

Similarly, with 2-methylbut-2-ene the hydrogen goes to the CH carbon and not to the $C(CH_3)_2$ carbon. The major product is 2-chloro-2-methylbutane, $CH_3CH_2CCl(CH_3)_2$, and *not* 3-chloro-2-methylbutane, $CH_3ClCH(Cl)CH(CH_3)_2$:

$$CH_3CH=C(CH_3)_2 + HCl \rightarrow CH_3CH_2CCl(CH_3)_2$$
2-methylbut-2-ene 　　　　 2-chloro-2-methylbutane

> **Tip**
>
> Do not state that the secondary halogenoalkane is more stable than the primary halogenoalkane. They are equally stable. It is the *intermediate* secondary carbocation that is more stable.

Addition of water

This is an important reaction in which alkenes produced from petroleum can be converted into alcohols.

The alkene is vaporised and mixed with steam and passed over an acidic catalyst such as phosphoric(v) acid, H_3PO_4. This is a reversible reaction and so the alcohol produced is removed from the equilibrium mixture by cooling and the remaining gases repassed over the catalyst. In this way up to 95% of the alkene can be converted.

With propene the main product is propan-2-ol.

$$CH_3CH=CH_2(g) + H_2O(g) \rightleftharpoons CH_3CH(OH)CH_3$$

The first step is the addition of the electrophile H^+ from the acid. This goes to the carbon with more hydrogen atoms according to Markovnikoff's rule. The lone pair of electrons on the oxygen of a water molecule then forms a σ-bond with the C^+ followed by loss of an H^+ from the water (Figure 10.32).

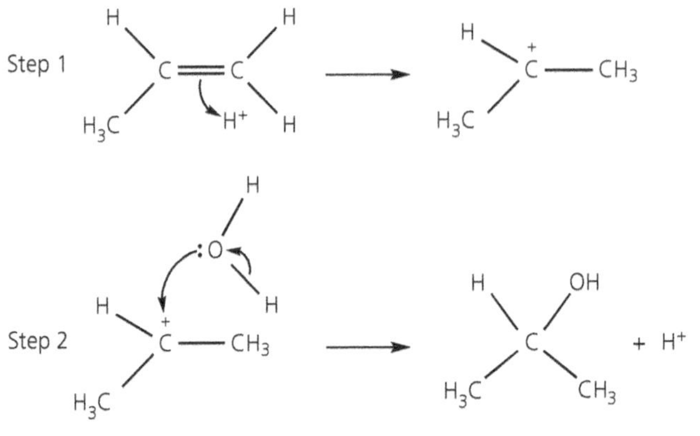

Figure 10.32

Reaction with potassium manganate(VII) solution

When ethene is shaken with a neutral or acidic solution of potassium manganate(VII), oxidation with addition takes place. The purple manganate(VII) ions are reduced to a precipitate of brown manganese(IV) oxide in a neutral solution or to colourless Mn^2 ions in acid solution. As the exact stoichiometry is not fully known, [O] is used in the equation as the symbol for the oxidising agent:

$$H_2C=CH_2 + [O] + H_2O \rightarrow HOCH_2-CH_2OH$$

Reagent: neutral potassium manganate(VII) solution

Conditions: shake together at room temperature

Observation: the purple solution goes colourless or to a brown precipitate

Product: ethane-1,2-diol

Reaction type: oxidation

Polymerisation reactions

Alkene molecules can react together in an **addition polymerisation** reaction. For example, one ethene molecule can break the π-bond in another ethene molecule and become attached. This is repeated with other ethene molecules so that, eventually, a long hydrocarbon chain containing thousands of carbon atoms is formed. This chain is called a **polymer**. Some addition polymers are illustrated in Table 10.7 on page 192.

A polymer is a chain of covalently bonded molecules.

Other alkenes, such as propene, and substituted alkenes, such as chloroethene, $ClCH=CH_2$, tetrafluoroethene, $CF_2=CF_2$, and phenylethene, $C_6H_5CH=CH_2$, also form polymers.

Polymer production

The usual procedure is to cause radicals to be formed that initiate the polymerisation reaction.

One method of polymerising ethene to poly(ethene) is to heat it under a pressure of 1000 atm in the presence of a trace of oxygen. The oxygen produces radicals that initiate the polymerisation (Figure 10.33).

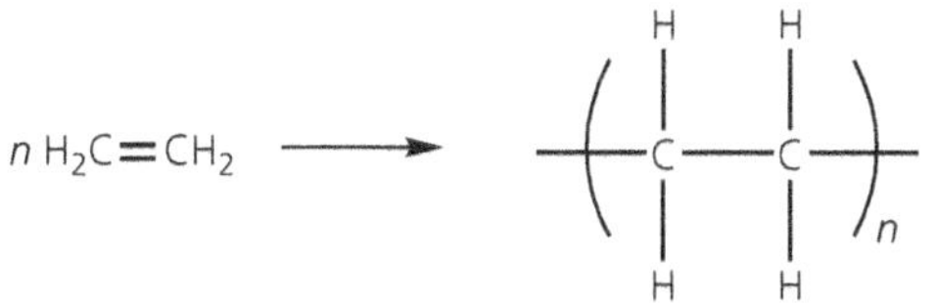

Figure 10.33

Table 10.7 Some common addition polymers

Monomer	Polymer — showing two repeat units	Name	Uses
Ethene, $H_2C=CH_2$	$\left(\!\!\begin{array}{cccc} H & H & H & H \\ | & | & | & | \\ C{-}&C{-}&C{-}&C \\ | & | & | & | \\ H & H & H & H \end{array}\!\!\right)$	Poly(ethene)	Low density — plastic bags; high density — water pipes, bottles, washing-up bowls, buckets
Propene, $CH_3CH=CH_2$	$\left(\!\!\begin{array}{cccc} H & CH_3 & H & CH_3 \\ | & | & | & | \\ C{-}&C{-}&C{-}&C \\ | & | & | & | \\ H & H & H & H \end{array}\!\!\right)$	Poly(propene)	Ropes, containers that have to withstand boiling water
Chloroethene, $CHCl=CH_2$	$\left(\!\!\begin{array}{cccc} H & Cl & H & Cl \\ | & | & | & | \\ C{-}&C{-}&C{-}&C \\ | & | & | & | \\ H & H & H & H \end{array}\!\!\right)$	Poly(chloroethene) or PVC	Window frames, guttering, drain pipes, electrical insulation
Tetrafluoroethene, $CF_2=CF_2$	$\left(\!\!\begin{array}{cccc} F & F & F & F \\ | & | & | & | \\ C{-}&C{-}&C{-}&C \\ | & | & | & | \\ F & F & F & F \end{array}\!\!\right)$	Poly(tetrafluoroethene) PTFE or Teflon	Non-stick coatings, low-friction bearings (burette taps, plumber's tape), electrical insulation
Propenenitrile, $H_2C=CHCN$	$\left(\!\!\begin{array}{cccc} CN & H & CN & H \\ | & | & | & | \\ C{-}&C{-}&C{-}&C \\ | & | & | & | \\ H & H & H & H \end{array}\!\!\right)$	Acrilan	Fibres for clothing
Phenylethene, $C_6H_5HC=CH_2$	$\left(\!\!\begin{array}{cccc} C_6H_5 & H & C_6H_5 & H \\ | & | & | & | \\ C{-}&C{-}&C{-}&C \\ | & | & | & | \\ H & H & H & H \end{array}\!\!\right)$	Polystyrene	Thermal insulation, packaging for fragile articles
Ethenol, $H_2C=CHOH$	$\left(\!\!\begin{array}{cccc} H & OH & H & OH \\ | & | & | & | \\ C{-}&C{-}&C{-}&C \\ | & | & | & | \\ H & H & H & H \end{array}\!\!\right)$	Poly(ethenol) or polyvinyl alcohol	Soluble laundry bags and liquitab capsules

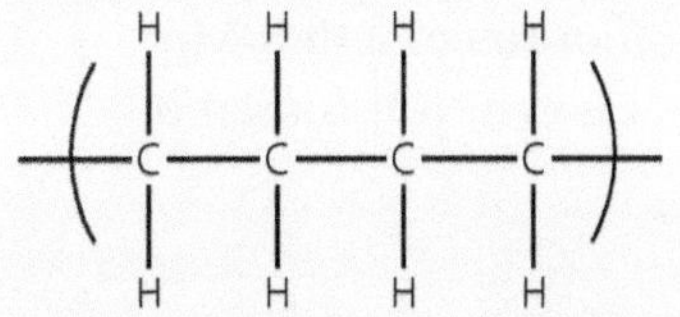

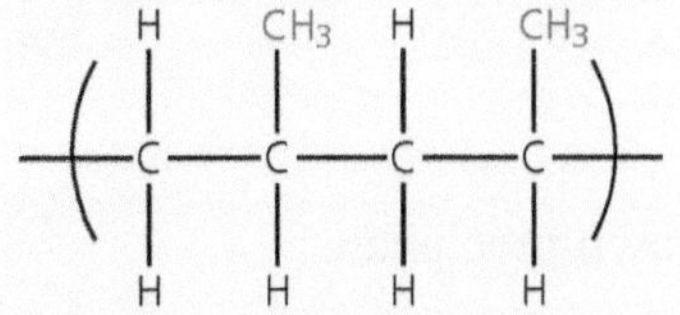

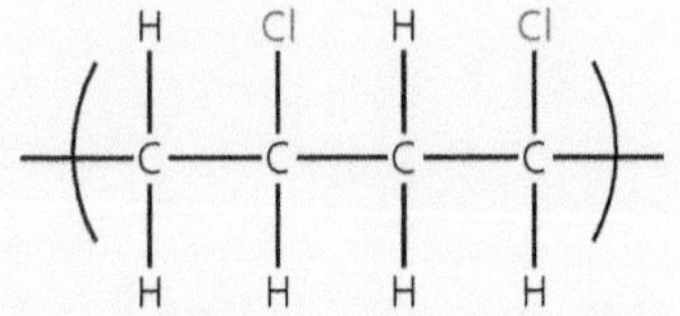

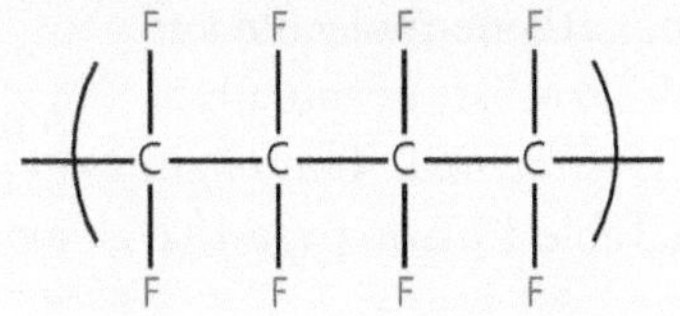

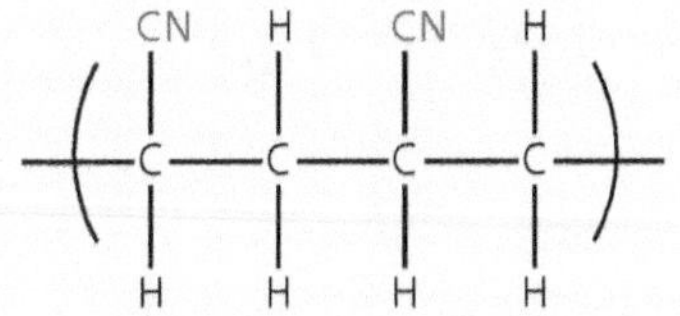

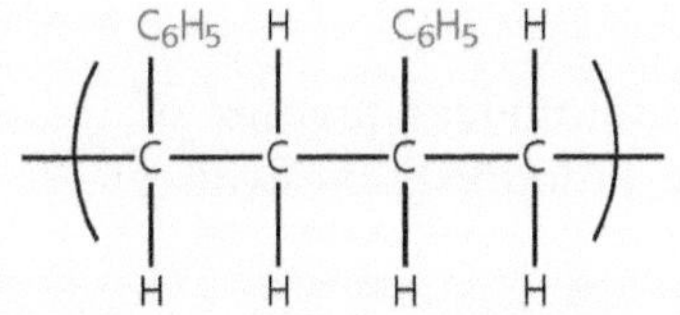

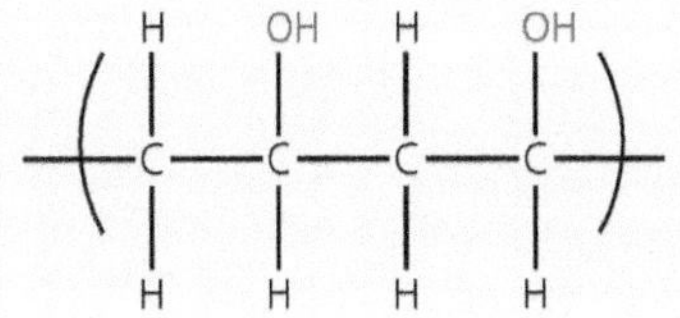

Propene is polymerised to poly(propene) by passing it over a catalyst of titanium tetrachloride and aluminium triethyl. In the equation in Figure 10.34 *two* repeat units are shown.

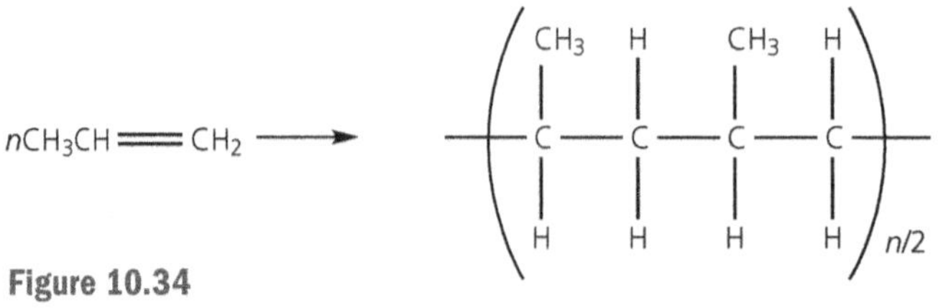

$$nCH_3CH=CH_2 \longrightarrow \left(\!\!\begin{array}{cccc} CH_3 & H & CH_3 & H \\ | & | & | & | \\ C{-}&C{-}&C{-}&C \\ | & | & | & | \\ H & H & H & H \end{array}\!\!\right)_{n/2}$$

Figure 10.34

The other method of producing poly(ethene) is to mix ethene with a solution containing alkylaluminium and titanium chloride catalysts. This method produces a harder, higher-density polymer with a higher melting temperature.

The reaction on page 191 for polymerising ethene is not as simple as implied by the equation given. A significant amount of branching occurs and the lengths of the polymer chains vary considerably. This results in the polymer softening over a range of temperatures before it becomes molten, rather than it having a definite melting temperature.

Test yourself

8 Draw a section of the polymer formed, showing two repeat units, when but-1-ene is polymerised.

Disposal of waste polymers (plastic)

Because of the large size of the molecules and the strength of the C—C and C—halogen bonds, addition polymers are resistant to chemical and biological attack. They are not naturally occurring substances, so no enzymes have evolved to break them down. This is both a disadvantage and an advantage. Resistance to corrosion and chemical attack are useful properties, in that they confer a long life to plastic objects. However, discarded plastic bags can litter the environment and bulky plastic objects can fill waste disposal sites.

The best practice is to separate the plastic into different types. These can then be melted down and reused. Alternatives are as follows:

- Using the waste plastic as feedstock for catalytic cracking, thus producing a mixture of short-chain alkenes.
- Combustion in specially designed incinerators and using the energy released to raise steam to turn turbines, thus producing electricity from waste plastic. This is done on a large scale in Switzerland. A major drawback is that combustion can produce toxic fumes such as carbon monoxide, while halogenated plastics such as PVC produce toxic hydrochloric acid vapour. These have to be removed before the gases can be released into the environment.
- Using biodegradable plastics such as polylactic acid and biopol (see Chapter 9 in *Edexcel A Level Chemistry Year 2*, by the same author).
- Use less plastic packaging and pass laws that make supermarkets charge for plastic bags, as is done in Wales.

The chemical industry is trying to use less energy in the manufacture of plastics and the government is trying to get the public to reuse or recycle plastic objects. All this will make the use of materials more sustainable.

Summary of alkene reactions

Propene is used as the example (Figure 10.35).

- The reactions in blue are free radical addition reactions.
- The reactions in red are electrophilic addition reactions.
- The reaction in green is oxidation.

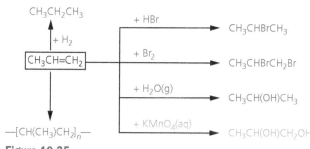

Figure 10.35

Hazard and risk

Many organic chemicals and some of the substances that they react with are hazardous. This means that they are potentially dangerous for anyone using them. Possible hazards include:

- toxicity (e.g. lead compounds)
- absorption through the skin (e.g. 1-bromobutane)
- irritation if inhaled (e.g. hydrogen chloride)
- corrosive compounds (e.g. concentrated sulfuric acid)
- high flammability (e.g. ethoxyethane, $C_2H_5OC_2H_5$)
- carcinogenic compounds (e.g. benzene, C_6H_6)

A reaction might be hazardous if it is rapid and highly exothermic or if it produces a volatile hazardous product.

The risk relates to how a hazardous material is used. For instance, using small quantities or taking specific precautions (e.g. wearing gloves or using a water bath for heating) makes the probability of harm occurring less and so reduces the risk. Hazardous materials used in small quantities with proper containment pose little risk.

It is important to understand the possible hazards when carrying out an experiment and to take precautions to reduce the risk. For example, alkenes react with bromine (a hazardous chemical) and the reaction between pure liquid bromine and a liquid alkene is fast and extremely exothermic. The risk is reduced by using a dilute solution of bromine in a suitable solvent. The reaction is then much slower. Therefore, the temperature does not rise dangerously quickly and the risk to the user is reduced considerably. However, bromine fumes are still present. Performing the reaction in a fume cupboard further reduces the risk.

Manufacturers spend large sums trying to find alternative processes that use less hazardous substances. Union Carbide Corporation manufactured the pesticide Sevin in a factory in Bhopal in India. The first step was to make methylisocyanate (MIC), $CH_3N=C=O$. This is extremely toxic and reacts with water in the presence of rust in a highly exothermic reaction. This happened in an old MIC storage tank, causing a runaway reaction. About 40 tonnes of MIC was released into the atmosphere through the tank's venting valve. It is estimated that more than 8000 people died as a result. Other companies used a less risky manufacturing process, which did not involve the extremely hazardous MIC as an intermediate.

Summary tasks

Make sure that you can:

- list three reagents that react with alkanes and state the reaction conditions
- draw a spider diagram showing the names of the reagents and the structural formulae of the products for the reactions of the alkane hexane
- list six reagents that react with alkenes and state the reaction conditions
- draw a spider diagram showing the names of the reagents and the structural formulae of the products for the reactions of the alkene propene
- draw a spider diagram showing the structural formulae for the five isomers of C_4H_8 (are they all alkenes?)

Questions

1 Name the following compounds:
   a) $CH_3CH(OH)CH_2Br$
   b) CH_2ClCH_2COOH
   c) $CH_2=CHC(CH_3)_3$

2 Give the formulae of the following compounds:
   a) 1,2-dichloro-1,2-difluoroethene
   b) 1-hydroxybutanone
   c) 2-amino-3-chloropropanoic acid

3 Identify the functional groups in the following:
   a) $CH_2OHCOCH(NH_2)COOH$
   b) $CH_2=CHCH(OH)CHO$

4 Draw and name all the structural isomers of $C_3H_6Br_2$.

5 Draw and name five isomers of the alkene C_5H_{10}.

6 Identify the major organic product when ethane and *excess* chlorine are exposed to white light for a long period of time.

7 Iodine monochloride, ICl, reacts with ethene to form 1-chloro-2-iodoethane, CH_2ClCH_2I. Identify the electrophile in this addition reaction and draw the mechanism for the first step.

8 What would you observe when but-2-ene and a neutral solution of potassium manganate(VII) are shaken together? Name the organic product and give its formula.

9 Explain why bromine reacts rapidly with alkenes, but only reacts slowly with alkanes, even in the presence of light.

10 a) 11-*cis*-retinal is attached to the protein opsin in human eyes. When light is absorbed it isomerises to all *trans*-retinal. Refer to Wikipedia or another internet source, and write out the structure of 11-cis-retinal and circle the double bond that rotates and forms all *trans*-retinal when light is absorbed.
   b) Explain, in terms of bonding orbitals, why energy is required to cause this isomerisation.

11 Explain why the *E-/Z-* system of naming geometric isomers is better than the *cis-/ trans-* method for an alkene such as $CH_2OHCH_2CH=C(CH_3)C_2H_5$.

Exam practice questions

1 a) Alkanes show structural isomerism. The number of structural isomers that have the formula C_5H_{12} is:

   A 2   **C** 4

   B 3   **D** 5   (1)

b) Explain why but-2-ene exhibits geometric isomerism whereas but-1-ene does not. (2)

c) Which exhibits geometric (E/Z) isomerism?

   A cyclohexene   **C** 2-methylpropene

   B propene   **D** pent-2-ene   (1)

d) The number of isomers of formula C_4H_8, excluding cycloalkanes, is:

   A 2   **C** 4

   B 3   **D** 5   (1)

e) i) Define the term **electrophile.** (2)

   ii) Which is *not* formed when ethene reacts with bromine water, Br_2(aq), in the presence of dissolved sodium chloride?

      A CH_2BrCH_2Br

      B CH_2ClCH_2Cl

      C $CH_2(OH)CH_2Br$

      D CH_2BrCH_2Cl (1)

   iii) The organic product of the reaction of alkaline potassium manganate(VII) solution with propene is:

      A $CH_3CH(OH)CH_2OH$

      B $CH_2(OH)CH_2CH_2OH$

      C $CH_3CH(OH)CH_2OK$

      D $CH_3CH(OK)CH_2OH$ (1)

      (Total 9 marks)

2 a) Chlorine reacts with ethane and with ethene.

   i) Classify the reaction with ethane. (1)

   ii) Classify the reaction with ethene. (1)

b) Ethene and but-1-ene are members of the same homologous series.

   i) Explain what is meant by the term 'homologous series'. (3)

   ii) Write the equation for the reaction of but-1-ene with bromine. (1)

   iii) Write the mechanism for the reaction between but-1-ene and bromine. (3)

   iv) Identify the major product of the reaction of but-1-ene with bromine water. (1)

   v) But-1-ene reacts with an aqueous solution of potassium manganate(VII).

Describe what you would see and identify the organic compound produced. (3)

   vi) But-2-ene can be polymerised to poly(but-1-ene). Draw a section of the structure of the polymer that shows one repeating unit. (2)

      (Total 15 marks)

3 When propene reacts with hydrogen bromide a mixture of 1-bromopropane and 2-bromopropane is produced.

a) Draw the mechanism for the reaction that produces the major product. (3)

b) Explain, in terms of the mechanism, why this is the major product. (2)

   (Total 5 marks)

4 Bromine water contains dissolved Br_2 molecules, H^+ ions, Br^- ions, HOBr molecules and water molecules.

a) When bromine water is added to an alkene such as ethene, the carbocation $CH_2Br{-}$ CH_2^+ is formed as an intermediate. Explain how this causes the final products of this reaction to include 1,2–dibromoethane and 2-bromoethanol. (3)

b) Under the same conditions a different carbocation can also be formed and this leads to a mixture of bromoethane and ethanol. Suggest a mechanism for this. (3)

   (Total 6 marks)

5 a) The alkene below can form a polymer.

Write the displayed formula of two repeat units of this polymer. (2)

b) The same polymer can be formed from an isomer of the alkene in (a). Write its displayed formula and explain why it forms the same polymer. (3)

c) Polyethenol exists but its theoretical monomer CH=CHOH does not. It would spontaneously revert to ethanal, CH_3CHO. Suggest a mechanism for this change. (3)

   (Total 8 marks)

6 Methane and chlorine react in the presence of light to form chloromethane and hydrogen chloride.

a) Use the table of bond energies below to calculate ΔH for this reaction. (3)

Bond	C–H	Cl–Cl	C–Cl	H–Cl
Bond energy/ kJmol^{-1}	435	243	346	432

b) i) Step 1 of the mechanism is the homolytic fission of the Cl−Cl bond into two •Cl radicals.
Define the term **homolytic fission**. (2)

ii) In step 2, HCl molecules and •CH$_3$ radicals are formed. In step 3, the methyl radicals react with more chlorine molecules to form chloromethane and •Cl radicals.
Draw the mechanism of step 3 using the correct type of curly arrows. (2)

iii) Some ethane is also produced. Draw the mechanism, using curly arrows, for this. (1)

c) i) Draw the mechanism for the reaction of propene with hydrogen bromide. (3)

ii) Explain why the major product is the one that you have drawn. (3)

d) Suggest why ethene does not react with iodine. (2)

(Total 16 marks)

11 Further organic chemistry (Topic 6)

Halogenoalkanes

> ### Key term
>
> A **halogenoalkane** is a compound in which one or more hydrogen atoms in an alkane has been replaced by halogen atoms and which has only single bonds in the molecule.

Halogenoalkanes have the general formula $C_nH_{(2n+1)}X$, where X is a halogen atom. They are named from the parent alkanes, with a number representing the carbon atom in the chain to which the halogen is joined.

The skeletal formulae, names and structural formulae of some halogenoalkanes are shown in Figure 11.1.

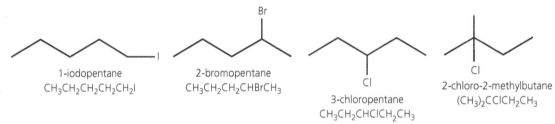

Figure 11.1
Some examples of halogenoalkanes

1-iodopentane
$CH_3CH_2CH_2CH_2CH_2I$

2-bromopentane
$CH_3CH_2CH_2CHBrCH_3$

3-chloropentane
$CH_3CH_2CHClCH_2CH_3$

2-chloro-2-methylbutane
$(CH_3)_2CClCH_2CH_3$

Primary halogenoalkanes have no more than one carbon atom directly attached to the carbon in the C−halogen group. Some examples are shown in Figure 11.2.

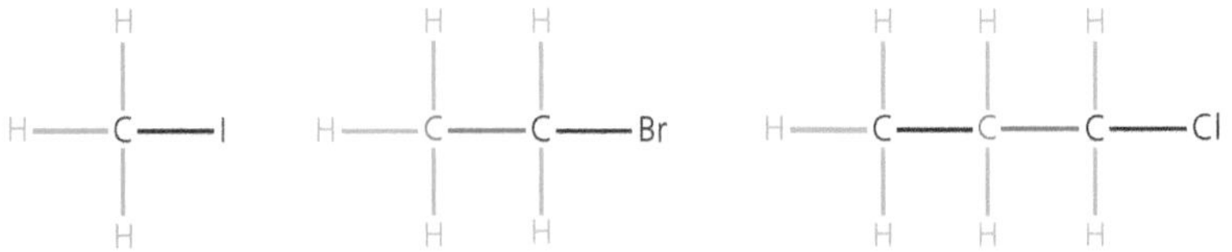

Figure 11.2 Primary halogenoalkanes

Iodomethane   Bromoethane   1-chloropropane

Secondary halogenoalkanes have two carbon atoms (and hence only one hydrogen atom) directly attached to the carbon in the C−halogen group, for example, 2-chloropropane (Figure 11.3).

Tertiary halogenoalkanes have three carbon atoms (and hence no hydrogen atoms) directly attached to the carbon in the C−halogen group, for example, 2-chloro-2-methylpropane (Figure 11.4).

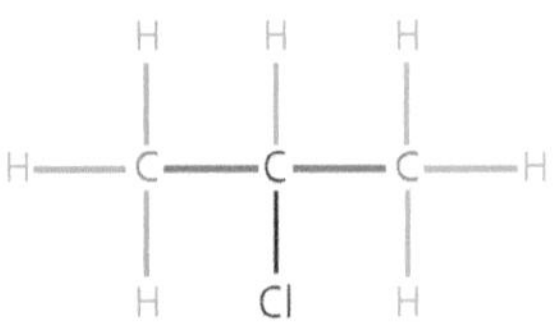

Figure 11.3 The structural formula of 2-chloropropane

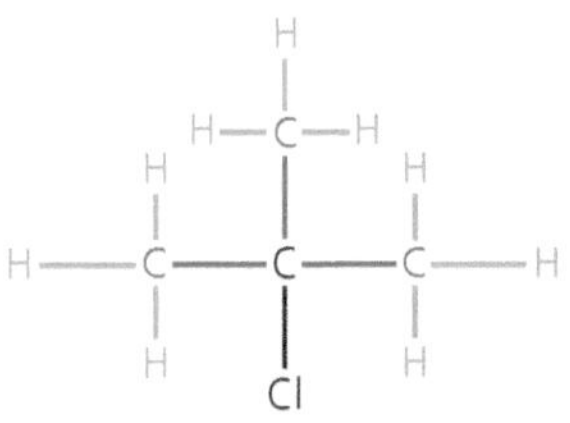

Figure 11.4 The structural formula of 2-chloro-2-methylpropane

Halogens are electronegative elements. The carbon–halogen bond in halogeno-alkanes is polarised, making the carbon atom $\delta+$ and the halogen atom $\delta-$ as shown in Figure 11.5.

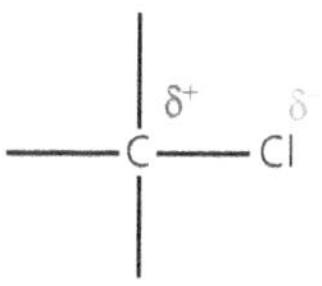

Figure 11.5 The polar nature of halogenoalkanes

Figure 11.5 The polar nature of halogenoalkanes

Test yourself

1 Draw the skeletal formulae of the isomers of C_4H_9Br stating whether they are primary, secondary or tertiary.

Physical properties

Chloromethane, bromomethane and chloroethane are gases at room temperature. Iodomethane and higher members of the homologous series are liquids. The boiling temperatures of halogenoalkanes are higher than those of alkanes, primarily because halogenoalkanes contain more electrons and so have stronger instantaneous induced dipole–induced dipole (London) forces between the molecules. In addition, because the molecules are polar, there are permanent dipole–dipole forces between the molecules which strengthen the intermolecular forces and so increase the boiling temperature.

Even though they are polar molecules, halogenoalkanes are insoluble in water. This is because the molecules contain neither $\delta+$ hydrogen atoms nor small $\delta-$ atoms with a lone pair of electrons, so they cannot hydrogen-bond with water. They are, however, soluble in a variety of organic solvents, such as ethanol and ethoxyethane (ether), $C_2H_5OC_2H_5$.

Test yourself

2 Explain why iodoethane has a higher boiling temperature than iodomethane.

Chemical reactions

Nucleophilic substitution reactions

Key terms

A **substitution reaction** is a reaction in which an atom or group is replaced by another atom or group. There are always two reactants and two products in a substitution reaction.

A **nucleophile** is a species with a lone pair of electrons that is used to form a covalent bond with a $\delta+$ atom in another molecule.

The halogen atom in a halogenoalkane molecule can be replaced by an −OH, −CN or −NH$_2$ group. These reactions are examples of nucleophilic substitution because the attacking group is a nucleophile. In these reactions, the reagent forms a bond to the carbon using its lone pair of electrons and the halide ion is released.

Reaction with aqueous alkali
When a halogenoalkane is heated under reflux with an *aqueous* solution of an alkali, such as potassium hydroxide or sodium hydroxide, the halogen is replaced by

an −OH group and an alcohol is produced. For example with 1-bromopropane:

$$CH_3CH_2CH_2Br + KOH \rightarrow CH_3CH_2CH_2OH + KBr$$

The ionic equation for this reaction is:

$$CH_3CH_2CH_2Br + OH^-(aq) \rightarrow CH_3CH_2CH_2OH + Br^-(aq)$$

Reagent: potassium (or sodium) hydroxide

Conditions: warmed under reflux in *aqueous* solution

Product: propan-1-ol

Reaction type: nucleophilic substitution (also called hydrolysis)

A lone pair of electrons on the oxygen atom in the OH^- ion attacks the δ^+ carbon in the carbon−bromine bond and forms a new carbon−oxygen σ-bond. The bromine gains the electrons from the carbon−bromine σ-bond, which breaks, forming a Br^- ion. In this example, the OH^- ion is the nucleophile.

The rate of this reaction varies considerably according to the halogen in the halogenoalkane. The rate of reaction is in the order:

iodo- > bromo- > chloro- > fluoro-

The reason for this is the difference in bond enthalpies of the C−halogen bonds, as given in Table 11.1.

A weaker carbon−halogen bond means that there is a smaller activation energy (page 261) for a reaction that involves breaking that bond. The C−I bond is the weakest and so reactions involving iodoalkanes will have the lowest activation energy and thus the fastest rate.

The rate of reaction also varies considerably according to the type of halogenoalkane involved. The rate of reaction is in the order:

tertiary > secondary > primary

The explanation for this is complex. A CH_3 group (and to a lesser extent a CH_2 group) has a tendency to push electrons in the σ-bond away from itself. This facilitates the release of the negative halide ion because there is a general shift of electrons away from the CH_3 group towards the halogen atom.

Reaction with water containing silver nitrate solution

The halogenoalkane reacts with the water to form an alcohol and a solution that contains the halide as an anion:

$$R{-}X(aq) + H_2O(l) \rightarrow R{-}OH(aq) + H^+(aq) + X^-(aq)$$

(where X represents a halogen).

The reaction involves nucleophilic attack on the carbon atom joined to the halogen by the lone pair of electrons on the oxygen in water. Since water is not as good a nucleophile as hydroxide ions, the reaction is much slower than that with aqueous potassium hydroxide.

The halide ion formed then reacts with silver ions from the silver nitrate to form a precipitate of silver halide:

$$X^-(aq) + Ag^+(aq) \rightarrow AgX(s)$$

This reaction is sometimes carried out with the halogenoalkane dissolved in alcohol and the alkali dissolved in water. This is because the organic compound is not water soluble, and so little contact would occur between it and the hydroxide ions. If a solution of the alkali in *ethanol* is used, a different reaction occurs, particularly with secondary and tertiary halogenoalkanes (pages 205–06).

Table 11.1 Bond enthalpies

Bond	Average bond enthalpy/ kJ mol^{-1}
C−F	+484
C−Cl	+338
C−Br	+276
C−I	+238

This is similar to the stabilisation of a secondary carbocation in the addition of HBr to an asymmetrical alkene (see page 189).

The rates of the reaction of the halogenoalkanes can be compared by noting the time taken for the precipitates to appear.

Equal volumes of each halogenoalkane are placed in test tubes, which are then put in a water bath at 60°C. Some silver nitrate solution is then added and the time taken for a precipitate of the silver halide to appear is noted.

- Primary halogenoalkanes hardly react with water. The C–Cl bond is too strong for any noticeable precipitate to be observed. 1–bromoalkanes give a precipitate very slowly; 1–iodoalkanes give a precipitate slightly more quickly.
- Secondary halogenoalkanes react slowly to form a secondary alcohol and a precipitate is soon observed. Precipitate formation is quicker with secondary iodoalkanes than with secondary bromoalkanes, which in turn form precipitates more quickly than secondary chloroalkanes.
- Tertiary halogenoalkanes react rapidly to produce a tertiary alcohol. A precipitate is seen as soon as the silver nitrate is added.

The halogenoalkanes are sometimes mixed with equal volumes of ethanol in order to improve solubility in the aqueous silver nitrate.

The carbon–halogen bond has been broken by water, so the reaction is called hydrolysis.

> **Test yourself**
>
> 3 Explain why 2-iodopropane reacts with aqueous silver nitrate at a faster rate than 2-chloropropane.

Reaction with potassium cyanide

When a halogenoalkane dissolved in ethanol is warmed with aqueous potassium cyanide, a substitution reaction takes place and a nitrile which contains a $C≡N$ is formed. With 1-bromopropane the reaction is:

$$CH_3CH_2CH_2Br + KCN \rightarrow CH_3CH_2CH_2CN + KBr$$

Reagent: potassium cyanide, KCN

Conditions: warmed under reflux in aqueous ethanol solution

Product: 1-butanenitrile

Reaction type: nucleophilic substitution

This reaction is an example of an increase in the carbon chain length. The lone pair of electrons on the carbon atom of the CN^- ion attacks the δ^+ carbon atom of the halogenoalkane, forming a new carbon–carbon σ-bond.

The rate of this reaction depends on the halogen and on whether the halogenoalkane is primary, secondary or tertiary (see page 198).

Rate: I > Br > Cl > F and tertiary > secondary > primary

Nitriles are useful intermediate compounds in synthesis. They can be hydrolysed to an acid or reduced to a primary amine.

$$RCN + H^+ + 2H_2O \rightarrow RCOOH + NH_4^+$$

$$RCN + 4[H] \rightarrow RCH_2NH_2$$

Reaction with ammonia

The reaction between a halogenoalkane and ammonia produces an amine.

Ammonia is a gas that is soluble in water. However, a solution cannot be heated under reflux because ammonia gas would be liberated. This would then escape because it

Hazard: cyanides are extremely toxic and experiments involving them should never be carried out in schools.

The product here has four carbon atoms in a single bonded chain and so the stem name is butan-.

> **Key term**
>
> An **amine** is a molecule containing the $–NH_2$, $>N–H$ or $>N–$ group.

would not be condensed by the reflux condenser. The halogenoalkane and the ammonia solution must therefore be heated in a sealed container. Alternatively, a concentrated ammonia solution can be used and the mixture left at room temperature for a long time.

A simplified equation for the reaction between 1-chloropropane and ammonia is:

$$CH_3CH_2CH_2Cl + 2NH_3 \rightarrow CH_3CH_2CH_2NH_2 + NH_4Cl$$

Reagent: excess ammonia

Conditions: concentrated solution of ammonia at room temperature or heated in a sealed tube

Product: 1-aminopropane

Reaction type: nucleophilic substitution

The product, 1-aminopropane, can react with more 1-chloropropane to produce the secondary amine, $(CH_3CH_2CH_2)_2NH$, and some tertiary amine, $(CH_3CH_2CH_2)_3N$.

Tip

Under these alkaline conditions, the salt NH_4Cl is produced rather than the acidic HCl. Stating that HCl is a product of this reaction is a common error.

Mechanism of nucleophilic substitution

Halogenoalkanes react with nucleophiles such as OH^-, H_2O, NH_3 and CN^- in substitution reactions. This is because the carbon atom joined to the halogen is slightly δ^+ and is, therefore, attacked by nucleophiles.

There are two distinct mechanisms by which halogenoalkanes react. Which mechanism is followed depends on whether they are primary, secondary or tertiary halogenoalkanes.

Primary halogenoalkanes

These react in an S_N2 reaction. The mechanism is a single step that goes through a transition state.

Key terms

An S_N2 reaction is so called because it is a substitution (S), is nucleophilic (N) and there are two species involved at the beginning of the mechanism.

A transition state is not a species that can be isolated. It changes immediately into the product. An analogy is that the transition state is like the top of a pass going from one valley to another.

Mechanism of reaction with OH^-(aq)

An example of an S_N2 mechanism involving a transition state is the reaction between hydroxide ions and bromoethane, as shown in Figure 11.6.

The red curly arrow in Figure 11.6 shows the movement of a lone pair of electrons from the oxygen to the carbon as a covalent bond forms. The green arrow represents the electrons in the C–Br σ-bond moving to the bromine atom as the bond breaks.

Tip

Do not forget to include the negative charge on the transition state, or the δ^+ and δ^- charges on the halogenoalkane.

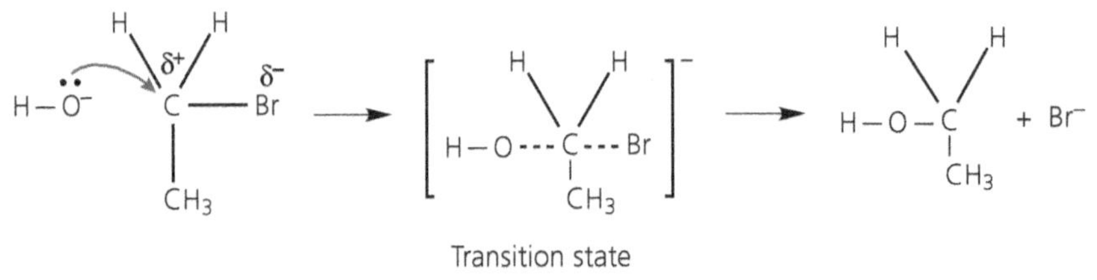

Transition state

Figure 11.6 The reaction between hydroxide ions and bromoethane, showing the transition state

The transition state occurs when the new O−C bond is half-formed and the C−Br bond is half-broken.

The mechanism for the reaction with cyanide ions, ⁻CN, is similar, with the lone pair of electrons on the carbon atom forming a bond with the δ+ carbon atom of the halogenoalkane.

The reaction profile diagram for this type of reaction is shown in Figure 11.7.

Tip

Make sure that the curly arrow starts from the carbon atom of the cyanide ion and not the nitrogen atom.

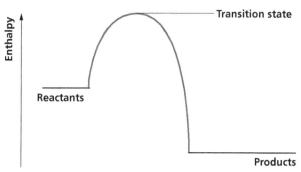

Figure 11.7 Reaction profile for an S$_N$2 reaction involving a transition state

The energy released in the formation of the O−C bond is enough to provide the energy to break the C−halogen bond. The weaker the C−halogen bond, the faster the rate of the reaction. Therefore, since the C−Cl bond is the strongest and the C−I bond is the weakest, the rate order is:

C−I > C−Br > C−Cl

Key term

The mechanism is called S$_N$1 because it is a substitution (S), is nucleophilic (N) and there is only one species involved at the beginning of the mechanism.

Tertiary halogenoalkanes

Tertiary halogenoalkanes react by S$_N$1 mechanisms.

This type of reaction takes place in two steps.

Step 1: the carbon–halogen bond breaks, a carbocation is formed and a halide ion is released. This is the slower rate-determining step.

Figure 11.8

Step 2: the carbocation is attacked by the nucleophile in a faster reaction.

Figure 11.9

The rate of the first step is slower than that of the second step. Therefore, the activation energy for the first step is greater than that of step 2. This is shown in Figure 11.10.

Tip

The S$_N$1 mechanism has a lower activation energy with a tertiary halogenoalkane than with a primary one. This is because the carbocation intermediate is stabilised by the pushing effect of the three alkyl groups (see page 190).

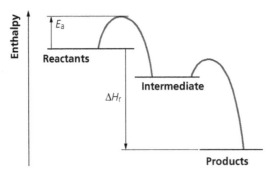

Figure 11.10 Reaction profile for an S_N1 reaction involving an intermediate.

> **Tip**
> When drawing diagrams like Figure 11.11, it does not matter whether you put the – sign on the C or on the N, but the curly arrow must start from the carbon atom.

With cyanide ions as the nucleophile, the second step is the attack on the carbocation by the lone pair of electrons on the carbon atom of the cyanide ion, CN^-, thus forming a new carbon–carbon single bond.

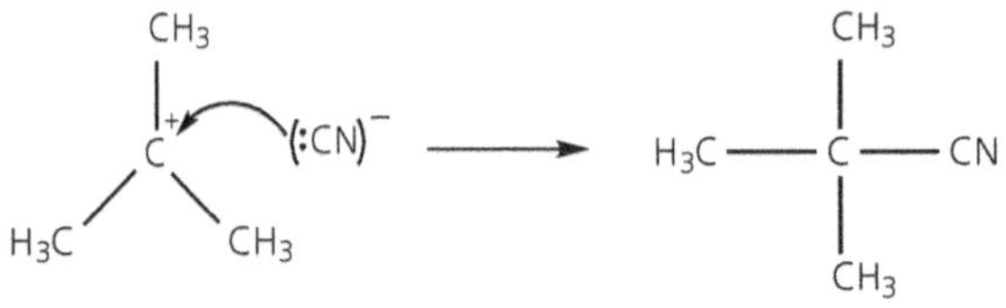

Figure 11.11

Secondary halogenoalkanes

The rate of reactions with S_N2 mechanisms decreases in the order:

primary > secondary > tertiary halogenoalkane

The rate of reactions with S_N1 mechanisms increases in the order:

primary < secondary < tertiary halogenoalkane

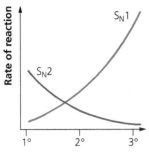

Figure 11.12 Different rates of S_N1 and S_N2 reactions

These relationships are shown graphically in Figure 11.12. Primary (1°) halogenoalkanes react almost entirely by an S_N2 mechanism and tertiary (3°) halogenoalkanes react by an S_N1 mechanism. Secondary (2°) halogenoalkanes react by both mechanisms. However, S_N1 is often faster and is, therefore, the dominant mechanism.

The overall rate is fastest with a tertiary halogenoalkane and slowest with a primary. For example, 2-chloro-2-methylpropane, $(CH_3)_3CCl$, produces an instant precipitate of silver chloride with aqueous silver nitrate, whereas 1-chloropropane gives a precipitate only after heating for a long period.

Mechanism of reaction with ammonia

With primary halogenoalkanes

The lone pair of electrons on the nitrogen atom attacks the δ^+ carbon atom. Ammonia is therefore the nucleophile. As this happens, the C–halogen bond breaks as in the S_N2 reaction on page 202. Note that the intermediate is neutral, because the attacking species is neutral (Figure 11.13).

Figure 11.13

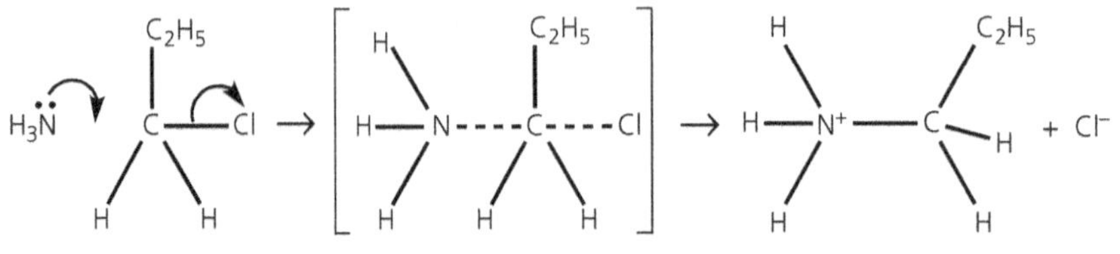

The final step is the loss of H^+, which is removed by a second NH_3 molecule (Figure 11.14).

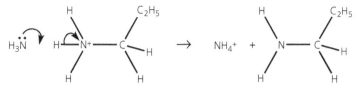

Figure 11.14

With tertiary halogenoalkanes

The first step is identical to the S_N1 reaction with aqueous OH^- ions.

The carbocation is then attacked by the lone pair of electrons in the NH_3 molecule. The last step is loss of H^+ as in the S_N2 mechanism shown in Figure 11.15.

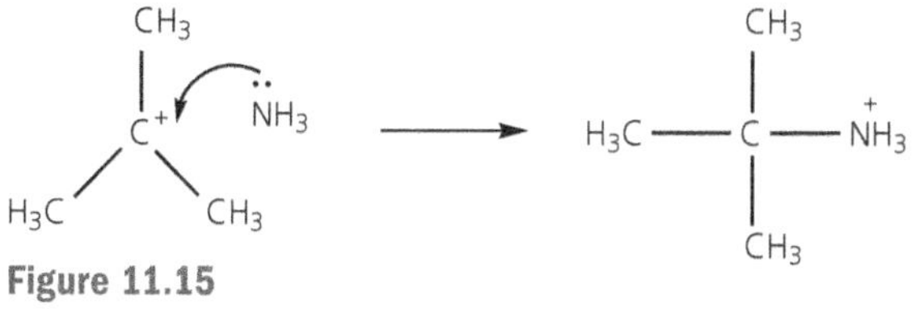

Figure 11.15

Elimination reaction

Key term

An **elimination reaction** is a reaction in which two atoms, or one atom and one small group, are removed from adjacent carbon atoms, forming an unsaturated compound.

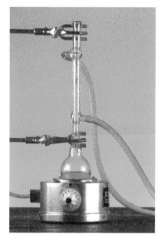

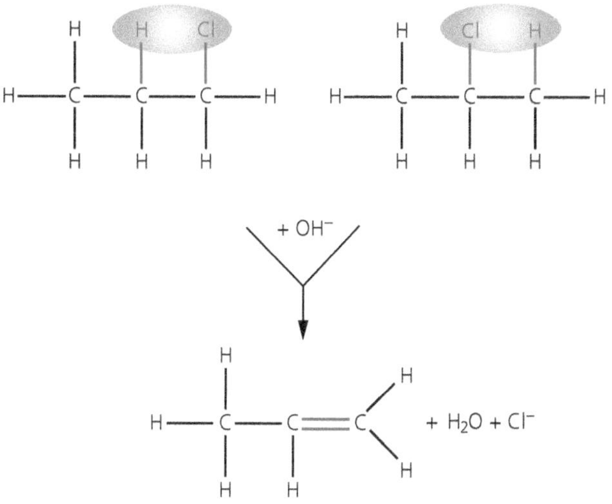

Heating under reflux

When a halogenoalkane is heated under reflux with a concentrated solution of potassium hydroxide in *ethanol*, the halogen atom is removed from the carbon atom to which it is attached and a hydrogen atom is removed from an adjacent carbon atom. The organic product is an alkene or a mixture of alkenes.

With either 1-chloropropane or 2-chloropropane, the only elimination product is propene, as shown in Figure 11.16.

Figure 11.16 The elimination of HCl

Reagent: concentrated potassium hydroxide

Conditions: heat under reflux in solution in *ethanol*

Product: propene

Reaction type: elimination

1-chlorobutane produces but-1-ene:

$$CH_3CH_2CH_2CH_2Cl + OH^- \rightarrow CH_3CH_2CH{=}CH_2 + H_2O + Cl^-$$

However, 2-chlorobutane produces a mixture of but-1-ene and both geometric isomers of but-2-ene (Figure 11.17).

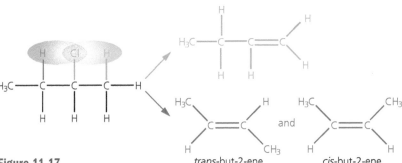

Figure 11.17   *trans*-but-2-ene   *cis*-but-2-ene

In practice, the situation is more complex because as well as elimination reactions, substitution reactions take place. Elimination is favoured by high temperatures in reactions with strong bases such as OH^- and involving tertiary halogenoalkanes. Substitution is favoured by moderate temperatures in reactions with weak bases such as H_2O and NH_3 and involving primary halogenoalkanes. The reaction of bromoethane with hot ethanolic potassium hydroxide produces only about 1% ethene, whereas the reaction using 2-bromopropane gives about 80% propene. Tertiary halogenoalkanes give almost 100% alkenes as the product under these conditions.

Test yourself

4 Name and give the formula of the organic product of the reaction of 1-bromo-2-methylpropane with:

a) an aqueous solution of potassium hydroxide

b) a concentrated solution of sodium hydroxide in ethanol

c) excess concentrated ammonia

Summary of reactions of halogenoalkanes

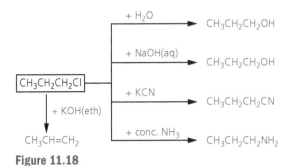

Figure 11.18

- The reactions in red are nucleophilic substitution reactions.
- The reaction in blue is elimination.

Test for halogenoalkanes

- Add a few drops of the halogenoalkane to an aqueous solution of sodium hydroxide and warm for several minutes.
- Cool.
- Add dilute nitric acid until the solution is just acidic to litmus.
- Add silver nitrate solution.

Result

- Chloroalkanes give a white precipitate that is soluble in dilute ammonia solution.
- Bromoalkanes give a cream precipitate that is insoluble in dilute ammonia solution but soluble in concentrated ammonia.
- Iodoalkanes give a pale yellow precipitate that is insoluble in dilute and concentrated ammonia.

The sodium hydroxide solution hydrolyses the halogenoalkane and liberates the halide ion. The solution has to be made acidic to prevent the precipitation of silver oxide when the silver nitrate is added. The precipitates are silver chloride (soluble in dilute ammonia), silver bromide (soluble only in concentrated ammonia) and silver iodide (insoluble in concentrated ammonia).

Uses of halogenoalkanes

Solvents

Compounds with several halogen atoms are used as solvents to remove grease from metals before electroplating. An example is 1,1,2-trichloroethane.

Refrigerants

Fully substituted compounds, such as the CFCs freon 12, CF_2Cl_2, and freon 113, $CF_2ClCFCl_2$, were used as coolants in refrigerators and in air conditioning. They are chemically inert, non-toxic and non-flammable. When released, however, their inert nature causes an environmental problem. They diffuse unchanged up into the stratosphere, where they are decomposed by ultraviolet radiation, producing chlorine radicals. The chlorine radicals break down ozone in a chain reaction.

It has been estimated that a single chlorine atom will cause the decomposition of 100000 ozone molecules. During the Antarctic winter, the chlorine radicals build up on ice crystals in the air, and when the ice is melted by the spring sun, massive depletion of the polar ozone occurs, causing a hole in the ozone layer in the southern hemisphere.

New refrigerant coolants, which contain hydrogen atoms as well as chlorine and fluorine, have been developed. An example is HCFC-22, which has the formula $CHClF_2$. HCFCs are more reactive and are broken down at lower altitudes, avoiding harm to the ozone layer. However, like CFCs, they are potent greenhouse gases.

Herbicides and pesticides

Herbicides kill plants. Two examples are 2,4-D and 2,4,5-T, which have structures as shown in Figure 11.19.

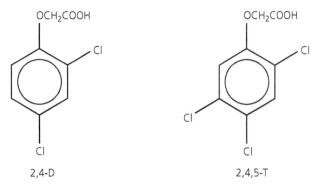

2,4-D 2,4,5-T

Figure 11.19 The structural formulae of two herbicides

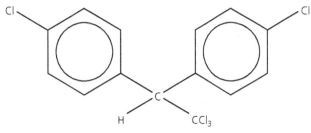

Figure 11.20 The structural formula for DDT

Pesticides kill insects. One of the most effective was DDT (dichlorodiphenyltrichloroethane — Figure 11.20). Unfortunately, it was found that its concentration built up in the fat of animals high in the food chain, causing problems with reproduction. Therefore, its use has been banned in many countries. DDT eradicated malaria from some countries and helped to control it in others. Since its ban, deaths from malaria in some tropical countries have risen.

The problem associated with the use of halogen-containing herbicides and pesticides is that they are inert to chemical and biological attack. They remain in the environment for a very long period. In the 1970s, the US military sprayed the forests of Vietnam with the defoliant Agent Orange, a mixture of 2,4-D and 2,4,5-T, and its adverse effects are still being seen. These chemicals are inert mainly because of the strength of the carbon–chlorine bond, which is particularly strong if bonded to benzene rings (Figure 11.20).

Alcohols

Key term

Alcohols are compounds that contain the hydroxyl, C–OH, group.

In an alcohol, the other atoms attached to the carbon of the C–OH group must be either hydrogen or carbon.

Alcohols have the general formula $C_nH_{(2n+1)}OH$. They are named from the parent alkanes, with a number representing the carbon atom in the chain to which the –OH group is joined. The skeletal formulae, names and structural formulae of some alcohols are shown in Figure 11.21.

Figure 11.21 The structures of some common alcohols

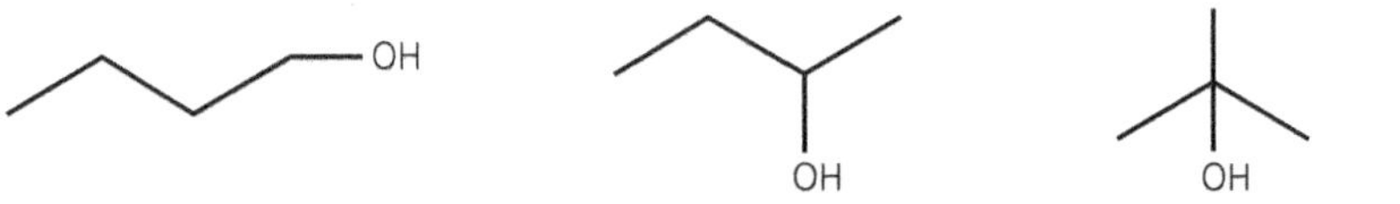

Butan-1-ol $CH_3CH_2CH_2CH_2OH$ | Butan-2-ol $CH_3CH_2CH(OH)CH_3$ | 2-methylpropan-2-ol $(CH_3)_3COH$

Primary alcohols have no more than one carbon atom attached directly to the carbon of the C–OH group. Methanol, CH_3OH, ethanol, CH_3CH_2OH, and propan-1-ol, $CH_3CH_2CH_2OH$, are all primary alcohols. All primary alcohols contain the $-CH_2OH$ group.

Secondary alcohols have two carbon atoms (and hence only one hydrogen atom) directly attached to the carbon of the C–OH group. Propan-2-ol, $CH_3CH(OH)CH_3$, is a secondary alcohol. All secondary alcohols contain the CH(OH) group.

Tertiary alcohols have three carbon atoms (and hence no hydrogen atoms) directly attached to the carbon of the C–OH group. 2-methylpropan-2-ol is a tertiary alcohol. Its structure is shown in Figure 11.22.

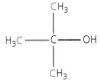

Figure 11.22 A tertiary alcohol, 2-methylpropan-2-ol

Physical properties

Most alcohols are liquids at room temperature. This is because there is hydrogen bonding between alcohol molecules. The oxygen–hydrogen bond is very polar because of the difference in the electronegativity of the two elements. The δ^- oxygen in one alcohol molecule forms a hydrogen bond with the δ^+ hydrogen atom in another molecule (Figure 11.23). This intermolecular force is stronger than, and in addition to, the instantaneous induced dipole–induced dipole (London) forces such as those acting between alkane molecules and those between the polar halogenoalkane molecules. As the forces are stronger, more energy is required to separate the molecules, resulting in a higher boiling temperature.

The lower members of the homologous series of alcohols are all completely miscible with water. This means that they dissolve in water in all proportions. Higher members are less soluble because the large hydrocarbon part interferes with the hydrogen bonding between water molecules. The reason for the solubility is the hydrogen bonding between alcohol and water molecules (Figure 11.24). This is similar in strength to the hydrogen bonding in pure water and in pure alcohol.

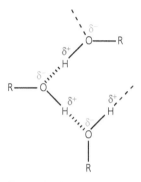

Figure 11.23
Hydrogen bonding between alcohol molecules

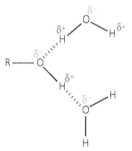

Figure 11.24 Hydrogen bonding between water and alcohol molecules

Reactions of alcohols

Combustion

Alcohols, like almost all organic chemicals, burn to form carbon dioxide and water. Ethanol burns with a clean flame:

$$C_2H_5OH + 3O_2 \rightarrow 2CO_2 + 3H_2O$$

Ethanol can be made by fermenting sugar or grain. Therefore, its use, when mixed with ordinary petrol, helps to reduce the carbon footprint of the fuel.

Halogenation (substitution by a halogen)

In a halogenation reaction, the −OH group of an alcohol molecule is replaced by a halogen atom. The reactions below are the standard ways of preparing halogenoalkanes in the laboratory.

Chlorination

When solid phosphorus pentachloride is added to a dry alcohol, clouds of hydrogen chloride fumes are produced, mixed with the gaseous chloroalkane. Phosphorus oxychloride remains in the vessel:

$$CH_3CH_2OH + PCl_5 \rightarrow CH_3CH_2Cl + POCl_3 + HCl$$

Tertiary alcohols are much more easily converted into halogenoalkanes in a substitution reaction. 2-chloro-2-methylpropane can be prepared from 2-methylpropan-2-ol by heating it under reflux with concentrated hydrochloric acid:

$$(CH_3)_3COH + HCl \rightarrow (CH_3)_3CCl + H_2O$$

The tertiary alcohol and an excess of concentrated hydrochloric acid are shaken together in a stoppered flask until a separate layer is formed on top of the acid. The mixture is transferred to a separating funnel and the lower aqueous layer discarded. The organic layer is washed with a solution of sodium hydrogencarbonate in order to remove any dissolved hydrochloric acid. The lower aqueous layer is discarded as before and the organic layer is dried with anhydrous sodium sulfate until the cloudy liquid goes clear. The product, a tertiary halogenoalkane, is poured into a distillation flask and distilled, collecting the liquid that boils off at the correct boiling temperature.

Bromination

When an alcohol is heated under reflux with a mixture of potassium bromide and 50% sulfuric acid, hydrogen bromide is first produced, which then reacts with the alcohol to form a bromoalkane:

$$KBr + H_2SO_4 \rightarrow KHSO_4 + HBr$$

$$CH_3CH_2OH + HBr \rightarrow CH_3CH_2Br + H_2O$$

The acid used is only 50% concentrated to prevent the hydrogen bromide that is produced from being oxidised (by sulfuric acid) to bromine (page 114).

Iodination

Warming a mixture of damp red phosphorus and iodine produces phosphorus triiodide, which then reacts with the alcohol to form the iodoalkane and phosphorus(III) acid:

$$2P + 3I_2 \rightarrow 2PI_3$$

$$3CH_3CH_2OH + PI_3 \rightarrow 3CH_3CH_2I + H_3PO_3$$

The moisture is to bring the iodine and phosphorus, both of which are solids, into contact so that they can react.

Table 11.2 summarises the substitution reactions of alcohols with halogens.

Table 11.2 Halogenation of alcohols

	Chlorination	Bromination	Iodination
Reagent	PCl$_5$ or conc. HCl	KBr and 50% H$_2$SO$_4$	I$_2$ and moist red phosphorus
Conditions	Room temperature or heat under reflux	Heat under reflux	Warm
Product	a chloroalkane	a bromoalkane	an iodoalkane
Reaction type	Substitution	Substitution	Substitution

Oxidation

Primary and secondary alcohols are oxidised by a solution of potassium dichromate(VI) and dilute sulfuric acid. The orange potassium dichromate(VI) solution turns green because it is reduced to hydrated Cr^{3+} ions.

Tertiary alcohols are unaffected by this oxidising agent, which remains orange in colour.

Oxidation of a primary alcohol to an aldehyde

If a *primary* alcohol is heated with a mixture of potassium dichromate(VI) and sulfuric acid and the volatile product is allowed to escape, an aldehyde is produced. For example:

$$CH_3CH_2OH + [O] \longrightarrow \underset{H_3C}{\overset{H}{>}}C{=}O + H_2O$$

Tip

[O] can always be used in the equations for oxidation reactions in organic chemistry.

The aldehyde is not hydrogen bonded and so has a lower boiling temperature than the alcohol. Therefore it boils off from the hot reaction mixture. A suitable apparatus is shown in Figure 11.25.

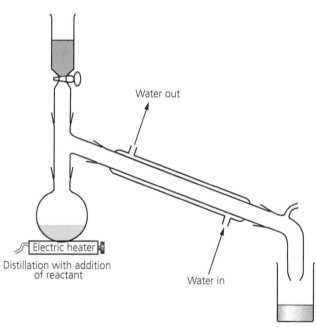

Figure 11.25 Apparatus for the oxidation of a primary alcohol to an aldehyde

Reagents: potassium dichromate(VI) and sulfuric acid

Conditions: add the oxidising agent to a mixture of excess hot ethanol and acid and distil off the aldehyde as it forms

Product: ethanal

Reaction type: oxidation

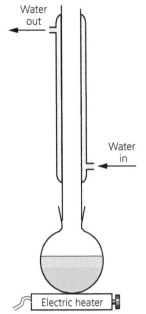

Figure 11.26 Reflux apparatus for the production of carboxylic acids and ketones

Oxidation of a primary alcohol to a carboxylic acid

If a primary alcohol is heated under reflux with the oxidising mixture, a carboxylic acid is formed. For example:

$$CH_3C]H_2OH + 2[O] \rightarrow CH_3COOH + H_2O$$

The acid can be distilled off after the reaction has gone to completion.

Reagents: excess potassium dichromate(VI) and sulfuric acid

Conditions: heat the mixture under reflux

Product: ethanoic acid

Reaction type: oxidation

A suitable apparatus is shown in Figure 11.26. The orange potassium dichromate goes green as it is reduced to Cr^{3+} ions. After the reaction has finished the ethanoic acid is distilled off, using normal distillation apparatus.

Oxidation of a secondary alcohol to a ketone

If a secondary alcohol is heated under reflux with the oxidising mixture, a ketone is produced. For example:

$$CH_3CH(OH)CH_3 + [O] \rightarrow + H_2O$$

$$CH_3CH(OH)CH_3 + [O] \longrightarrow \begin{array}{c} H_3C \\ \diagdown \\ C = O + H_2O \\ \diagup \\ H_3C \end{array}$$

Reagents: potassium dichromate(VI) and sulfuric acid

Conditions: heat the mixture under reflux

Product: propanone

Reaction type: oxidation

A suitable apparatus is shown in Figure 11.26.

Tip

If you are asked to draw apparatus, make sure that:

- the apparatus is made up of specific pieces, such as the flask and the condenser, rather than one continuous piece of glassware
- the apparatus is open and not sealed (for heating under reflux, the apparatus is open at the top; for distillation, it is open at the receiving flask)
- you take care when drawing condensers; show the water going in at the bottom and out at the top

---

Heating under reflux prevents volatile reactants from escaping the reaction mixture, so that a good conversion to product is achieved. After the reaction has finished, the reflux condenser is removed and the apparatus reassembled for ordinary distillation. Pure product is then obtained.

Elimination

If a water molecule is eliminated from an alcohol, an alkene is formed. For example propan-2-ol forms propene:

$$CH_3CH(OH)CH_3 - H_2O \rightarrow CH_3CH=CH_2$$

There are two ways of carrying out this elimination:

1 pass the alcohol over heated aluminium oxide

2 mix the alcohol with phosphoric(v) acid and warm.

Cyclohexene can be prepared by mixing cyclohexanol with phosphoric(v) acid in a 2:1 ratio and heating gently. The cyclohexene distils off and can be collected after being condensed (see Figure 11.27).

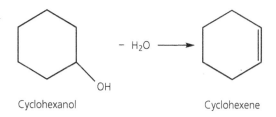

Cyclohexanol   Cyclohexene

The reaction mixture is gently heated and the vapour that comes off between 82°C and 85°C is condensed and collected. The cyclohexene has a lower boiling temperature than cyclohexanol as it is not hydrogen bonded. Thus it boils off, leaving the less volatile alcohol behind.

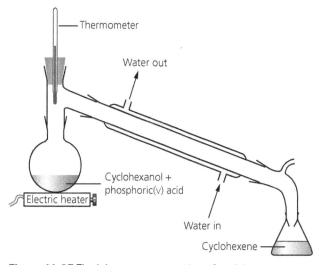

Figure 11.27 The laboratory preparation of cyclohexene

Summary of reactions of alcohols

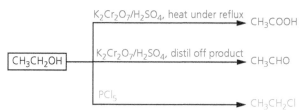

Figure 11.28 Summary of alcohol reactions

- The reactions in red are oxidation reactions.
- The reaction in green is substitution (halogenation).

Test for alcohols

Tip

Do not say that *white fumes* or *white smoke* are produced. The steamy fumes of hydrogen chloride produce a white smoke (of ammonium chloride) when a glass rod dipped in concentrated ammonia is held in the fumes. A common error is to state that a positive result with this test means that the unknown is an alcohol. The correct answer for a positive PCl_5 test is that the unknown substance contains an −OH group.

Add phosphorus pentachloride to the *dry* substance under test. All alcohols will produce steamy fumes of hydrogen chloride. This is a test for an −OH group, so the same result is obtained with carboxylic acids.

To distinguish between an acid and an alcohol, test the pH of the substance. Alcohols are neutral, whereas the pH of acids is less than 7.

Test to distinguish a tertiary alcohol from primary and secondary alcohols

- Warm with acidified potassium dichromate(VI).
- Tertiary alcohols are not oxidised by a heated solution of potassium dichromate(VI) and sulfuric acid and so the solution stays orange.
- Primary and secondary alcohols reduce the dichromate(VI) ions and so turn the solution from orange to green.

Tip

Do not forget to give the colour *before* as well as *after*.

Tip

Both Fehling's and Benedict's are alkaline solutions containing blue complex copper(II) ions. The red precipitate is copper(I) oxide.

Test to distinguish a primary alcohol from a secondary alcohol

- Warm with acidified potassium dichromate(VI) and distil off the product.
- A primary alcohol will be oxidised to an aldehyde which then gives a red precipitate when warmed with blue Fehling's or Benedict's solution.
- Secondary alcohols give a ketone that does not react with Fehling's or Benedict's which will stay blue.

Summary of types of reaction

Addition: two reactants form a single product. An example is the addition of hydrogen to an alkene:

$$CH_2=CH_2 + H_2 \rightarrow CH_3-CH_3$$

Substitution: one atom or group of atoms replaces another atom or group of atoms in a molecule. An example is the reaction between hydroxide ions and bromoethane:

$$CH_3CH_2Br + OH^- \rightarrow CH_3CH_2OH + Br^-$$

Elimination: two atoms are removed from adjacent carbon atoms in a molecule of an organic substance. An example is the removal of a hydrogen and a chlorine atom from 2-chloropropane to form propene:

$$CH_3CHClCH_3 + OH^- \rightarrow CH_3CH=CH_2 + Cl^- + H_2O$$

Polymerisation: thousands of monomer molecules join together to form a long polymeric chain. An example is the polymerisation of ethene to poly(ethene):

$$nCH_2=CH_2 \rightarrow (CH_2-CH_2)_n$$

Oxidation: in organic chemistry, oxidation is best defined as the addition of oxygen or the removal of hydrogen.

Secondary alcohols are oxidised to ketones. Two hydrogen atoms are removed from the alcohol. Therefore, it is oxidised:

$$CH_3CH(OH)CH_3 + [O] \rightarrow CH_3COCH_3 + H_2O$$

Hydrolysis: water, often with a catalyst of acid or alkali, splits an organic molecule into two parts. The $-OH$ group joins one part and the hydrogen atom joins the other part. An example is the hydrolysis of 2-iodopropane:

$$CH_3CHICH_3 + HOH \rightarrow CH_3CH(OH)CH_3 + HI$$

Summary of types of reagent

A **free radical** is an atom or group of atoms with an unpaired electron that it uses to form a covalent bond. A free radical is formed when a bond breaks homolytically, with one electron going to each atom in the bond. When chlorine is exposed to ultraviolet light, the $Cl-Cl$ bond breaks homolytically and two chlorine radicals are produced. A fishhook arrow shows the movement of each electron:

$$Cl-Cl \rightarrow Cl\cdot + Cl\cdot$$

A **nucleophile** is a species with a lone pair of electrons that it uses to form a covalent bond. Nucleophiles can be:

- negative ions — for example, OH^-, I^- and CN^-
- neutral molecules containing oxygen or nitrogen atoms — for example, water and ammonia

Nucleophiles attack δ^+ centres in molecules.

An **electrophile** is a species that attacks places of high electron density, for example, the C=C group in alkenes. The electrophile forms a covalent bond with a pair of electrons from the electron-rich site. Electrophiles can be:

- positive ions, for example, H^+
- δ^+ atoms in molecules, for example, the δ^+ hydrogen atom in HBr
- neutral molecules that can be polarised, for example, $Br-Br$

Understanding organic reactions

Organic reactions can be learnt or they can be understood. The first thing to do is to look at the molecule and ask yourself some questions:

- Is it polar with a δ^+ site? If so, it is likely to be attacked by nucleophiles. A halogenoalkane has a δ^+ carbon joined to the halogen and so undergoes substitution reactions with nucleophiles, resulting in the loss of a halide anion. As ions are formed during this type of reaction, it is usually carried out under aqueous conditions.
- Does it have an electron-rich site such as a non-polar π-bond? If so, it is likely to be attacked by an electrophile and the π-electrons will form a new bond with the electrophile. Alkenes are attacked by electrophiles.
- Is the molecule non-polar, without a site of high electron density? If so, it will react with free radicals. Light or peroxides are usually needed to produce the free

radicals, so a non-aqueous solvent (or gaseous-phase reaction) and ultraviolet light will probably be necessary. Alkanes react in this way.

● Which bond will break in an organic molecule? Rarely will a C–H or a C–C σ-bond break. C=C, O–H or C–OH are more likely to be broken.

Quantitative organic chemistry

Formulae

The **molecular formula** of a compound shows the number of atoms of each element in one molecule of the substance. For example, the molecular formula of ethanoic acid is $C_2H_4O_2$ and that of glucose is $C_6H_{12}O_6$.

The **empirical formula** of a substance is the simplest whole number ratio of the atoms of each element in the substance. For example, the empirical formula for both ethanoic acid and glucose is CH_2O.

The **structural formula** is an unambiguous structure that shows how the atoms in the molecule are arranged (see Figure 11.29). The *displayed* or *full* structural formula of a compound shows every atom and every bond. Glucose also exists as a six-membered ring compound.

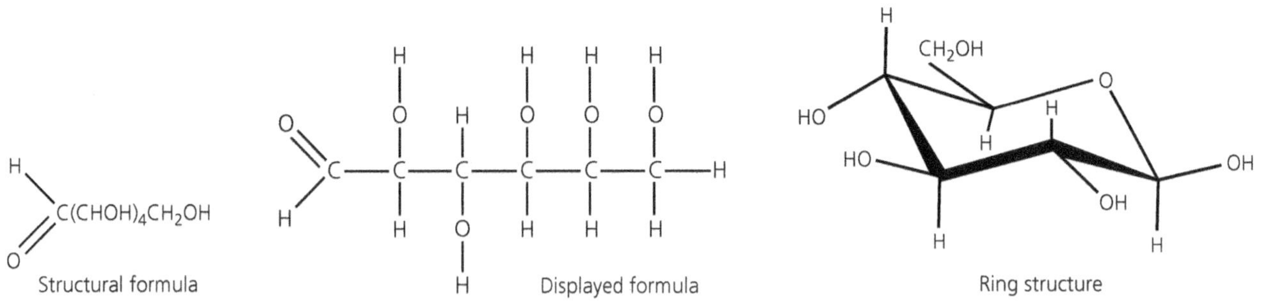

Structural formula   Displayed formula   Ring structure

Figure 11.29 Different ways of showing glucose

Empirical formula
This can be worked out from the percentage by mass of each element in the compound. The calculation is done in three stages.

Step 1: divide each percentage by the relative atomic mass of the element to give the number of moles of each element in 100 g of the compound.

Step 2: these values, which are the relative number of moles of each element, are then divided by the smallest value. Give the results to one decimal place.

Step 3: if the numbers are not whole numbers, multiply by 2 to see if that converts them into integers. If not, try multiplying by 3 and so on, until all the values are whole numbers.

The integers obtained in the final step are the simplest ratio of the numbers of each element present in the compound. The empirical formulae can now be written.

> Make sure you use atomic masses, *not* atomic numbers, in step 1.

> The calculation is best done in the form of a table.

Worked example

A compound contains 62.1% carbon, 10.3% hydrogen and 27.6% oxygen by mass. Calculate its empirical formula.

Answer

Element	%	Divide by RAM	Divide by the smallest	Ratio
Carbon	62.1	$\dfrac{62.1}{12} = 5.175$	$\dfrac{5.175}{1.725} = 3$	3
Hydrogen	10.3	$\dfrac{10.3}{1} = 10.3$	$\dfrac{10.3}{1.725} = 5.97 \rightarrow 6$	6
Oxygen	27.6	$\dfrac{27.6}{16} = 1.725$	$\dfrac{1.725}{1.725} = 1$	1

The empirical formula is C_3H_6O.

A second method for calculating empirical formulae involves the use of combustion analysis.

Worked example

When 1.00 g of a compound containing carbon, hydrogen and oxygen only was burnt in excess air, 1.74 g of carbon dioxide and 0.947 g of water were formed. Calculate its empirical formula.

Answer

$$\text{moles of } CO_2 = \frac{1.74}{44} = 0.0395 = \text{moles of C}$$

mass of carbon $= 0.0395 \times 12 = 0.475$ g

$$\text{moles of } H_2O = \frac{0.947}{18} = 0.526$$

moles of H $= 2 \times 0.526 = 0.105 = $ mass of hydrogen

mass of oxygen $= 1.00 - (0.475 + 0.105) = 0.42$ g

$$\text{moles of O} = \frac{0.42}{16} = 0.02625$$

To get ratio by moles divide by the smallest moles (oxygen):

$$\text{carbon} = \frac{0.0395}{0.02625} = 1.5$$

$$\text{hydrogen} = \frac{0.105}{0.02625} = 4$$

oxygen $= 1$

The simplest whole number ratio is 3C : 8H : 2O, so the empirical formula is $C_3H_8O_2$.

Molecular formula

If the molar mass is known, the molecular formula can be calculated from the empirical formula. This is done in three stages.

Step 1: calculate the empirical mass.

Step 2: divide the molar mass by the empirical mass. The answer is a whole number.

Step 3: multiply the number of atoms of each element by the integer found in Step 2 to give the actual numbers of atoms of each element in the molecule.

Worked example

A substance X has the empirical formula, CH. The molar mass of X is $78\,g\,mol^{-1}$. Calculate the molecular formula.

Answer

Step 1: empirical mass = $12 + 1 = 13$

Step 2: $\dfrac{\text{molar mass}}{\text{empirical mass}} = \dfrac{78}{13} = 6$

Step 3: molecular formula = C_6H_6

Reaction yield

Theoretical yield

The theoretical yield is calculated in three steps:

Step 1: calculate the amount of reactant in moles.

Step 2: use the reaction stoichiometry to calculate the amount of product in moles.

Step 3: convert moles of product to mass of product.

Worked example

Calculate the theoretical yield when 1.23 g of buta-1,3-diene reacts with excess bromine according to the equation:

$$CH_2=CH-CH=CH_2 + 2Br_2 \rightarrow CH_2BrCHBrCHBrCH_2Br$$

Answer

Step 1: molar mass of buta-1,3-diene = $54\,g\,mol^{-1}$

amount of buta-1,3-diene $= \dfrac{1.23\,g}{54\,g\,mol^{-1}} = 0.0228\,mol$

Step 2: The ratio of product to reactant is 1:1.
The bromine is in excess, so the ratio of product to buta-1,3-diene is 1:1.

amount of product = 0.0228 mol

Step 3: molar mass of product = $54 + (4 \times 80) = 374\,g\,mol^{-1}$
theoretical yield = amount of product (moles) × molar mass
$= 0.0228\,mol \times 374\,g\,mol^{-1} = 8.53\,g$

Percentage yield

The actual yield is the measured mass of the product obtained in the experiment and is usually given in the question. The theoretical yield has to be calculated from the equation and the mass of reactant.

Worked example

When 3.21 g of propan-2-ol was heated under reflux with 50% sulfuric acid and potassium bromide, 4.92 g of 2-bromopropane was produced. Calculate the percentage yield.

$$CH_3CH(OH)CH_3 + HBr \rightarrow CH_3CHBrCH_3 + H_2O$$

Answer

$$\text{amount of propan-2-ol} = \frac{3.21\,\text{g}}{60\,\text{g mol}^{-1}} = 0.0535\,\text{mol}$$

ratio of product to reactant = 1:1

amount of 2-bromopropane = 0.0535 mol

theoretical yield = $0.0535 \times 123\,\text{g mol}^{-1} = 6.58\,\text{g}$

$$\% \text{ yield} = \frac{4.92\,\text{g} \times 100}{6.58\,\text{g}} = 74.8\%$$

If a reaction takes place in two steps, each with a 60% yield, the percentage yield for the overall reaction is:

$$60\% \text{ of } 60\% = \frac{60}{100} \times \frac{60}{100} \times 100 = 36\%$$

Summary tasks

Make sure you can:
- draw skeletal formulae for alcohols and halogenoalkanes
- give examples of primary, secondary and tertiary alcohols and halogenoalkanes
- explain why ethanol is soluble in water whereas chloroethane is not

Check that you can write equations for the reactions of alcohols such as propan-1-ol with:
- oxygen (combustion)
- oxidising agents such as acidified potassium dichromate(VI)
- phosphorus(V) chloride
- phosphorus(III) iodide
- concentrated sulfuric acid

Do you know:
- the test for alcohols and for halogenoalkanes?
- the laboratory preparation of halogenoalkanes?

Make sure that you can write equations for the reactions of halogenoalkanes such as 2-bromopropane with:
- dilute aqueous OH^- ions
- water in the presence of Ag^+ ions
- concentrated OH^- ions dissolved in ethanol
- excess ammonia

Make sure you can draw, using curly arrows, S_N1 and S_N2 mechanisms and know which is correct for a given halogenoalkane.

Copy the diagram below and make sure that you know the correct reagents and any necessary conditions.

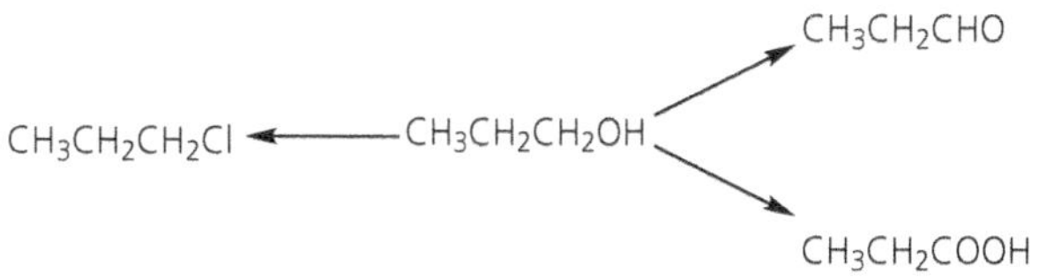

$CH_3CH_2CH_2Cl \longleftarrow CH_3CH_2CH_2OH$

CH_3CH_2CHO

CH_3CH_2COOH

Copy the diagram below and make sure that you know the correct reagents and any necessary conditions.

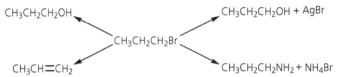

Questions

1 Which of the following is the most polar molecule and which is the least polar?
   a) chloromethane, bromomethane or iodomethane
   b) fluoromethane or methanol

2 Explain why fluoromethane is insoluble in water, whereas methanol is totally soluble.

3 Give an example of a halogenated polymer. State one use of this polymer and one environmental problem related to its disposal.

4 You are given three unlabelled samples of organic liquids. You know that one is hexene, one is hexanol and the other is hexanoic acid. Describe how you would identify each substance.

5 Describe the mechanism of the reaction between 2-bromobutane and aqueous hydroxide ions.

6 Suggest the mechanism for the reaction between 2-chloropropane and cyanide ions ($^-C\equiv N$) in aqueous solution.

7 Explain why it is necessary to have some ethanol present for the reaction between dilute aqueous sodium hydroxide and 2-iodopentane.

8 A chloroalkane contains 37.2% carbon and 55.0% chlorine by mass. Calculate its empirical formula.

9 A carboxylic acid contains 50% carbon, 5.6% hydrogen and 44.4% oxygen by mass. It turns brown bromine water colourless.
   a) Calculate the empirical formula of the acid.
   b) Suggest the simplest structural formula for this acid.

10 A compound X contains 53.3% carbon, 11.1% hydrogen and 35.6% oxygen by mass.
   a) Calculate the empirical formula of X.

b) The molar mass of X is $90\,g\,mol^{-1}$. Deduce the molecular formula of X.

c) When excess phosphorus pentachloride was added, $9.0\,g$ of dry X gave off $4.8\,dm^3$ of hydrogen chloride gas. Suggest one structural formula for X, giving your reasons. (Under the conditions of the experiment, 1 mol of gas occupies $24\,dm^3$.)

11 $5.67\,g$ of ethanol was added to a hot solution of potassium dichromate(VI) and sulfuric acid. The ethanal produced was distilled off and $4.88\,g$ of pure ethanal was obtained. Calculate the percentage yield.

12 2-iodopropane can be made from 1-chloropropane by the two-stage synthesis:

$$CH_3CH_2CH_2Cl \rightarrow CH_3CH=CH_2$$
$$\rightarrow CH_3CHICH_3$$

If stage 1 has a 30% yield and stage 2 has a 90% yield, calculate the mass of 2-iodopropane made from $78.5\,g$ of 1-chloropropane.

13 $100\,g$ of the fat glyceryl tristearate was boiled with excess sodium hydroxide and the soap, sodium stearate, salted out. The yield of soap was $87.1\,g$. The reaction is as given below:

$$
\begin{array}{l}
C_{17}H_{35}COOCH_2 \\
\quad | \\
C_{17}H_{35}COOCH + 3NaOH \longrightarrow 3C_{17}H_{35}COONa \\
\quad | \qquad\qquad\qquad\qquad\qquad + CH_2(OH)CH(OH)CH_2OH \\
C_{17}H_{35}COOCH_2
\end{array}
$$

Calculate the percentage yield.

14 Outline a synthetic route in not more than three steps to convert the following. For each step give the reagent and the conditions.
   a) $CH_2CH_2CH_2Cl$ to CH_3CH_2COOH
   b) $CH_3CH=CH_2$ to CH_3COCH_3

Exam practice questions

1 a) Which is **not** a nucleophile?

    A CH_3NH_2 **C** H_3O^+

    B H_2O **D** I^- (1)

b) i) Which describes the reaction between 2-chloropropane and aqueous sodium hydroxide?

    A free radical substitution

    B nucleophilic substitution

    C electrophilic addition

    D oxidation   (1)

  ii) Identify the product in b)i).   (1)

c) Which describes the reaction between bromine and methane?

    A free radical substitution

    B nucleophilic substitution

    C electrophilic addition

    D oxidation   (1)

d) Which describes the reaction between ethanol and excess acidified potassium dichromate(VI)?

    A free radical substitution

    B nucleophilic substitution

    C electrophilic addition

    D oxidation   (1)

e) i) Which describes the reaction between hydrogen bromide and propene?

    A free radical substitution

    B nucleophilic substitution

    C electrophilic addition

    D oxidation   (1)

  ii) Identify the major product in e)i).   (1)

(Total 7 marks)

2 a) Define the term **nucleophile**.   (2)

b) Cyanide ions react with 1-bromopropane in a nucleophilic substitution reaction.

$$CH_3CH_2CH_2Br + :CN^- \rightarrow$$
$$CH_3CH_2CH_2CN + Br^-$$

  i) Draw a mechanism for this reaction. (3)

  ii) Explain why the reaction between cyanide ions and 1-iodopropane is faster.   (2)

  iii) Explain why the reaction of a nucleophile such as cyanide ions with 2-methyl-2-bromopropane goes via a different mechanism.   (2)

(Total 9 marks)

3 a) You are given three unlabelled bottles containing halogenoalkanes with different halogens. Describe a test that you would do to find which was a bromoalkane.   (2)

b) Name the organic product of the reaction of 2-bromopropane with:

  i) excess ammonia   (1)

  ii) a concentrated solution of potassium hydroxide in ethanol.   (1)

c) 2-bromo-2-methylpropane can be prepared from 2-methylpropan-2-ol.

  i) Name the reagents and the conditions.   (2)

  ii) In the preparation the halogenoalkane boils off leaving behind any unreacted alcohol. Explain why this is so.   (2)

d) Write skeletal formulae of the three branched-chain primary alcohols of formula $C_5H_{11}OH$.   (3)

(Total 11 marks)

4 Consider the following series of reactions and then answer the questions that follow:

$$C_4H_8 \underset{\text{ethanolic KOH}}{\overset{\text{HBr}}{\rightleftarrows}} C_4H_9Br \xrightarrow{\text{NaOH(aq)}} C_4H_9OH$$

    A   **B**   **C**

a) i) Compound A is an alkene that has two geometric isomers. Draw their structural formulae.   (2)

  ii) State the two features of the molecule that makes this isomerism possible.   (2)

  iii) Stating what you would see, give a simple chemical test for the functional group present in compound A.   (2)

  iv) What type of reaction is the conversion of compound A to compound B?   (1)

  v) Draw the mechanism for the reaction of compound A with hydrogen bromide. In your mechanism, the alkene (A) can be represented simply as: (3)

$$>C=C<$$

  vi) What type of reaction is the conversion of compound B to compound A?   (1)

b) i) The reaction of compound B to give compound C is a nucleophilic substitution. What is meant by the term nucleophile? (1)

ii) Give the full structural formula of compound C. (1)

iii) Give a simple chemical test for the functional group in compound C. Describe what you would see as a result of this test. (2)

iv) Give the full structural formula for the compound obtained by heating compound C with acidified potassium dichromate solution. (2)

c) The alkene 3-methylpent-2-ene has two geometric isomers. Giving your reasons, state whether the isomer shown below is the *E*-isomer or the *Z*-isomer. (2)

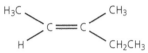

(Total 19 marks)

5 a) Draw the mechanism for the substitution reaction of 2-methyl-2-bromopropane with ammonia. You should include all relevant lone pairs of electrons. (4)

b) Suggest the skeletal formula of the product of reacting iodoethane with the primary amine $C_2H_5NH_2$. (2)

c) Explain why water at room temperature and not hot aqueous sodium hydroxide is used for the hydrolysis of a tertiary halogenoalkane. (2)

d) Explain why the major product of the reaction of gaseous hydrogen bromide with propene is 2-bromopropane and not 1-bromopropane. (3)

(Total 11 marks)

6 a) Methanol is manufactured by the reversible reaction between hydrogen and carbon monoxide over a suitable catalyst at a moderate temperature.

$$2H_2(g) + CO(g) \rightleftharpoons CH_3OH(g)$$
$$\Delta H = -101 \, kJ \, mol^{-1}$$

Explain why
i) a high temperature is not used
ii) a high pressure is used
iii) a catalyst is used (6)

b) Explain why methanol is very soluble in water. (2)

c) Write structural formulae, showing any double bonds, of the organic products of the reactions of methanol with:
i) excess acidified potassium dichromate(VI) when heated under reflux
ii) sodium
iii) damp red phosphorus and iodine. (3)

d) When the product of c)ii) is mixed with water, the solution turns phenolphthalein red. Explain this observation. (2)

e) Which of the following alcohols does not produce a green solution when warmed with acidified potassium dichromate(VI)?
A ethanol
B butan-2-ol
C 2-methylbutan-2-ol
D hexan-3-ol (1)

(Total 14 marks)

12 Modern analytical techniques (Topic 7)

Mass spectrometry

A diagram and an explanation of how a mass spectrometer works can be found on pages 12–13. Some examples of its use are given on pages 14–15.

Valuable information about the molecular structure of an organic molecule can be obtained from a **mass spectrum**. The first thing to look for in a mass spectrum is the peak due to the **molecular ion**. This is normally the peak with the highest m/z value. However, sometimes there is a peak with an m/z value 1 more than that of the molecular ion peak — the $M+1$ peak. This is caused by the presence of the carbon-13 isotope. The carbon-13 content of natural carbon is 1.1%, so a molecule containing six carbon atoms has an $M+1$ peak about 7% of the height of the molecular ion peak (see Figure 12.1 on page 224).

> **Tip**
>
> In some mass spectra the molecular ion peak is missing. This is caused by the high energy of the ionisation process, which is sufficient to split all the molecular ions into fragments.

Worked example

a) An organic compound has the empirical formula C_2H_4O. The largest m/z value in its mass spectrum is 88. Calculate the molecular formula of the compound.

b) When phosphorus pentachloride is added to this compound, 1 mol of HCl per mole of the organic compound is liberated. Suggest possible formulae for the compound.

Answer

a) The mass of $C_2H_4O = (2 \times 12) + 4 + 16 = 44$. This is half of 88, so the molecular formula is $C_4H_8O_2$.

b) The HCl is produced in a 1:1 ratio, so there can be only one –OH group in the molecule. Some possible substances are:

$CH_3CH_2CH_2COOH$

$(CH_3)_2CHCOOH$

$CH_3COCH_2CH_2OH$

Further study of the mass spectrum can help to identify the substance.

Fragmentation of the molecular ion

The ionisation process causes the molecular ion to be in a high-energy state. Many of these ions break down into two fragments — a radical and a positive ion. Various functional groups cause molecules to break apart in characteristic ways. Ketones tend to break where the C=O group bonds onto one of the alkyl groups — for example, butanone, $CH_3CH_2COCH_3$ gives a molecular ion peak at $m/z = 72$ and peaks at m/z values of 57 (loss of CH_3), 43 (loss of C_2H_5), 15 (caused by CH_3^+) and 29 (caused by $C_2H_5^+$). A typical fragmentation would be:

$$CH_3CH_2COCH_3^+ \rightarrow CH_3\bullet + CH_3CH_2CO^+$$

The fragments give clues to the groups that are present in the molecule. A CH_3 group has a mass of 15 units, so an ion of mass $(M - 15)$ indicates that the substance has a CH_3 group:

$$(RCH_3)^+ \rightarrow R^+ + CH_3\bullet$$

The masses of some common fragments that are often lost are given in Table 12.1.

The mass spectrum of the substance in the worked example above (highest m/z value 88) also had peaks at m/z values 43 (88 − 45) and 59 (88 − 29). These fragments show that the substance has a COOH group ($m/z = 45$) and a C_2H_5 or a CHO group ($m/z = 29$). It cannot have a CHO group as well as a COOH group as there are only two oxygen atoms in the substance. Of the three suggested formulae in the worked example — $CH_3CH_2CH_2COOH$, $(CH_3)_2CHCOOH$ and $CH_3COCH_2CH_2OH$ — only the first has a C_2H_5 and a COOH group, so this is the compound.

Propan-1-ol and propan-2-ol can be oxidised to propanal and propanone respectively. The mass spectra of the oxidation products are shown in Figures 12.1 and 12.2. The molecular ion peaks at $m/z = 58$ can be seen clearly in both spectra. In the spectrum for propanal there is a large peak at $m/z = 29$, which is due to a combination of the $C_2H_5^+$ and CHO^+ peaks:

$$C_2H_5CHO^+ \rightarrow C_2H_5^+ + CHO\bullet \quad \text{and} \quad C_2H_5CHO^+ \rightarrow C_2H_5\bullet + CHO^+$$

Table 12.1 Common fragments lost

m/z value	Group
15	CH_3
29	C_2H_5 or CHO
31	CH_2OH
45	COOH
77	C_6H_5

Note the small $(M + 1)$ peaks in both spectra. These are caused by a ^{13}C atom in the molecule. These $(M + 1)$ peaks are sometimes missed out of mass spectra in A-level questions.

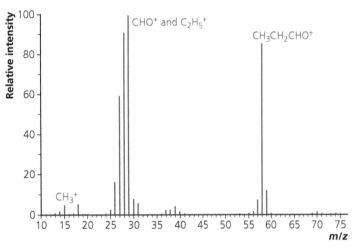

Figure 12.1 Mass spectrum of propanal

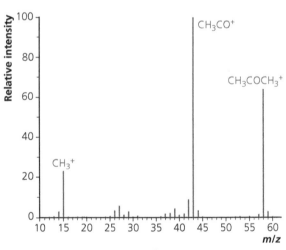

Figure 12.2 Mass spectrum of propanone

The spectrum of propanone shows peaks due to fragments at $m/z = 15$ (CH_3^+) and $m/z = 43$ (CH_3CO^+):

$$CH_3COCH_3^+ \rightarrow CH_3^+ + CH_3CO\bullet \quad \text{and} \quad CH_3COCH_3^+ \rightarrow CH_3\bullet + CH_3CO^+$$

Test yourself

1 The mass spectrum of butanoic acid, $CH_3CH_2CH_2COOH$, has a peak at $m/z = 43$. Write the equation for the formation of the particle that causes this peak.

12 Modern analytical techniques (Topic 7)

Mass spectrometers in the pharmaceutical industry

When potential drugs are developed, their identity must be confirmed. The reaction mixture is first separated into pure components by high-performance liquid chromatography (HPLC). The theory is the same as that of the chromatography studied at GCSE but, in HPLC, the solution mixture is forced under pressure through a column containing a solid adsorbent material. The different components are separated quickly and effectively. Samples are then analysed by a specialised mass spectrometer.

Most pharmaceuticals are not thermally stable. Therefore, the usual method of bombarding their vapour with electrons would cause considerable decomposition. Instead, molecules containing a base, such as an $-NH_2$ group, are protonated by adding methanoic acid. This causes the potential drug molecule to become positively charged. A solution of the charged molecule is sprayed into the spectrometer and the solvent is rapidly evaporated using a laser. The positive ions pass through the spectrometer and their molar masses are determined. Molecules containing an acidic group (such as COOH) are treated with ammonia, which deprotonates them and produces negative ions. The molecules are then sprayed into the spectrometer.

Mass spectrometer

Infrared absorption

Electromagnetic radiation

Electromagnetic radiation consists of an oscillating electric and magnetic field of a wide range of frequencies (Table 12.2). In a vacuum, light travels at a speed of $3.00 \times 10^8\,m\,s^{-1}$ (670 000 000 miles per hour).

Table 12.2 Frequency, wavenumber and energy of different types of electromagnetic radiation

Type of radiation	Frequency/MHz	Wavenumber/cm⁻¹	Energy/J per photon
X-rays	$> 10^{11}$	$> 3 \times 10^6$	$> 7 \times 10^{-17}$
Ultraviolet	1×10^9	3×10^4	7×10^{-19}
Visible — blue	6×10^8	2.1×10^4	4.2×10^{-19}
Visible — yellow	5×10^8	1.6×10^4	3.2×10^{-19}
Visible — red	4×10^8	1.4×10^4	2.8×10^{-19}
Infrared	$< 3 \times 10^8$	< 10000	$< 2 \times 10^{-19}$
Microwaves	$< 3 \times 10^4$	< 1	$< 2 \times 10^{-22}$
Radiowaves	< 100	$< 3 \times 10^{-3}$	$< 7 \times 10^{-26}$

Frequency is measured in hertz, Hz ($1\,Hz = 1\,s^{-1}$). The frequency determines the colour and the energy of the light, which is calculated by the expression formulated by Max Planck:

$$E = h\nu$$

where h is Planck's constant and ν is the frequency.

The speed of light, its frequency and the wavelength are combined in the equation:

$$c = \lambda\nu$$

where c is speed of light and λ is the wavelength.

When electromagnetic radiation is passed through a diffraction grating, it is split up into a spectrum according to the frequency of the radiation. Visible light is split by passing it through a prism. Blue light is refracted (bent) more than red light.

A rainbow is caused by droplets of rain splitting up white light into its component colours.

Infrared radiation is a form of electromagnetic radiation that has a lower frequency, or longer wavelength, than that of visible light. It is more convenient to use wavenumber, rather than hertz, for frequency, because this is a more manageable number.

$$\text{wavenumber} = \frac{\text{frequency}}{\text{speed of light}}$$

where the units of wavenumber are cm^{-1}.

The larger the wavenumber, the higher is the frequency and the larger is the energy of the radiation.

Infrared light has a wavenumber below $10\,000\,cm^{-1}$, whereas yellow light has a wavenumber of $17\,000\,cm^{-1}$. An infrared line at $1720\,cm^{-1}$ has a frequency of $5 \times 10^{13}\,Hz$ and a wavelength of $6000\,nm$.

Absorption of energy

A molecule can absorb energy in a number of ways:

- **Translational energy** — a molecule gains kinetic energy and moves faster. Heating a substance causes it to gain kinetic energy.
- **Rotational energy** — a molecule rotates about its centre of mass. Absorption of microwaves causes an increase in rotational energy.
- **Vibrational energy** — the atoms in a molecule vibrate in different ways. The bonds can stretch or bend. Absorption of infrared energy causes an increase in vibrational energy.
- **Electron excitement** — an electron in an atom or bond is promoted to a higher energy level. Absorption of visible or ultraviolet light results in electron excitement. In some cases, the electron is excited to such a high level that a covalent bond breaks. For example, the absorption of ultraviolet or visible light by chlorine results in the Cl−Cl bond breaking homolytically.

Infrared absorption

For a molecule to absorb in the infrared, the vibration must involve a change in the **dipole moment** of the molecule. Molecules with non-polar bonds, such as oxygen and nitrogen, do not absorb infrared radiation. This is why they are not **greenhouse gases**.

Non-polar molecules

Non-polar molecules that have polar bonds absorb in the infrared. These include carbon dioxide and methane.

Carbon dioxide

Oxygen is more electronegative than carbon, so the carbon atom in carbon dioxide is δ^+ and the oxygen atom is δ^-. However, the molecule is linear, so the dipoles cancel out and the molecule is non-polar. There are three ways in which the molecule can vibrate (Figure 12.3).

Figure 12.3 Carbon dioxide stretching and bending

The symmetrical stretching does not cause a change in dipole moment and so does not absorb infrared radiation. The other two modes cause a change in dipole moment from zero and are said to be 'infrared active'. Carbon dioxide, therefore, absorbs infrared radiation and is a greenhouse gas. The infrared spectrum of carbon dioxide is shown in Figure 12.4.

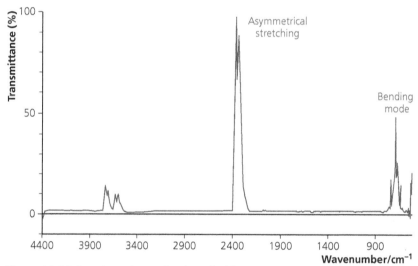

Figure 12.4 Infrared spectrum of carbon dioxide

Methane

The C–H bond is polar — the electronegativity of carbon is 2.5 and that of hydrogen is 2.1. However, the methane molecule is tetrahedral, so the dipoles cancel and the molecule has no dipole moment. Any asymmetrical bending or stretching causes the molecule to have a dipole moment. Therefore, methane absorbs infrared radiation.

Polar molecules

All polar molecules are infrared active.

Water

The oxygen atom in a molecule of water is δ^- and has two lone pairs of electrons. This results in the molecule being non-linear and, therefore, polar. It absorbs infrared radiation in all its bending and stretching modes. It is the major greenhouse gas in the atmosphere.

Oxides of nitrogen

The electronegativity of nitrogen is 3.0 and that of oxygen is 3.5. Therefore, all bonds between nitrogen and oxygen are polar. Nitric oxide, NO, is a diatomic polar molecule and has a dipole moment of 0.16 D. Nitrogen dioxide, NO_2, is a V-shaped molecule with a dipole moment of 0.40 D. Therefore, both oxides absorb infrared radiation and are greenhouse gases.

Infrared spectroscopy

An infrared spectrometer measures the amounts of radiation absorbed. It does this by splitting the incident beam of radiation into two. One beam passes through a reference cell and then goes to the detector; the other goes through the sample to the detector (Figure 12.5). The difference between the two amounts of radiation arriving at the detector is the amount absorbed by the chemical. The angle of the diffraction grating is slowly altered so that different frequencies sweep through the apparatus. The liquid sample is sandwiched between two plates of transparent sodium chloride.

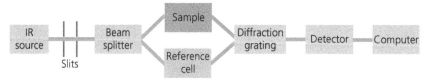

Figure 12.5 Representation of an infrared spectrometer

Different bonds in a covalent molecule absorb radiation of different frequencies, which are normally measured as wavenumbers. An infrared spectrum usually has a range from $4000\,cm^{-1}$ to $600\,cm^{-1}$.

The C=O bond absorbs at around $1700\,cm^{-1}$, but the actual value depends on the other atoms attached to the C=O group. This is shown in Table 12.3.

Table 12.3 Absorption frequencies of different C=O groups

Type of compound	Wavenumber/cm^{-1}
Alkyl aldehyde	1725–1740
Aryl aldehyde	1690–1715
Alkyl ketone	1710–1725
Aryl ketone	1680–1700
Carboxylic acid	1700–1725
Ester	1735–1750
Acid chloride	1815–1825
Amide	1640–1680

Aryl refers to compounds containing a C_6 benzene ring.

Other types of bond absorb at different frequencies, but the actual value again depends on the neighbouring atoms and groups (Table 12.4).

Table 12.4 Absorption frequencies of some common groups

Bond	Functional group	Wavenumber/cm^{-1}
O–H	Alcohols (hydrogen bonded)*	3200–3600
	Alcohols (not hydrogen bonded)	3600–3700
	Carboxylic acids*	2500–3300
N–H	Amines (hydrogen bonded)*	3300–3500
C–H	Alkanes	2850–3000
	Alkenes and arenes	3000–3100
	Aldehydes*	2800–3000 and 2700–2750
C–C	Alkanes	1360–1490
C=O	See Table 12.3	
C=C	Alkenes	1650–1700

*These peaks are very broad because of intermolecular hydrogen bonding.

The region below about 1300 cm^{-1} is known as the fingerprint region. It shows a complex series of peaks that depends on the exact compound being analysed. Just as human fingerprints can be matched by computer to give a unique identification, so computer analysis of the fingerprint region can be used to identify a pure unknown organic substance.

In the infrared spectrum of propan-2-ol shown in Figure 12.6:

- the broad peak at around 3330 cm^{-1} is due to hydrogen-bonded O–H
- the peak at 2970 cm^{-1} is due to the C–H bonds
- the peak at 1380 cm^{-1} is due to the C–C bonds

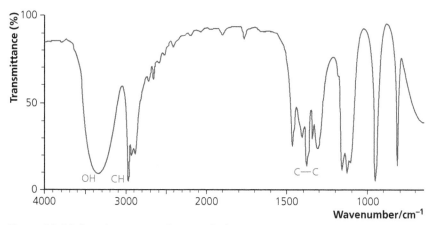

Figure 12.6 Infrared spectrum of propan-2-ol

Worked example

Examine the infrared spectrum of ethanoic acid.

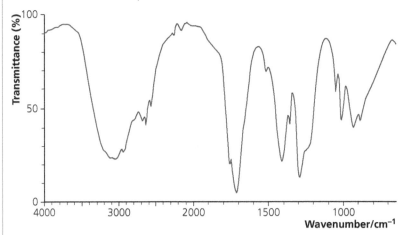

a) Assign the peaks at 3000 cm^{-1}, 1700 cm^{-1} and 1400 cm^{-1}.

b) Why is the peak at 3000 cm^{-1} very broad?

Answer

a) The peak at 3000 cm^{-1} is due to the O–H bond in the carboxylic acid group.

   The peak at 1700 cm^{-1} is due to the C=O bond in the carboxylic acid group.

   The peak at 1400 cm^{-1} is due to the C–C bond.

b) The peak at 3000 cm^{-1} is very broad because of the effects of intermolecular hydrogen bonding.

The absorption by C–H bonds is often masked by the broad peak due to the O–H bond at similar frequencies.

Test yourself

2 Suggest the wavenumbers of the peaks you would see in the range 3500–1600 cm^{-1} of the infrared spectrum of ethyl ethanoate, $CH_3COOCH_2CH_3$.

Success of reaction

Infrared spectroscopy can be used to show whether a reaction has taken place. The spectrum of the final product is compared with that of the original reactant. For example, if an alcohol is being oxidised to an aldehyde or a ketone, the peak between 3200 and 3600 cm^{-1} caused by the stretching of the O–H bond should not be found in the spectrum of the product, but a peak between 1700 and 1740 cm^{-1} due to the C=O bond should be clearly visible.

If butan-2-ol is heated with an oxidising agent, butanone should be produced. By looking at the spectra before and after the experiment (Figures 12.7 and 12.8) and comparing them with a library of spectra (www.aist.go.jp or www.rod.beavon.clara.net), it can be seen whether or not the oxidation took place.

Note that the broad peak due to O−H at 3350 cm⁻¹ has disappeared and a sharp peak at 1715 cm⁻¹ due to C=O has appeared. This confirms the oxidation of the CH(OH) group to a C=O group.

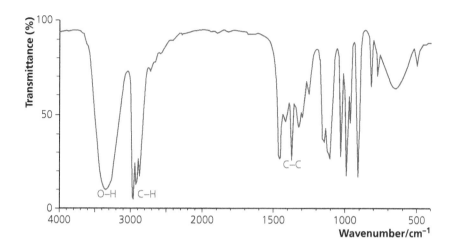

Figure 12.7 Infrared spectrum of butan-2-ol

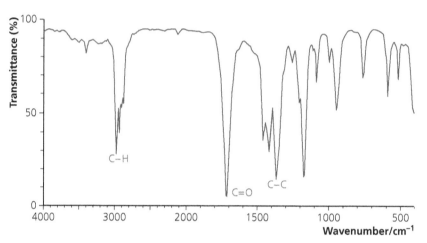

Figure 12.8 Infrared spectrum of butanone

Summary tasks

Make sure you can you identify:

- the fragments in a mass spectrum by their *m/z* ratio
- the bonds in a group that cause absorptions in infrared spectra, given a data booklet
- the formula of a substance given either or both of mass and infrared spectra

Questions

1 Bromine has two isotopes, ^{79}Br and ^{81}Br, in approximately equal proportions. Sketch the mass spectrum of bromine in the range m/z 155 to 165.

2 Ethanal, CH_3CHO, has a peak at $m/z = 29$ in its mass spectrum.
   a) Identify the species responsible for this peak.
   b) Write the equation for its formation.

3 The mass spectrum below is that of propanone.

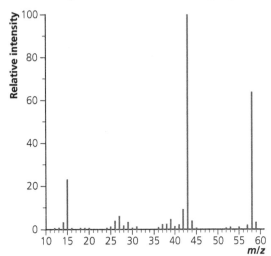

Identify the peaks at m/z values of 58, 43 and 15 and write equations to show the formation of the species responsible for these peaks.

4 Calculate the energy of 1 mol of photons of green light of frequency 5.7×10^{14} Hz.

(Avogadro constant = 6.02×10^{23} mol^{-1}; Planck's constant, $h = 6.63 \times 10^{-34}$ Js)

5 Calculate the frequency required to break a chlorine molecule homolytically.

(Cl–Cl bond enthalpy = +242 kJ mol^{-1}; Avogadro constant = 6.02×10^{23} mol^{-1}; Planck's constant, $h = 6.63 \times 10^{-34}$ Js)

6 Examine the infrared spectra A and B below. One spectrum is that of propanal; the other is that of propanoic acid.

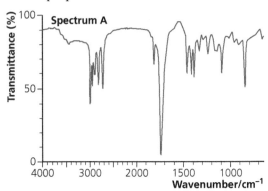

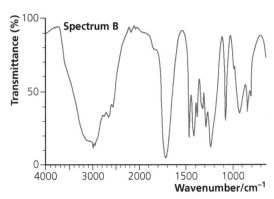

Identify the peaks in A at 1715 cm^{-1} and 1421 cm^{-1} and the peaks in B at 2986 cm^{-1}, 1716 cm^{-1} and 1416 cm^{-1}. Hence, decide which spectrum is that of propanoic acid.

Exam practice questions

1 a) Consider a mass spectrometer. State:
   i) how the positive ions are produced
   ii) how the ions are accelerated
   iii) how the ions are deflected (3)

b) A compound of molar mass $74\,\text{g}\,\text{mol}^{-1}$ has a molecular formula of $C_3H_6O_2$. It has been identified as either compound X, formula $CH_3CH(OH)CHO$, or compound Y, formula CH_2OHCH_2CHO. The mass spectrum has peaks at m/z values of 74, 29 and 31 but none at 15 or 59. Identify the compound. Justify your answer. (4)

c) Which would *not* produce a fragment at $m/z = 29$ in its mass spectrum?
   A $(CH_3)_2CHCHO$
   B $CH_2{=}CHCH(OH)CH_3$
   C $C_2H_5COCH_3$
   D $CH_2{=}C(OH)C_2H_5$ (1)

d) A substance has peaks in its mass spectrum at m/z values of 88, 45 and 29 and peaks in its infrared spectrum at $1715\,\text{cm}^{-1}$ and $3010\,\text{cm}^{-1}$. The substance is:
   A $CH_2OHCH{=}CHCH_2OH$
   B $CH_3CH_2CH_2COOH$
   C $(CH_3)_2CHCOOH$
   D $C_2H_5COCH_2OH$ (1)

(Total 9 marks)

2 a) Compound X of mass $1.10\,\text{g}$ was burnt in excess oxygen and $2.62\,\text{g}$ of carbon dioxide and $1.34\,\text{g}$ of water were produced. Calculate the empirical formula of X. (6)

b) It was found that the molecular formula of X is the same as its empirical formula.

i) When a small piece of sodium was added to X, a gas was evolved which ignited when lit.
   Identify the gas and state what this reaction tells about the nature of X. (2)

ii) When X is warmed with acidified potassium dichromate(VI), the orange solution goes green.
   Write the skeletal formulae of three compounds that could be X. (3)

iii) The mass spectrum of X had peaks at m/z of 74 and 31 but none at 29 or at 43.
   Identify X. Justify your choice. (2)

iv) Write the equation showing the formation of the species of $m/z = 31$ from the molecular ion. (2)

c) When the organic product of the reaction of X with sodium was added to water a strongly alkaline solution was obtained. Write the equation for this reaction. (2)

d) When X was reacted with acidified potassium dichromate(VI) two organic compounds could be produced. Write the structural formulae of these two compounds and state how infrared spectroscopy could distinguish between them. (3)

(Total 20 marks)

13 Energetics (Topic 8)

The **first law of thermodynamics** states that energy can neither be created nor destroyed. However, one form of energy can be converted into another. This law is sometimes called the **law of conservation of energy**. For example, when petrol burns in a car engine, the chemical energy of the petrol–air mixture is converted into the kinetic energy of the car, as well as into heat and sound.

There are various forms of energy:

- **Work** — when a force moves an object.
- **Kinetic energy** — the energy due to the motion of a body. The value is equal to half the mass of the body multiplied by the square of its speed.
- **Gravitational potential energy** — the energy due to the position of the object relative to the centre of the Earth. For example, the water in a reservoir is at a higher potential energy than the water below the dam.
- **Chemical potential energy** — the energy stored in a molecule that can be used to do work.
- **Radiant energy** — the energy in light and sound. Light of high frequency has more energy than low-frequency light of the same intensity. The energy of a photon of radiation is given by the expression $E = h\nu$, where h is Planck's constant and ν is the frequency of the radiation. A single photon of blue light has energy, $E = 6.63 \times 10^{-34} \times 6.4 \times 10^{14} = 4.2 \times 10^{-19}\,\text{J}$.
- **Electrical energy** — this can be in the form of electric potential energy or the energy due to an electric current.

> Radiation consists of a stream of packets of electromagnetic energy called photons. Visible light photons have more energy than infrared photons, because they have a higher frequency (for blue light, $\nu = 6.4 \times 10^{14}\,\text{Hz}$; for infrared radiation, ν is around $3.0 \times 10^{14}\,\text{Hz}$).

Einstein suggested that mass is related to energy by the equation $E = mc^2$, where c is the speed of light. The conversion of mass to energy only occurs during nuclear reactions, such as the emission of radioactivity, nuclear fission and nuclear fusion.

Heat is a form of kinetic energy. When an object is heated, the random motion of the atoms and molecules in that body increases. This motion can be in the form of vibration, rotation or the movement of molecules. Heat flows spontaneously from a hotter object to a colder object.

The SI unit of energy is the **joule**, symbol J, but the energy changes of chemical reactions are usually expressed in **kilojoules**, symbol kJ.

$$1\,\text{kJ} = 1000\,\text{J}$$

When a substance is heated, its temperature increases. The amount of heat transferred and the temperature change are given by the expression:

heat transferred = mass × specific heat capacity × the rise in temperature

$$\text{heat} = m \times c \times \Delta T$$

The two temperatures can be measured in degrees celsius, °C, or kelvin, K. The numerical value of ΔT is the same.

The specific heat capacity of water is $4.18\,\text{J}\,\text{g}^{-1}\,°\text{C}^{-1}$.

> **Tip**
>
> Do not confuse heat with temperature. Temperature is determined by the *average* energy of the random motion of the atoms and molecules. A beaker of water at 50°C is hotter than a bath full of water at 40°C, but the amount of heat energy in the bathwater is considerably greater than the heat energy of the water in the beaker.

Key term

The **specific heat capacity** of a substance is the heat required to increase the temperature of 1 g of the substance by 1°C.

Worked example

Calculate the heat required to increase the temperature of $100\,cm^3$ of water from 17.6°C to 50.5°C.

Answer

density of water $= 1\,g\,cm^{-3}$

mass of $100\,cm^3$ of water $= 100\,g$

$\Delta T = 50.5 - 17.6 = 32.9°C$

heat required $= m \times c \times \Delta T = 100\,g \times 4.18\,J\,g^{-1}\,°C^{-1} \times 32.9°C$

$\qquad = 13\,800\,J = 13.8\,kJ$

Test yourself

1 Calculate the temperature reached when 100 g of water at 18.2°C absorbs 9.45 kJ of heat energy. The specific heat capacity of water is $4.18\,J\,g^{-1}\,°C^{-1}$.

Enthalpy changes

Key terms

In an **exothermic** reaction, chemical energy is converted into heat energy and the temperature of the system rises.

In an **endothermic** reaction, heat energy is converted into chemical energy and the temperature of the system falls.

The **enthalpy**, H, is the chemical energy in the system at constant pressure that can be converted into heat.

All the chemical changes that are discussed in this chapter are carried out in a container that is open, such as a simple calorimeter. This means that the reactions take place at constant pressure (1 atm or 100 kPa).

When a chemical reaction takes place, chemical energy is interchanged with heat and work. If chemical energy is changed into heat energy, the chemicals become hot and heat then flows to the surroundings. Reactions that produce heat are said to be exothermic. For example, when a mixture of powdered aluminium and iron(III) oxide is heated, a violent reaction takes place. The temperature rises so much that the iron produced melts. This exothermic reaction is used to join railway lines together.

The term **system** is used in thermochemistry to represent the reaction mixture, including any solvent and the reaction vessel. The **surroundings** are everything outside the system, which in practice is the air in the room in which the experiment is taking place.

If, during a reaction, the mixture cools, the reaction is said to be endothermic. For example, when ethanoic acid is added to solid sodium hydrogencarbonate a rapid reaction takes place and the temperature drops considerably.

Thermite (exothermic) reaction creating molten iron

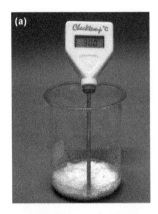

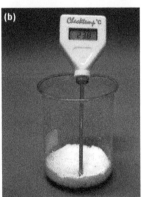

An example of an endothermic reaction – ethanoic acid and solid sodium hydrogencarbonate (a) at the start of the reaction and (b) after 15 minutes

Tip

It is essential to put state symbols into all thermochemical equations.

The release or absorption of heat energy by a system at constant pressure is caused by a change in the enthalpy of the chemicals.

Absolute enthalpy values cannot be found. The only value that can be measured is the difference in enthalpy when a reaction or physical change takes place. For example, when 1 mol of methane, CH_4, is burnt in excess oxygen, 890 kJ of heat energy is produced. This means that the enthalpy change, ΔH, is $-890\,kJ\,mol^{-1}$.

In a chemical change, the enthalpy of the products will be different from the enthalpy of the reactants. The change in enthalpy, ΔH, is given by:

$$\Delta H = H_{products} - H_{reactants}$$

If enthalpy is converted into heat energy (an *exothermic* reaction), the value of $H_{products}$ is less than $H_{reactants}$, so ΔH is *negative*. This is shown in an enthalpy level diagram (Figure 13.1). An enthalpy level diagram shows the enthalpy of the reactants and the products with the enthalpy change, ΔH, marked on the arrow, which always points from the enthalpy of the reactants to that of the products. It does *not* include the activation energy, which must be shown in a reaction profile diagram (see page 267).

If heat energy is converted into enthalpy (an *endothermic* reaction), the value of $H_{products}$ is greater than $H_{reactants}$, so ΔH is *positive*. This is shown in Figure 13.2.

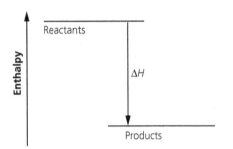

Figure 13.1 An enthalpy level diagram for an exothermic reaction

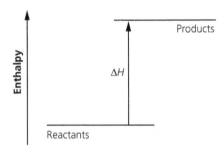

Figure 13.2 An enthalpy level diagram for an endothermic reaction

Test yourself

2 Draw a labelled enthalpy level diagram for the reaction:

$$S(s) + O_2(g) \rightarrow SO_2(g) \qquad \Delta H^\circ = -297\,kJ\,mol^{-1}$$

Thermochemical equations

A thermochemical equation is one that includes the value of ΔH as well as the chemical equation.

The thermochemical equation for the combustion of 1 mol of methane is:

$$CH_4(g) + 2O_2(g) \rightarrow CO_2(g) + 2H_2O(l) \quad \Delta H = -890\,kJ\,mol^{-1}$$

In practice, most enthalpy changes are quoted as **standard enthalpy changes**. This means that the heat produced is measured under **standard conditions**, which are:

- a pressure of 100 kPa, which is the same as 1 atm
- a stated temperature (usually 25°C which is 298 K)
- all solutions at a concentration of $1\,mol\,dm^{-3}$

- physical state of each substance in the change (for instance $C_{graphite}$ for carbon or $H_2O(l)$ for water)

The symbol for standard conditions is a superscript $\ominus$, as in $\Delta H^{\ominus}$.

Hot and cold packs

Self-heating soup tins have two compartments. One compartment contains the soup and the other contains solid calcium oxide and a sachet of water. When the sachet is broken, the water reacts with the calcium oxide in an exothermic reaction and the heat produced warms the soup in the inner container.

$$CaO(s) + H_2O(l) \rightarrow Ca(OH)_2(aq) \quad \Delta H = -80 \, kJ \, mol^{-1}$$

20 g of calcium oxide mixed with water causes the temperature of 200 cm^3 of soup to rise by about 25°C.

It is important that when an athlete pulls a muscle, a cold pack is applied quickly. One such pack consists of a divided plastic bag, one part of which contains a salt. The other part contains water. When crushed, the two mix and the salt dissolves endothermically. The salt most commonly used is ammonium nitrate:

$$NH_4NO_3(s) + aq \rightarrow NH_4^+(aq) + NO_3^-(aq) \quad \Delta H = +26 \, kJ \, mol^{-1}$$

20 g of ammonium nitrate causes the temperature of 100 cm^3 of water to fall by 15°C.

Hess's law

Hess's law is usually stated as:

The enthalpy change for any reaction is independent of the route taken from reactants to products.

Consider the cycle shown in Figure 13.3.

The enthalpy change from A + B *directly* to C + D is ΔH_1.

The enthalpy change from A + B to C + D *via* X and Y is $\Delta H_2 + \Delta H_3$.

Thus, by Hess's law:

$$\Delta H_1 = \Delta H_2 + \Delta H_3 \quad \text{or} \quad \Delta H_3 = \Delta H_1 - \Delta H_2$$

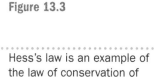

Figure 13.3

Hess's law is an example of the law of conservation of energy.

It is impossible to measure the enthalpy change directly for the reaction below because if the molar quantities as in the equation were used, a mixture of unburnt carbon, carbon monoxide and carbon dioxide would be formed.

$$C(s) + \tfrac{1}{2}O_2(g) \rightarrow CO(g)$$

However, by using excess oxygen, the enthalpy changes for the following reactions can be measured:

$$C(s) + O_2(g) \rightarrow CO_2(g) \quad \Delta H_1 = -394 \, kJ \, mol^{-1}$$

$$CO(g) + \tfrac{1}{2}O_2(g) \rightarrow CO_2(g) \quad \Delta H_2 = -283 \, kJ \, mol^{-1}$$

A Hess's law triangle can be drawn (Figure 13.4) and the enthalpy change for the first equation can be calculated.

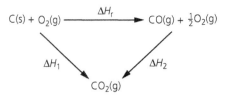

Figure 13.4

The enthalpy change from $C(s)$ to $CO_2(g)$ *directly* is ΔH_1.

The indirect enthalpy change from $C(s)$ to $CO_2(g)$ *via* $CO(g)$ is $\Delta H_r + \Delta H_2$.

By Hess's law these are equal, so:

$$\Delta H_1 = \Delta H_r + \Delta H_2$$

$$\Delta H_r = \Delta H_1 - \Delta H_2 = -394 - (-283) = -111 \, \text{kJ mol}^{-1}$$

This can also be shown by an enthalpy level diagram (Figure 13.5).

$$\Delta H_r + (-283) = -394$$

$$\Delta H_r = -394 + 283 = -111 \, \text{kJ mol}^{-1}$$

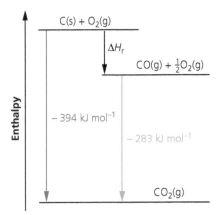

Figure 13.5

Worked example

Copper(II) sulfate exists as an anhydrous sulfate, $CuSO_4(s)$ and as a hydrated one, $CuSO_4.5H_2O(s)$.

The enthalpy change for the hydration of the anhydrous salt cannot be measured directly but can be calculated using Hess's law.

a) A polystyrene beaker was filled with 50.0 cm^3 of water and its temperature measured. Then 6.38 g of anhydrous copper(II) sulfate was added and the mixture stirred until all the solid had dissolved. The final temperature was measured. The temperature rose by 12.6°C.

Calculate the enthalpy change, ΔH_1, for the reaction:

$$CuSO_4(s) + aq \rightarrow CuSO_4(aq)$$

(Specific heat capacity of the solution = 4.18 J K^{-1} mol^{-1})

b) The experiment was repeated with 9.98 g of hydrated copper(II) sulfate. The temperature fell by 2.2°C. Calculate the enthalpy change, ΔH_2, for the reaction:

$$CuSO_4.5H_2O(s) + aq \rightarrow CuSO_4(aq)$$

c) Draw a Hess's law diagram and use it and the answers to (a) and (b) to calculate the enthalpy change for the reaction:

$$CuSO_4(s) + 5H_2O(l) \rightarrow CuSO_4.5H_2O(s)$$

d) Suggest one source of error in the method and explain how you would modify the experiment so as to remove this error.

Answer

a) amount (moles) of anhydrous salt $= \dfrac{\text{mass}}{\text{molar mass}} = \dfrac{6.38\,\text{g}}{159.5\,\text{g mol}^{-1}} = 0.0400\,\text{mol}$

heat transferred = mass × specific heat capacity × temperature change

$$= 50.0 \times 4.18 \times 12.6 = 2633\,\text{J} = 2.633\,\text{kJ}$$

$\Delta H_1 = \dfrac{\text{heat transferred}}{\text{moles}} = \dfrac{-2.633}{0.0400} = -65.8\,\text{kJ mol}^{-1}$

The value is negative because the temperature rose (reaction exothermic).

b) amount of hydrated salt $= \dfrac{9.98\,\text{g}}{249.5\,\text{g mol}^{-1}} = 0.0400\,\text{mol}$

heat transferred $= 50.0 \times 4.18 \times 2.2 = 459.8\,\text{J} = 0.4598\,\text{kJ}$

$\Delta H_2 = +\dfrac{0.4598}{0.400} = +11.5\,\text{kJ mol}^{-1}$

The value is positive because the temperature fell (reaction endothermic).

c)

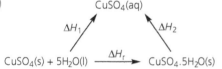

$$CuSO_4(s) + 5H_2O(l) \xrightarrow{\Delta H_r} CuSO_4.5H_2O(s)$$

$\Delta H_r = \Delta H_1 - \Delta H_2 = -65.8 - (+11.5) = -77.3\,\text{kJ mol}^{-1}$

d) The dissolving of the salts is slow and this will cause a significant heat loss in experiment 1. The experiment could be modified by measuring the temperature of the water at intervals of time, adding the anhydrous salt and then measuring the temperature at regular intervals. A graph of temperature against time would then be plotted and extrapolated to get a more accurate temperature rise.

Test yourself

3 Draw a Hess's law cycle and use it, together with the data given, to calculate the enthalpy change for the reaction:

$$P(s) + 1\tfrac{1}{2}Cl_2(g) \rightarrow PCl_3(l)$$

Data:

$$P(s) + 2\tfrac{1}{2}Cl_2(g) \rightarrow PCl_5(s) \qquad \Delta H^\ominus = -463\,\text{kJ mol}^{-1}$$

$$PCl_3(l) + Cl_2(g) \rightarrow PCl_5(s) \qquad \Delta H^\ominus = -124\,\text{kJ mol}^{-1}$$

Standard enthalpies

Standard enthalpy of formation, $\Delta H_f^{\ominus}$

> **Key term**
>
> The **standard enthalpy of formation** is the enthalpy change when *1 mol* of a substance is formed from its *elements* in their *standard* states at 100 kPa (1 atm) pressure and at a stated temperature, usually 298 K (25°C). The units are kJ mol^{-1}.

Standard state means the form in which the element is normally found under the quoted conditions of pressure and temperature. This means that bromine is a liquid and sulfur is a solid.

The standard enthalpy of formation of carbon monoxide is the heat change for the reaction:

$$C(s) + \tfrac{1}{2}O_2(g) \rightarrow CO(g)$$

The standard enthalpy of formation of ethanol is the heat change for the reaction:

$$2C(s) + 3H_2(g) + \tfrac{1}{2}O_2(g) \rightarrow C_2H_5OH(l)$$

> **Tip**
>
> Note that state symbols are always included in thermochemical equations. The value for the enthalpy of formation of gaseous ethanol is different from that for liquid ethanol:
>
> $\Delta H_f^{\ominus}$ (C$_2$H$_5$OH(l)) = -277.1 kJ mol^{-1}
>
> $\Delta H_f^{\ominus}$ (C$_2$H$_5$OH(g)) = -238.5 kJ mol^{-1}

Standard enthalpy of reaction, $\Delta H_r^{\ominus}$

> **Key term**
>
> The **standard enthalpy of reaction** is the enthalpy change when the number of moles of the substances in the equation *as written* react under standard conditions of 100 kPa (1 atm) pressure and a stated temperature, usually 298 K (25°C). The units are kJ mol^{-1}.

Consider the reaction:

$$2Na(s) + Cl_2(g) \rightarrow 2NaCl(s)$$

The enthalpy change for the reaction is the enthalpy change when 2 mol of solid sodium reacts with 1 mol of gaseous chlorine to produce 2 mol of solid sodium chloride. The value of $\Delta H_r^{\ominus}$ is -822 kJ.

Compare this with the reaction:

$$Na(s) + \tfrac{1}{2}Cl_2(g) \rightarrow NaCl(s)$$

The value of -411 kJ mol^{-1} is also $\Delta H_f^{\ominus}$ of NaCl(s)

The value of $\Delta H_r^{\ominus}$ is -411 kJ, which is half the value for the first reaction. This is because half the amounts of sodium and chlorine are reacting.

Calculation of enthalpy of reaction from standard enthalpy of formation data

The enthalpy of reaction can be calculated from the standard enthalpy of formation using a Hess's law cycle (Figure 13.6).

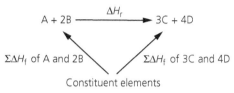

Figure 13.6

$$\Delta H_f \text{ of A} + 2 \times \Delta H_f \text{ of B} + \Delta H_r = 3 \times \Delta H_f \text{ of C} + 4 \times \Delta H_f \text{ of D}$$

$$\Delta H_r = [3\Delta H_f(C) + 4\Delta H_f(D)] - [(\Delta H_f(A) + 2\Delta H_f(B)]$$

A formula that enables the enthalpy of a reaction to be calculated from enthalpy of **formation** data is:

$$\Delta H_r = \Sigma \Delta H_f(\text{products}) - \Sigma \Delta H_f(\text{reactants})$$

> The symbol Σ means 'the sum of'.

> This 'formula' can *only* be used when enthalpy of **formation** data are given in the question.

Worked example

Use the data below to draw a Hess's law diagram and hence calculate the enthalpy change for the reaction:

$$CH_2=CH-CH=CH_2(g) + 2HBr(g) \rightarrow CH_3CHBrCHBrCH_3(g)$$

Substance	Enthalpy of formation/kJ mol^{-1}
Butadiene, $CH_2=CH-CH=CH_2(g)$	+162
Hydrogen bromide, HBr(g)	−36.4
2,3-dibromobutane, $CH_3CHBrCHBrCH_3(g)$	−103

> **Tip**
> The correct formulae and state symbols, including those of any elements, must be shown in the cycle.

Answer

$$CH_2=CH-CH=CH_2(g) + 2HBr(g) \xrightarrow{\Delta H_r} CH_3CHBrCHBrCH_3(g)$$

with ΔH_f (butadiene), $2 \times \Delta H_f$ (HBr), ΔH_f (2,3-dibromobutane) pointing to

$$4C(s) + 4H_2(g) + Br_2(l)$$

$$\Delta H_f(\text{butadiene}) + 2\Delta H_f(\text{HBr}) + \Delta H_r = \Delta H_f(\text{2,3-dibromobutane})$$

$$\Delta H_r = \Delta H_f(\text{2,3-dibromobutane}) - [\Delta H_f(\text{butadiene}) + 2\Delta H_f(\text{HBr})]$$

$$= -103 - [+162 + (2 \times -36.4)] = -192.2\,kJ\,mol^{-1}$$

If the question had not asked for a Hess's law diagram, the answer could have been obtained by using the formula:

$$\Delta H_r = \Sigma \Delta H_f(\text{products}) - \Sigma \Delta H_f(\text{reactants})$$

$$\Delta H_r = \Delta H_f(\text{2,3-dibromobutane}) - [\Delta H_f(\text{butadiene}) + 2\Delta H_f(\text{hydrogen bromide})]$$

$$= -103 - [+162 + (2 \times -36.4)] = -192.2\,kJ\,mol^{-1}$$

> Note that, because there are 2 mol of HBr in the equation, the cycle contains $2 \times \Delta H_f$ of HBr.

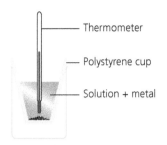

Thermometer

Polystyrene cup

Solution + metal

Figure 13.7 Experiment to determine enthalpy of reaction

Calculation of enthalpy of reaction from an experiment using an insulated container

If a reaction takes place at a reasonable rate at room temperature, the heat change can be measured using an expanded polystyrene cup as a calorimeter (Figure 13.7). Polystyrene is a thermal insulator. Not only does it minimise heat loss to the surroundings, it absorbs little heat itself. A polystyrene cup can be used when measuring the temperature change that occurs when zinc reacts with copper(II) sulfate solution according to the equation:

$$Zn(s) + CuSO_4(aq) \rightarrow ZnSO_4(aq) + Cu(s)$$

The enthalpy of the reaction is measured using the following procedure:

- A measured volume of copper(II) sulfate solution of known concentration is pipetted into an expanded polystyrene cup held in a glass beaker.
- Some powdered zinc metal is weighed out, such that the metal is in excess.
- The temperature of the aqueous copper(II) sulfate is measured every 30 seconds for 2 minutes. At 2.5 minutes, the powdered metal is tipped in.
- The solution is stirred and the temperature recorded every 30 seconds until a maximum temperature is reached, and then for a further 2 minutes.

Three quantities have to be evaluated before the enthalpy of the reaction can be calculated:

1 the **amount** (moles) of copper(II) sulfate that reacts:

    moles of copper(II) sulfate = concentration × volume in dm³

> An alternative method is to weigh the empty polystyrene cup, add the copper(II) sulfate solution and weigh it again. The difference is the mass of the copper(II) sulfate solution.

2 the **mass of solution** that was heated. This is assumed to be numerically the same as the volume in cm³.

3 the **temperature rise**. The reaction is slow, so some heat is lost to the surroundings during the experiment. This would be a significant source of error. To find a more accurate value of ΔT than simply the difference between the temperature at the start and that at the finish, a temperature–time graph is plotted and the value of ΔT found by extrapolation:
   - Draw a straight line through the first five points and extend (extrapolate) the line to at least 3 minutes.
   - Draw a straight line from the maximum to the final temperature and extrapolate it backwards to before the metal was added.
   - Measure the *difference* in height between these two lines at the time that the metal was added (2.5 minutes in the experiment described above). This height is ΔT (Figure 13.8).

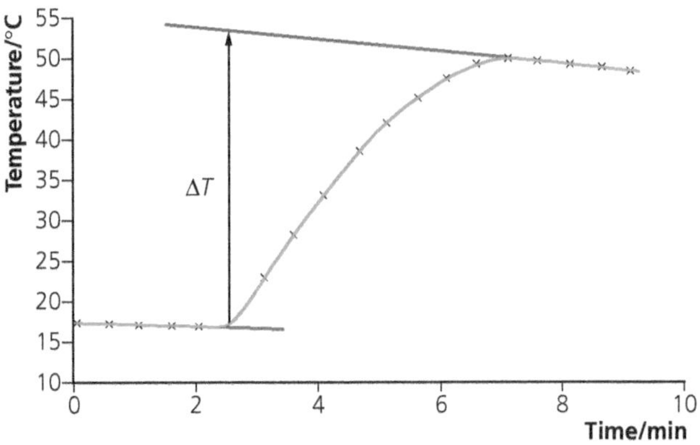

Assumptions

- It is assumed that the density of the solution is the same as pure water ($1\,g\,cm^{-3}$) and that its specific heat capacity is the same as that of water. Therefore, if $50.0\,cm^3$ of copper(II) sulfate solution had been used, the mass in the expression heat = $mc\Delta T$ would have been $50.0\,g$.
- The amount of heat absorbed by the polystyrene cup, the stirrer or the thermometer is negligible.

Figure 13.8 A temperature-time graph for determining enthalpy of reaction

Worked example

Use the data given to calculate the enthalpy of reaction for:

$$Fe(s) + CuSO_4(aq) \rightarrow FeSO_4(aq) + Cu(s)$$

In this experiment:

- volume of $1.00 \, mol \, dm^{-3}$ copper sulfate solution $= 50.0 \, cm^3$
- temperature rise (from Figure 13.8) $= 53.3 - 16.9 = 36.4°C$
- specific heat capacity of solution $= 4.18 \, J \, g^{-1} \, °C^{-1}$

Answer

mass of solution = volume × density

$$= 50.0 \, cm^3 \times 1 \, g \, cm^{-3} = 50.0 \, g$$

heat produced = mass × specific heat capacity × rise in temperature

$$= 50.0 \, g \times 4.18 \, J \, g^{-1} \, °C^{-1} \times 36.4°C$$

$$= 7610 \, J = 7.61 \, kJ$$

amount of copper sulfate taken $= 1.00 \, mol \, dm^{-3} \times \dfrac{50.0}{1000} \, dm^3$

$$= 0.0500 \, mol$$

heat produced per mol $= \dfrac{\text{heat produced}}{\text{number of moles}}$

$$= \dfrac{7.60 \, kJ}{0.0500 \, mol} = 152 \, kJ \, mol^{-1}$$

$$\Delta H_r = -152 \, kJ \, mol^{-1}$$

All the exams at AS and A level will contain questions on practical experiments that the student should have performed. These will be in the form of describing the method or evaluating the result in terms of assumptions made and possible sources of error.

Possible sources of error

- The reaction is slow, so some heat is lost to the surroundings. Extrapolating the graph, rather than calculating ΔT as $T_{max} - T_{start}$, allows for most of this heat loss. The error makes the experimentally determined value of ΔH_r less exothermic than the correct value.
- Some heat will be absorbed by the iron metal and by the thermometer. This also makes the experimentally determined value of ΔH_r less exothermic than the correct value.

A lid on the calorimeter would help to reduce heat loss.

Rapid reactions

A similar method, but without measuring the temperature over a period of time, can be used for any rapid reaction that takes place in solution — for example, the precipitation of insoluble salts such as barium sulfate.

- Measure out $25.0\,cm^3$ of $1.0\,mol\,dm^{-3}$ barium chloride solution into a polystyrene cup and measure its temperature.
- Measure out $25.0\,cm^3$ of $1.1\,mol\,dm^{-3}$ sulfuric acid solution into a beaker and measure its temperature.
- Average the two temperatures.
- Pour the contents of the beaker into the polystyrene cup, stir the mixture with the thermometer and measure the temperature reached.

Calculation

mass of solution = $50.0\,g$

specific heat of solution = $4.18\,J\,g^{-1}\,^{\circ}C^{-1}$

temperature change = final temperature − mean temperature

heat transferred = $50.0\,g \times 4.18\,J\,g^{-1}\,^{\circ}C^{-1} \times$ temperature change

amount of Ba^{2+} ions reacted = $1.0 \times \dfrac{25.0}{1000} = 0.0250\,mol$

This reaction is exothermic so the sign of ΔH is negative.

$$\Delta H = \frac{\pm\ \text{heat transferred}}{0.0250}\,J\,mol^{-1}$$

There is no need to plot a temperature time curve, because the reaction is rapid and the heat loss to the surroundings is negligible.

Standard enthalpy of combustion, $\Delta H_c^{\ominus}$

> ### Key term
> The **standard enthalpy of combustion** is the enthalpy change when *1 mol* of the substance is burnt in *excess* oxygen under *standard conditions* of 100 kPa (1 atm) pressure and a stated temperature (usually 25°C). The units are $kJ\,mol^{-1}$.

Tip

Note that all combustion reactions are exothermic, and so all ΔH_c values are negative.

The standard enthalpy of combustion for ethanol is the enthalpy change when 1 mol of ethanol reacts according to the equation:

$$C_2H_5OH(l) + 3O_2(g) \rightarrow 2CO_2(g) + 3H_2O(l)$$

For ethane, it is the enthalpy change when 1 mol of ethane reacts according to the equation:

$$C_2H_6(g) + 3\tfrac{1}{2}O_2(g) \rightarrow 2CO_2(g) + 3H_2O(l)$$

> **Tip**
>
> There must only be 1 mol of the substance on the left-hand side in an enthalpy of combustion equation. The normal balanced equation for the combustion of ethane is:
>
> $$2C_2H_6(g) + 7O_2(g) \rightarrow 4CO_2(g) + 6H_2O(l)$$
>
> Therefore, for the enthalpy of combustion of ethane, this equation must be halved, so that there is only 1 mol of ethane on the left-hand side:
>
> $$C_2H_6(g) + 3\tfrac{1}{2}O_2(g) \rightarrow 2CO_2(g) + 3H_2O(l)$$

Experimental method to find the enthalpy of combustion of a liquid

To find the enthalpy of combustion of a liquid, a known mass of the liquid is burnt and the heat produced used to warm up a known volume of water. An appropriate laboratory apparatus is shown in Figure 13.9. The following procedure is used:

- The spirit burner containing the liquid is weighed.
- A known volume of water is added to the copper calorimeter.
- The temperature of the water in the calorimeter is measured every minute for 4 minutes.
- The burner is lit after 4.5 minutes.
- The temperature of the water is measured every minute.
- When the temperature has reached about 20°C above room temperature, the flame in the spirit burner is extinguished and the burner immediately reweighed.
- The temperature readings are stopped 5 minutes after the temperature has reached a maximum value.

Three quantities have to be evaluated before the enthalpy of combustion can be calculated:

- the **mass of water** that was heated. The density of water is $1\,g\,cm^{-3}$. Therefore, if $100\,cm^3$ of water had been measured out, the mass would have been $100\,g$.

- the **temperature rise**. A significant amount of heat is lost during the experiment, so to find a more accurate value of ΔT, a temperature–time graph is plotted and the value of ΔT found by extrapolation:

  - Draw a straight line through the first five points and extend (extrapolate) it to at least 3 minutes.
  - Draw a straight line from the maximum temperature to the final temperature and extrapolate it backwards to before the time when the burner was lit.
  - Measure the difference in heights between these two lines at the time when the heating started. This difference is ΔT (Figure 13.10).

- the **amount in moles** of ethanol burnt. The mass of ethanol used is the mass of the burner and ethanol at the start minus the mass after burning:

$$\text{amount in moles} = \frac{\text{mass used}}{\text{molar mass}}$$

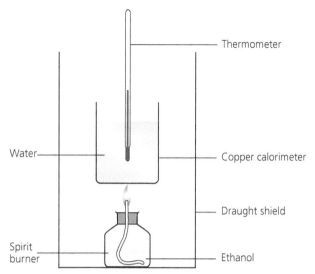

Figure 13.9 Apparatus used to determine the enthalpy of combustion of a liquid

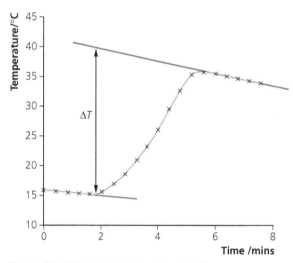

Figure 13.10 A temperature-time graph for determining enthalpy of combustion

Worked example

Use the data given to calculate the enthalpy of combustion of ethanol. The equation is:

$$C_2H_5OH(l) + 3O_2(g) \rightarrow 2CO_2(g) + 3H_2O(l)$$

In this experiment:

- mass of water = 100 g
- temperature rise (from Figure 13.10) = 24.6°C
- mass of ethanol burnt = 0.388 g

The specific heat capacity of water is $4.18\,J\,g^{-1}\,°C^{-1}$.

Answer

heat transferred = mass of water heated × specific heat capacity of water × ΔT

$$= 100\,g \times 4.18\,J\,g^{-1}\,^{\circ}C^{-1} \times 24.6^{\circ}C = 10\,282\,J = 10.28\,kJ$$

$$\text{amount of ethanol burnt} = \frac{\text{mass}}{\text{molar mass}} = \frac{0.388\,g}{46\,g\,mol^{-1}} = 0.00843\,mol$$

$$\text{heat transferred per mol} = \frac{\text{heat produced}}{\text{number of moles}} = \frac{10.28\,kJ}{0.00843\,mol}$$

$$= 1219\,kJ\,mol^{-1}$$

ΔH_c of ethanol $= -1219 = -1.22 \times 10^3\,kJ\,mol^{-1}$ (3 significant figures)

Possible sources of error

The experimentally determined value in the example ($-1220\,kJ\,mol^{-1}$) is less exothermic than the accepted data book value. This is caused by a number of factors:

- As the experiment takes a long time, not all the heat lost to the surroundings is compensated for by the extrapolation of the graph.
- Some of the heat released in burning heats up the air and not the water.
- The beaker absorbs some of the heat produced.
- Some of the ethanol may not burn completely to carbon dioxide and water. (Incomplete combustion would cause black soot to be deposited on the bottom of the beaker.)
- The conditions are not standard. Water vapour, and not liquid water, is produced.

These errors result in less heat being absorbed by the water, so the value for ΔT is too low. Hence, the value calculated for ΔH_c is less negative.

Calculation of standard enthalpy of formation from combustion enthalpy data

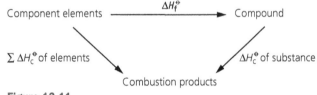

Figure 13.11

Many enthalpies of formation cannot be measured directly. However, their values can be calculated from enthalpy of combustion data, using Hess's law (Figure 13.11).

$$\Delta H_f^{\ominus} + \Delta H_c^{\ominus} \text{ of compound} = \Sigma \text{ of } \Delta H_c^{\ominus} \text{ of elements}$$

$$\Delta H_f^{\ominus} = \Sigma \Delta H_c^{\ominus} \text{ of elements} - \Delta H_c^{\ominus} \text{ of compound}$$

Worked example

Calculate the enthalpy of formation of ethanol, C_2H_5OH, given the following enthalpy of combustion data:

Substance	$\Delta H_c^{\ominus}/kJ\,mol^{-1}$
Ethanol, $C_2H_5OH(l)$	−1371
Carbon, C(s)	−394
Hydrogen, $H_2(g)$	−286

The Hess's law cycle is:

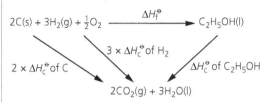

$$2 \times \Delta H_c^\ominus \text{ of } C + 3 \times \Delta H_c^\ominus \text{ of } H_2 = \Delta H_f^\ominus \text{ of ethanol} + \Delta H_c^\ominus \text{ of ethanol}$$

$$\Delta H_f^\ominus \text{ of ethanol} = 2 \times (-394) + 3 \times (-286) - (-1371) = -275 \, \text{kJ mol}^{-1}$$

The sum of the enthalpies of combustion of the elements equals the sum of the enthalpy changes via the formation of ethanol, and its combustion.

Test yourself

4 Write the equation that represents the standard enthalpy of formation of glucose, $C_6H_{12}O_6(s)$, and calculate its value using the values of standard enthalpies of combustion below.

Substance	$\Delta H_c^\ominus / \text{kJ mol}^{-1}$
Carbon, C(s)	–393.5
Hydrogen, $H_2(g)$	–285.8
Glucose, $C_6H_{12}O_6(s)$	–2816

Standard enthalpy of neutralisation, $\Delta H_{neut}^\ominus$

For hydrochloric acid, the standard enthalpy of neutralisation is the enthalpy change represented by:

$$HCl(aq) + NaOH(aq) \rightarrow NaCl(aq) + H_2O(l)$$

For sulfuric acid, it is the enthalpy change for:

$$\tfrac{1}{2}H_2SO_4(aq) + NaOH(aq) \rightarrow \tfrac{1}{2}Na_2SO_4(aq) + H_2O(l)$$

All strong acids are completely ionised in solution. Therefore, the ionic equation representing the enthalpy of the neutralisation of any strong acid by a strong base is:

$$H^+(aq) + OH^-(aq) \rightarrow H_2O(l) \qquad \Delta H^\ominus = -57.9 \, \text{kJ mol}^{-1}$$

Key term

The **standard enthalpy of neutralisation** is the enthalpy change when *1 mol of water is produced* by the neutralisation of a solution of an acid by *excess* base under standard conditions, with all solutions of concentration $1 \, \text{mol dm}^{-3}$. The units are kJ mol^{-1}.

Experimental method to find the enthalpy of neutralisation of an acid

The acid should have a concentration of $1.00 \, \text{mol dm}^{-3}$. The alkali used to neutralise it must be in slight excess, so that all the acid reacts. The following procedure is used:

- Using a pipette, measure out $25.0 \, \text{cm}^3$ of the $1.00 \, \text{mol dm}^{-3}$ acid solution into an expanded polystyrene cup.
- Measure the temperature of the acid.
- Measure the temperature of the alkali (usually sodium hydroxide solution of concentration $1.1 \, \text{mol dm}^{-3}$).
- Calculate the mean of the two temperatures.
- Measure out $25.0 \, \text{cm}^3$ of the alkali using a pipette, and add it to the acid solution.
- Stir the mixture with the thermometer and measure the maximum temperature reached.

An alternative method uses measuring cylinders to measure out the acid and the alkali. Weigh the polystyrene cup before and after addition of the solutions.

The reaction is instantaneous, so the heat lost to the surroundings is negligible. This is why a temperature–time graph is not needed.

The results of an experiment to find the enthalpy of neutralisation of hydrochloric acid were:

- volume of $1.00 \, mol \, dm^{-3}$ hydrochloric acid = $25.0 \, cm^3$
- volume of $1.1 \, mol \, dm^{-3}$ sodium hydroxide = $25.0 \, cm^3$
- initial temperature of acid = $17.4°C$
- initial temperature of alkali = $17.2°C$
- maximum temperature after mixing = $24.1°C$

(Specific heat capacity of the final solution = $4.18 \, J g^{-1} °C^{-1}$)

Calculate the enthalpy of neutralisation.

Answer

average starting temperature = $\frac{1}{2}(17.4 + 17.2) = 17.3°C$

$\Delta T = 24.1 - 17.3 = 6.8°C$

volume of solution that absorbed heat = $25.0 + 25.0 = 50.0 \, cm^3$

mass of solution = volume × density

$$= 50.0 \, cm^3 \times 1.00 \, g \, cm^{-3} = 50.0 \, g$$

heat transferred = mass × specific heat capacity × rise in temperature

$$= 50.0 \, g \times 4.18 \, J g^{-1} °C^{-1} \times 6.8°C$$

$$= 1421 \, J = 1.421 \, kJ$$

amount of acid = concentration × volume in dm^3

$$= 1.00 \, mol \, dm^{-3} \times \frac{25.0 \, dm^3}{1000} = 0.0250 \, mol$$

heat transferred per mole = $\dfrac{heat \, produced}{number \, of \, moles} = \dfrac{1.421 \, kJ}{0.0250 \, mol} = 56.8$

$$= 57 \, kJ mol^{-1} \text{ (to 2 s.f.)}$$

$\Delta H^{\ominus}_{neut} = -57 \, kJ \, mol^{-1}$

The mass in the 'heat produced' expression is the total mass of the solution (50.0 g), not the mass of the hydrochloric acid.

The temperature rose, so the reaction is exothermic. Therefore ΔH is *negative*.

The answer should only be given to 2 significant figures because ΔT is only measured to 2 significant figures.

Sources of error

The experimentally derived value for the standard enthalpy of neutralisation is slightly low because of heat absorbed by the polystyrene cup and by the thermometer.

5 Write the equation that represents the standard enthalpy changes of neutralisation of a) ethanoic acid, CH_3COOH and b) carbonic acid H_2CO_3.

Standard enthalpy of atomisation, $\Delta H_a^{\ominus}$

Key term

The **standard enthalpy of atomisation** of an element is the enthalpy change when *1 mol* of *gaseous* atoms is formed from the element in its standard state at 100 kPa (1 atm) pressure and a stated temperature (usually 298 K). The units are $kJ \, mol^{-1}$.

For bromine, it is the enthalpy change involved in the reaction:

$$\tfrac{1}{2}Br_2(l) \rightarrow Br(g)$$

For sodium, it is the enthalpy change involved in the reaction:

$$Na(s) \rightarrow Na(g)$$

Test yourself

6 Write the equation that represents the standard enthalpy change of atomisation of white phosphorus, P_4.

Bond enthalpy, ΔH_B

The mean A–B bond enthalpy is the average of the A–B bond enthalpies in a variety of molecules. For the mean O–H bond enthalpy it is the average of the O–H bond enthalpy in H_2O, the O–H bond enthalpy in CH_3OH and the O–H bond enthalpy in CH_3COOH etc.

The H–H bond enthalpy is the enthalpy change for:

$$H_2(g) \rightarrow 2H(g) \qquad \Delta H_B = +436\,kJ\,mol^{-1}$$

Some bond enthalpy values are given in Table 13.1. These are *average* values. For example, the C–H bond enthalpy is the average of the C–H bonds in methane, ethane, ethanol and so on.

Key term

Bond enthalpy is the enthalpy change when the bond in a gaseous molecule is broken. The units are $kJ\,mol^{-1}$.

Table 13.1 Some average bond enthalpies

Bond	Average bond enthalpy/kJ mol^{-1}	Bond	Average bond enthalpy/kJ mol^{-1}
C–C	+348	H–H	+436
C=C	+612	H–Cl	+431
C–H	+413	H–Br	+366
C–O	+360	H–I	+299
C=O	+743	O–H	+463
C–Cl	+338	Cl–Cl	+242
C–Br	+276	Br–Br	+193
C–I	+238	I–I	+151

The C–H bond enthalpy in methane is one-quarter of the total enthalpy change for:

$$CH_4(g) \rightarrow C(g) + 4H(g) \qquad \Delta H = +1740\,kJ\,mol^{-1}$$

$$\Delta H_B(C–H) = \frac{1740}{4} = +435\,kJ\,mol^{-1}$$

$$\Delta H_B(C–H) \text{ in ethane} = +420\,kJ\,mol^{-1}$$

The *average* C–H bond enthalpy in a large number of organic compounds is $+413\,kJ\,mol^{-1}$. If a bond enthalpy is worked out for a particular compound, the value obtained is slightly different from the average value.

Tip

Biologists sometimes refer to 'high-energy bonds' in ATP and the release of energy when a phosphate residue is removed from ATP and ADP is formed. This is an oversimplification. The breaking of the P–O bond as ATP is converted to ADP is endothermic. However, energy is then released in the hydration of the phosphate and hydrogen ions, making the overall process exothermic.

Calculation of enthalpy of reaction from average bond enthalpies

The simplest way to do this type of calculation is in three steps.

Step 1: list all the bonds broken. Write down the energy required (a **positive** number) to break each bond. Add, to find the total energy required.

Step 2: list the bonds made. Write down the energy released (a **negative** number) to make each bond. Add, to find the total energy released.

Step 3: add the two totals to give $\Delta H_r^{\ominus}$.

Tip

Bond breaking is endothermic; bond making is exothermic.

Tip

If you have any difficulty deciding which bonds break in the reaction, break *all* the bonds in the reactants and then make *all* the bonds in the products.

This is not a very accurate way of calculating $\Delta H_{reaction}$ as average bond enthalpies are used. For example, the C=C bond enthalpy in propene is not quite the same as the mean C=C bond enthalpy.

Given the enthalpy change for one of its reactions and all other relevant bond enthalpies, the bond enthalpy in a compound can be calculated by assigning it to an unknown, *z*, and proceeding as in Worked example 2.

Worked example 1

Use the data in Table 13.1 to calculate the enthalpy of the reaction:

Answer

Step 1:

Bonds broken	Bond enthalpy
C=C	+612
Cl–Cl	+242
Total	**+854**

Step 2:

Bonds made	Bond enthalpy
C–C	–348
2 × C–Cl	2 × (–338)
Total	**–1024**

Step 3: $\Delta H_r^{\ominus} = +854 + (-1024) = -170\,\text{kJ mol}^{-1}$

Worked example 2

Given the data in Table 13.1 and the enthalpy change of the reaction between buta-1,3-diene and chlorine, calculate the C=C bond enthalpy in buta-1,3-diene.

Answer

Let the C=C bond enthalpy in buta-1,3-diene = *z*.

Step 1:

Bonds broken	Bond enthalpy
2 × C=C	2z
2 × Cl–Cl	2 × (+242) = 484
Total	**(2z + 484)**

Step 2:

Bonds made	Bond enthalpy
2 × C–C	2 × (–348) = –696
4 × C–Cl	4 × (–338) = –1352
Total	**–2048**

Step 3: $\Delta H_r^{\ominus} = -328 = (2z + 484) - 2048$

$2z = -328 - 484 + 2048 = +1236$

C=C bond enthalpy in buta-1,3-diene = z

$$= \frac{+1236}{2} = +618\,kJ\,mol^{-1}$$

There is no need to break the six C–H bonds and then remake them in the product. Remember that there are two C=C bonds in buta-1,3-diene.

The bond that is likely to be broken in a chemical reaction can be indicated by bond enthalpies. For example, when hydroxide ions are added to iodomethane, either a C–H or the C–I bond could be broken and a new C–OH bond formed. The bond enthalpies of the two bonds are:

$+413\,kJ\,mol^{-1}$ for C–H   and $+238\,kJ\,mol^{-1}$ for C–I

The weaker C–I bond is the one predicted to break. This is borne out by the fact that methanol, CH_3OH, is formed rather than iodomethanol, $CH_2C(OH)I$ (Figure 13.12).

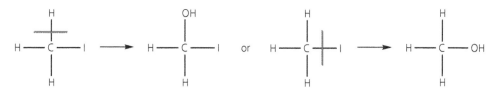

Figure 13.12

Bond enthalpies can also be used to predict relative rates of reaction.

Test yourself

7 Using the average bond enthalpies given in the table, calculate the enthalpy change for the reaction:

$CH_3CH=CH_2(g) + HBr(g) \rightarrow CH_3CHBrCH_3(g)$

Bond	$\Delta H_B/kJ\,mol^{-1}$	Bond	$\Delta H_B/kJ\,mol^{-1}$
C–C	+348	C–Br	+276
C=C	+612	H–Br	+366
C–H	+413		

Worked example

Use the data in Table 13.1 to predict the relative rates of the reaction of hydroxide ions with 1-chloropropane, 1-bromopropane and 1-iodopropane:

$CH_3CH_2CH_2X + OH^- \rightarrow CH_3CH_2CH_2OH + X^-$

where X is a halogen atom.

Enthalpy titrations

The concentration of a solution of an acid can be determined by measuring the temperature change when an alkaline solution of known concentration is added gradually, until it is in excess.

The method is as follows:

- Pipette $25.0\,cm^3$ of the acid solution into an expanded polystyrene cup.
- Measure the temperature of the acid.
- Add a standard $1.00\,mol\,dm^{-3}$ solution of sodium hydroxide from a burette in $2\,cm^3$ portions, stirring and measuring the temperature after each addition.
- Continue to add a further $8\,cm^3$ of the sodium hydroxide after the maximum temperature has been reached.
- Plot a graph of temperature against volume of sodium hydroxide.

To find the volume of alkali required for neutralisation, a line is drawn through the points up to one reading before the maximum temperature and then extrapolated. Another line is drawn from the maximum temperature to the last reading and extrapolated back. The point at which the two extrapolated lines intersect is the volume needed for neutralisation. For example, using the data in Figure 13.13, the volume needed for neutralisation is $20.6\,cm^3$.

Figure 13.13 An enthalpy titration graph

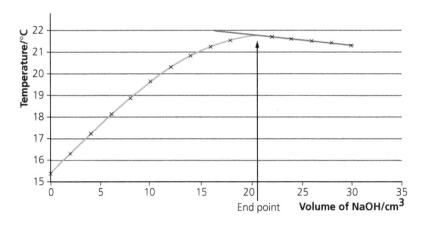

Worked example

In an enthalpy titration, the volume of alkali needed to neutralise $25\,cm^3$ of dilute hydrochloric acid was $20.6\,cm^3$. The equation for the reaction is:

$$HCl + NaOH \rightarrow NaCl + H_2O$$

Calculate the concentration of the acid.

Summary tasks

Make sure that you:

- know the definitions of $\Delta H_{\text{formation}}$, $\Delta H_{\text{reaction}}$, $\Delta H_{\text{combustion}}$, $\Delta H_{\text{neutralisation}}$, $\Delta H_{\text{atomisation}}$ and bond energy, including what the standard conditions are
- can draw a Hess's law diagram and be able to use it to calculate $\Delta H_{\text{reaction}}$ from $\Delta H_{\text{formation}}$ data, and vice versa
- can write the expression connecting heat change with temperature change and then use it to calculate $\Delta H_{\text{reaction}}$ or $\Delta H_{\text{neutralisation}}$
- can evaluate the change in temperature by extrapolation of a temperature/time graph
- know the experimental details of measuring temperature change for reactions in solution and when determining $\Delta H_{\text{combustion}}$
- can calculate $\Delta H_{\text{reaction}}$ from bond enthalpy data, and vice versa

Questions

1 Draw a labelled enthalpy level diagram for the reaction:

$6CO_2(aq) + 6H_2O(l) \rightarrow C_6H_{12}O_6(aq) + 6O_2(g)$
$\Delta H^\ominus = +2800 \, \text{kJ mol}^{-1}$

2 Draw a Hess's law diagram and calculate the enthalpy change for the reaction:

$C_2H_4(g) + H_2O(l) \rightarrow C_2H_5OH(l)$

Standard enthalpies of formation are given in the table below.

Substance	$\Delta H_f^\ominus / \text{kJ mol}^{-1}$
Ethene, $C_2H_4(g)$	+52.3
Water, $H_2O(l)$	−286
Ethanol, $C_2H_5OH(l)$	−278

3 Write the equation that represents the standard enthalpy of formation of glucose, $C_6H_{12}O_6(s)$,

and calculate its value. Standard enthalpies of combustion are given in the table below.

Substance	$\Delta H_c^\ominus / \text{kJ mol}^{-1}$
Carbon, $C(s)$	−393.5
Hydrogen, $H_2(g)$	−285.8
Glucose, $C_6H_{12}O_6(s)$	−2816

4 Write the thermochemical equation that represents the standard enthalpy of neutralisation of:
   a) nitric acid, $HNO_3(aq)$
   b) ethanedioic acid, $H_2C_2O_4(aq)$

5 Explain why the standard enthalpy of neutralisation of strong acids by aqueous sodium hydroxide is always close to $-58 \, \text{kJ mol}^{-1}$.

6 Calculate the C–Cl bond enthalpy in CH_2ClCH_2Cl, given the bond enthalpies in the table and the standard enthalpy of the reaction:

$$CH_2=CH_2(g) + Cl_2(g) \rightarrow CH_2ClCH_2Cl(g)$$
$$\Delta H_r = -217.4 \, kJ \, mol^{-1}$$

Bond	$\Delta H_B/kJ\,mol^{-1}$	Bond	$\Delta H_B/kJ\,mol^{-1}$
C–C	+348	C–H	+413
C=C	+612	Cl–Cl	+242

7 Plan an experiment that would enable you to calculate the exothermic enthalpy of dissolving anhydrous copper(II) sulfate, $CuSO_4(s)$, in water. The equation for the process, which is slow, can be represented by:

$$CuSO_4(s) + aq \rightarrow CuSO_4(aq)$$

Your answer should include what you would do, what measurements you would take and how you would use those measurements to calculate the enthalpy change.

8 Plan an experiment that would enable you to calculate the enthalpy change for the decomposition of calcium carbonate:

$$CaCO_3(s) \rightarrow CaO(s) + CO_2(g)$$

You are supplied with samples of calcium oxide, calcium carbonate and dilute hydrochloric acid, plus any laboratory equipment that you might require.

9 Ethanoic acid, CH_3COOH, is a weak acid. Therefore, its standard enthalpy of neutralisation is less exothermic than that of a strong acid. Use the following experimental data to calculate the standard enthalpy of neutralisation of a $1.00 \, mol \, dm^{-3}$ solution of ethanoic acid:
- volume of $1.00 \, mol \, dm^{-3}$ ethanoic acid solution = $40.0 \, cm^3$
- volume of $1.10 \, mol \, dm^{-3}$ sodium hydroxide solution = $40.0 \, cm^3$
- mass of mixed solution after the experiment = $80.0 \, g$

- average temperature of reactant solution at start = $18.5°C$
- maximum temperature after mixing = $24.9°C$

The specific heat capacity of the solution is $4.18 \, J \, g^{-1} \, °C^{-1}$.

10 A spirit burner was filled with methanol and weighed. It was then lit and placed underneath a beaker containing $175 \, cm^3$ of water at $18.5°C$. After a few minutes, the spirit lamp was blown out and the temperature of the water was found to be $40.2°C$. The burner was reweighed and was found to be $0.85 \, g$ lighter than at the start.

The density of water is $1.00 \, g \, cm^{-3}$ and its specific heat capacity is $4.18 \, J \, g^{-1} \, °C^{-1}$.

The equation for this combustion reaction is:

$$CH_3OH(l) + 1\tfrac{1}{2}O_2(g) \rightarrow CO_2(g) + 2H_2O(g)$$

a) Calculate the enthalpy of combustion of methanol, CH_3OH.
b) The data book value for the standard enthalpy of combustion of methanol is $-726 \, kJ \, mol^{-1}$. Give three reasons why this is significantly more exothermic than the value calculated from the experiment.

11 Propane gas, $C_3H_6(g)$, was burnt in a modified Bunsen burner that contained a flow meter to measure the volume of gas burnt. This was set up under a beaker containing $100 \, g$ of water, initially at $19.4°C$. After $208 \, cm^3$ of gas had been burnt, the temperature of the water had risen to $61.5°C$.

Calculate the enthalpy of combustion of propane gas.

Data:

Under the conditions of the experiment, 1 mol of gas has a volume of $24.0 \, dm^3$.

The specific heat capacity of water is $4.18 \, J \, g^{-1} \, °C^{-1}$.

Exam practice questions

1 Magnesium reacts with aqueous copper sulfate.

a) Write the ionic equation for this reaction. Include state symbols in your answer. (1)

b) The experiment was carried out in a beaker and the temperature change measured.

5 g (an excess) of magnesium was added to 25 cm³ of a 0.500 mol dm⁻³ solution of copper sulfate. The temperature rose from 18.3°C to 52.4°C.

(Assume that the solution has a density of 1.0 g cm⁻³ and a specific heat capacity of 4.2 J g⁻¹ °C⁻¹.)

i) The amount of heat produced, in joules, is:

A 3581   **C** 5502
B 4297   **D** 6602   (1)

ii) The amount (in moles) of copper sulfate that reacted is:

A 0.0125
B 0.02
C 0.05
D 12.5   (1)

c) In another experiment, 0.104 mol of copper sulfate reacted with excess magnesium and produced 29 790 J of heat energy. The enthalpy change, ΔHr, is:

A +286 kJ mol⁻¹
B −286 kJ mol⁻¹
C +286 000 kJ mol⁻¹
D −286 000 kJ mol⁻¹   (1)

(Total 4 marks)

2 a) Define the term **standard enthalpy of formation** as applied to butane, $C_4H_{10}(g)$. (3)

b) Which equation represents the change when the standard enthalpy of combustion of butane is measured?

A $C_4H_{10}(g) + O_2(g) \rightarrow C_4H_{10}O_2(l)$
B $2C_4H_{10}(g) + 9O_2(g) \rightarrow$
$\qquad 8CO(g) + 10H_2O(l)$
C $2C_4H_{10}(g) + 13O_2(g) \rightarrow$
$\qquad 8CO_2(g) + 10H_2O(l)$
D $C_4H_{10}(g) + 6\frac{1}{2}O_2(g) \rightarrow$
$\qquad 4CO_2(g) + 5H_2O(l)$ (1)

c) i) When methane, CH_4, burns, the products are carbon dioxide and water vapour:

$CH_4(g) + 2O_2(g) \rightarrow CO_2(g) + 2H_2O(g)$
$\Delta H = -803 \text{ kJ mol}^{-1}$

ΔH_f of $CO_2(g)$ is −394 kJ mol⁻¹
ΔH_f of $CH_4(g)$ is −75 kJ mol⁻¹
The enthalpy of formation of $H_2O(g)$ is:

A −484 kJ mol⁻¹
B +484 kJ mol⁻¹
C −242 kJ mol⁻¹
D +242 kJ mol⁻¹   (1)

ii) Ignoring the sign, would the enthalpy of formation of $H_2O(l)$ be numerically:

A greater than that for $H_2O(g)$?
B less than that for $H_2O(g)$?
C the same at a temperature of 25°C?
D the same at a temperature of 100°C?   (1)

(Total 6 marks)

3 a) Define the term **standard enthalpy of formation** and write an equation that represents the enthalpy of formation of chloroethane, CH_3CH_2Cl. (4)

b) Enthalpies of formation of organic compounds cannot usually be measured directly, but they can be calculated from enthalpy of combustion data. The thermochemical equation for the combustion of chloroethane, C_2H_5Cl, is:

$C_2H_5Cl(g) + 3O_2(g) \rightarrow$
$\qquad\qquad 2CO_2(g) + 2H_2O(l) + HCl(g)$
$\Delta H^\ominus_c = -1325 \text{ kJ mol}^{-1}$

i) Draw a labelled Hess's law diagram connecting the enthalpy of combustion of chloroethane with the enthalpies of formation of carbon dioxide, water and hydrogen chloride. (2)

ii) Use your diagram, the value of ΔH_c of chloroethane and the enthalpy of formation data in the table to calculate the enthalpy of formation of chloroethane. (2)

Substance	ΔH_f/kJ mol⁻¹
Carbon dioxide, $CO_2(g)$	−394
Water, $H_2O(l)$	−286
Hydrogen chloride, $HCl(g)$	−92.3

c) Chloroethane can be produced by the reaction of ethene with hydrogen chloride:

$$H_2C{=}CH_2(g) + H{-}Cl(g) \rightarrow H_3C{-}CH_2Cl(g)$$

i) Calculate the standard enthalpy change for this reaction given the following average bond enthalpies. (3)

Bond	Average bond enthalpy/kJ mol^{-1}
C=C	+612
C–H	+467
C–C	+347
H–Cl	+432
C–Cl	+346

ii) Draw a labelled reaction profile diagram for this reaction. (2)

iii) The standard enthalpy of this reaction, calculated from enthalpy of formation data, is −97 kJ mol^{-1}. Explain why this is different from the value obtained in c)i). (1)

(Total 14 marks)

4 Methyl ethanoate is a liquid ester and has the structure:

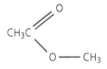

a) i) Write the molecular formula for methyl ethanoate. (1)

ii) Write the equation, including state symbols, for its complete combustion. (2)

b) i) Define the term **standard enthalpy of formation**. (3)

ii) Use the data below to calculate the standard enthalpy change of formation of methyl ethanoate. (3)

Substance	$\Delta H^{\ominus}_{combustion}$/kJ mol^{-1}
Carbon	−394
Hydrogen	−286
Methyl ethanoate	−1592

c) i) Enthalpies of formation can also be calculated from bond energy data. Use the data below to calculate the enthalpy of formation of methyl ethanoate. (3)

Bond	C–H	C–C	C–O	C=O
Mean bond energy/ kJ mol^{-1}	413	347	358	740

ii) Explain why your value in c)i) differs considerably from that in b)ii). (2)

(Total 14 marks)

14 Introduction to kinetics (Topic 9)

Rate of reaction

In chemistry, **kinetics** is the study of the speed, or rate, of reactions. Industrial processes must work sufficiently quickly to be economic, so knowledge of kinetics is important in chemical engineering.

Some reactions are extremely rapid. When solutions of silver nitrate and sodium chloride are mixed, a precipitate of silver chloride is produced instantaneously. The combustion of petrol in the engine of a Formula 1 car is very rapid and propels the car at high speeds. Conversely, rusting of iron is slow, as is the gradual deposition of calcium carbonate from dissolved calcium hydrogencarbonate in the formation of stalactites and stalagmites.

A Formula 1 car : 0-60 mph in 3.2 seconds

Stalactites and stalagmites : 0-2 cm in 100 years

Speed is measured by the amount a property changes in a given time. The average speed of a car is measured by the distance it travels in a given time (miles per hour or kilometres per hour).

> ### Key term
> The rate of reaction is the amount by which the concentration of a reactant or product changes in a given time. Its units are $mol\,dm^{-3}\,s^{-1}$.

> **Tip**
>
> The rate = −change in concentration of *reactant*/ time as its concentration decreases.

$$\text{rate of reaction} = -\frac{\Delta[\text{reactant}]}{\Delta\text{time}}$$

$$= +\frac{\Delta[\text{product}]}{\Delta\text{time}}$$

- The initial rate is the rate of reaction at the time when the reactants are mixed.
- It is the gradient at time $t = 0$ of a graph of concentration against time.

- The rate at time t is the gradient at time t of a graph of concentration against time.
- A good approximation of initial rate is the amount by which a reactant's or product's concentration has changed in a given time from mixing, *provided* its concentration has not changed by more than 10% in that time.

During a reaction, the concentration of the reactant falls. Therefore, the reaction rate falls, until there is no reactant left and the reaction stops. In a graph of the concentration of a reactant against time, the slope of the graph measures the rate of reaction. The magnitude of the slope decreases as the rate decreases and becomes zero (a horizontal line) when all the reactant has been used (Figure 14.1).

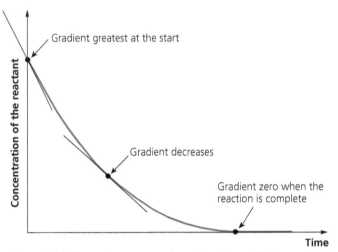

Figure 14.1 Change in concentration of reactant with time

Experimental methods

The rate of a reaction can be estimated in a number of ways. A common method is to measure the time, t, for a certain amount of the mixture to react or the time for a certain amount of product to be formed. The assumption is then made that $1/t$ is a measure of the rate. This is not strictly accurate because the rate will have been decreasing from the moment that the reactants were mixed. It is only a fair assumption if the concentrations of the reactants do not change significantly during the time of the experiment. A change of 10% or less is acceptable.

An example is the reaction between magnesium ribbon and dilute acid. Excess acid is added to a piece of magnesium and the time taken for all the magnesium to disappear is measured. The assumption is then made that the rate is proportional to $1/t$. This is only a fair assumption if the concentration of the acid falls by no more than 10% during the time of the experiment.

Measurable physical changes

There are a number of physical changes that can be used to estimate the rate of a chemical reaction.

Production of a gas

Either measure the volume produced at different times (collected over water or in a gas syringe) or the time to produce a fixed volume of gas. This is a suitable method for measuring the decomposition of hydrogen peroxide using, for example, either different catalysts or different concentrations of hydrogen peroxide:

$$2H_2O_2(aq) \rightarrow 2H_2O(l) + O_2(g)$$

This method is also suitable for studying the effect of temperature on the rate of reaction between magnesium and hydrochloric acid:

$$Mg(s) + 2HCl(aq) \rightarrow MgCl_2(aq) + H_2(g)$$

Production of a solid

The time taken to produce enough solid to hide a cross on a piece of paper under the reaction apparatus or on the side of the apparatus can be measured.

This method is used to measure the decomposition of sodium thiosulfate by acid. The solutions are mixed and placed in a boiling tube that has a felt-pen cross marked on the side. The time taken for enough sulfur to be produced to hide the cross, when viewed from the other side of the boiling tube, is measured. The experiment can then be repeated, for example, with either different concentrations or at different temperatures.

$$Na_2S_2O_3(aq) + 2HCl(aq) \rightarrow 2NaCl(aq) + SO_2(aq) + H_2O(l) + S(s)$$

An alternative method is to do the reaction in a beaker standing on a white tile marked with a cross.

Hazard: sulfur dioxide is an irritant gas.

> ### Test yourself
>
> 1 Explain why a dark thick cross should not be used in this experiment.

Colour change

The change in colour of either a reactant or a product is measured using a colorimeter.

A reaction that can be studied this way is the reaction between iodine and propanone. The decrease in the intensity of the colour of iodine can be measured with a colorimeter as a function of time.

Change in pH or conductivity

A reaction with an acid or alkali as a product or as a reagent can be followed by measuring the pH at intervals of time. This is not very accurate as pH is logarithmic and so if the initial $[H^+] = 1\,mol\,dm^{-3}$, 90% of the H^+ ions must react to give a change of 1 in pH.

Reactions where the number or type of ions change can be followed by measuring the electrical conductivity at intervals of time.

Clock reactions

In a 'clock' reaction, the reactants are mixed and the time taken to produce a fixed amount of product is measured. This gives the initial rate of the reaction.

The oxidation of iodide ions by hydrogen peroxide in acid solution can be followed as a clock reaction:

$$H_2O_2(aq) + 2I^-(aq) + 2H^+(aq) \rightarrow I_2(s) + 2H_2O(l)$$

- $25\,cm^3$ of hydrogen peroxide solution is mixed in a beaker with $25\,cm^3$ of water and a few drops of starch solution are added.
- $25\,cm^3$ of potassium iodide solution and $5\,cm^3$ of a dilute solution of sodium thiosulfate are placed in a second beaker.

- The contents of the two beakers are mixed and the time taken for the solution to go blue is measured.
- The experiment is repeated with the same volumes of potassium iodide and sodium thiosulfate but with other concentrations of hydrogen peroxide or at different temperatures.

The reaction produces iodine, which reacts with the sodium thiosulfate.

$$I_2 + 2S_2O_3^{2-} \rightarrow 2I^- + S_4O_6^{2-}$$

When all the sodium thiosulfate has been used up, the next iodine that is produced reacts with the starch to give an intense blue-black colour.

The amount of iodine produced in the measured time is proportional to the volume of sodium thiosulfate solution taken. Therefore, the average rate of reaction for each experiment is proportional to 1/time.

An alternative method is to monitor the reaction at intervals of time. The clock is started on mixing and when the blue-black colour is observed, the time is noted and a little more sodium thiosulfate added. The blue colour disappears and when it reappears the time is noted and more sodium thiosulfate is added and so on.

A graph of thiosulfate added against time is plotted and the rate at different times is measured from the graph as in Figure 14.1.

Calculation of rate from the gradient of a concentration–time graph

The concentration, or something proportional to it, is measured at intervals of time. The time must be long enough for at least 75% of the substance to react.

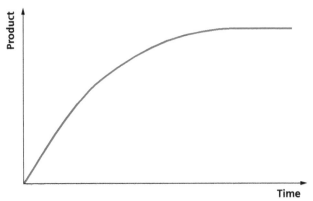

Figure 14.2 Change in concentration of product with time

The initial rate is that at the instant the reactants are mixed.

It is sometimes easier to measure the amount of product produced over time and plot a graph of the concentration of the product against time (Figure 14.2). As before, the slope measures the rate of reaction and gradually decreases as the reaction slows down. When the slope becomes zero (the graph becomes horizontal), the rate is zero. This is because all of the reactant has been used.

It is sometimes assumed that the rate of reaction can be calculated by measuring the time for a certain amount of a reactant to react or a certain amount of product to be formed. Then 1/time is assumed to be the rate of the reaction. This is not the *initial* rate but an *average* rate, which is meaningless unless less than 10% of the reaction has taken place. Then the approximation is acceptable.

Collision theory

The explanation of rates of reaction is based upon **collision theory**. Consider the reaction:

$$A + B \rightarrow C + D$$

The first requirement is for molecule A to collide with molecule B. However, this cannot be the *only* requirement, otherwise all reactions would be extremely fast.

There are about 10^{11} molecular collisions every second in $1\,cm^3$ of air in a room, and the frequency of collision is even greater in a liquid.

Collision theory also states that colliding molecules must hit each other with sufficient energy to cause a reaction.

Particles (e.g. molecules in a gas or ions in solution) move about randomly at various speeds. Maxwell and Boltzmann calculated the distribution of speeds of the molecules in a gas and hence their kinetic energies.

Maxwell–Boltzmann distribution of molecular energies

The Maxwell–Boltzmann distribution of molecular energies is plotted on a graph of the fraction of molecules with a particular energy against kinetic energy.

Figure 14.3 shows the distribution of molecular energies at two temperatures, T_1 (in blue) and T_2 (in red). T_2 is a higher temperature than T_1, and so the average kinetic energy of the molecules at T_2 is greater than that at T_1.

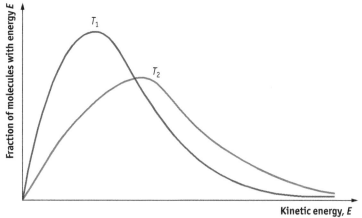

Figure 14.3 Maxwell–Boltzmann distribution of molecular energies at two temperatures

Tip

When drawing this distribution make sure that the curves do *not* hit the line on the right of the x-axis but approach it asymptotically.

Points to note about the graphs in Figure 14.3 are that:

- neither curve is symmetrical
- both curves start at the origin and finish by approaching the x-axis
- the area under both curves is the same (the number of molecules is the same)
- the peak of the T_2 (higher temperature) distribution is to the *right* and *lower* than the peak of the T_1 distribution

The second requirement of collision theory is that colliding molecules must possess, between them, at least the specific amount of kinetic energy required for a reaction to take place. The minimum energy that colliding molecules must have for the collision to result in reaction is called the activation energy.

The fraction of collisions that are successful is shown by the Maxwell–Boltzmann distribution in Figure 14.4. The *area* under the curve to the right of the activation energy line is the fraction of molecules that have the necessary energy to react on collision. For a reaction that proceeds steadily at room temperature, only about 1 in 10^{12} molecules possesses this energy.

Key term

The **activation energy** in a reaction, E_a, is the minimum kinetic energy that the colliding molecules must possess for the collision to be successful and result in the formation of product molecules.

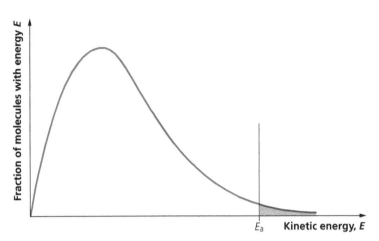

Figure 14.4 Fraction of molecules possessing the activation energy

If the activation energy is high, the number of colliding particles that have this energy at room temperature is extremely small, so the reaction does not take place. The system is then said to be **kinetically stable**. The reaction can occur only if the temperature is increased.

If the reactants are heated, enough molecules may gain energy equal to or greater than the activation energy, E_a, for the system to become kinetically unstable. An example is the reaction between hydrogen and oxygen. The mixture is thermodynamically very unstable relative to the product, water, but the activation energy is so high that the reaction does not occur at room temperature. The mixture is kinetically stable, but if it is heated with a spark, it becomes kinetically unstable and explodes.

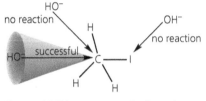

Figure 14.5 Importance of orientation for a successful collision

The third requirement of collision theory is that the colliding molecules must have the correct orientation on collision. For example, in the reaction between iodomethane, CH_3I, and hydroxide ions, OH^-, the collision has to be between the oxygen in the OH^- ion and the carbon of CH_3I. In addition, the OH^- ion has to approach from the side opposite from the iodine atom (Figure 14.5).

Summary of collision theory

- The molecules must collide. The rate of a reaction depends on the *frequency* of collision.
- A collision will only be successful if the colliding molecules have kinetic energy equal to or greater than the activation energy. A fast reaction has a low activation energy, so a greater *proportion* of collisions will be successful than in a reaction with a higher activation energy.
- The molecules must collide with the correct orientation. In a reaction involving complex molecules, fewer collisions will have the correct orientation than in a reaction between simpler molecules.

Factors affecting reaction rate

Concentration

For reactions in solution, an increase in concentration causes an increase in reaction rate. The frequency of collisions between solute molecules in solutions of concentration $2\,mol\,dm^{-3}$ is greater than the frequency in solutions of $1\,mol\,dm^{-3}$ concentration. The average kinetic energy is independent of the concentration, so as the collision frequency is higher, the frequency of *successful* collisions is also higher, so the rate of reaction is faster. Doubling the concentration of one reactant usually causes the rate of reaction to double.

The effect of increasing the concentration of acid on the rate of reaction between a piece of magnesium ribbon and excess aqueous hydrochloric acid is shown in Figure 14.6. The reaction is:

$$Mg(s) + 2HCl(aq) \rightarrow MgCl_2(aq) + H_2(g)$$

The blue curve is for acid of concentration $0.5\,mol\,dm^{-3}$; the green curve is for $1\,mol\,dm^{-3}$ acid. Note that the green line has a steeper *initial* slope (faster rate) than the blue line, but both lines flatten off at the same volume of hydrogen gas produced. This is because magnesium is the limiting reagent.

The red curve in Figure 14.6 shows the effect of increasing the temperature on the reaction between magnesium and $0.5\,mol\,dm^{-3}$ hydrochloric acid.

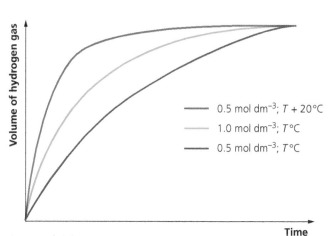

Figure 14.6 Reaction between magnesium and dilute hydrochloric acid

Pressure

For gaseous reactions, an increase in pressure, at constant temperature, results in an increase in reaction rate.

Pressure can be increased at a given temperature by:

- reducing the volume of the container
- pumping more reactant gas into the container

Either way, the result is the same. There is an increased number of gas particles per cm^3, so the *frequency* of collision is increased. The average kinetic energy of the particles remains the same, so the same proportion of collisions will result in reaction. However, as there are more collisions per second, the rate increases.

Marble chips reacting with (a) concentrated HCl and (b) dilute HCl

> **Tip**
>
> Do not just say that the number of collisions increases when the pressure or concentration increases. It is the number per second (or the frequency of collisions) that increases.

This applies to homogeneous reactions such as ethene and gaseous hydrogen bromide or heterogeneous reactions such as carbon and oxygen.

Surface area

For heterogeneous reactions involving a solid, a larger surface area of the solid results in a faster reaction.

> **Key terms**
>
> A **homogeneous reaction** is one that takes place in a single phase – for example, all the reactants are gases.
>
> A **heterogeneous reaction** is one in which the reactants are in two phases – for example, a solid and a gas or a solid and a solution.

When a solid, such as zinc, reacts with an acid, only collisions between hydrogen ions in the solution and zinc atoms on the *surface* of the solid zinc can result in reaction. If the zinc is powdered, the surface area is increased and so the frequency of collisions between H^+ ions and zinc atoms increases. Thus hydrogen gas is formed more quickly.

Temperature

An increase in temperature always causes an increase in reaction rate. There are two reasons for this. The more important is that the molecules have a higher average kinetic energy at the higher temperature. This means that a greater fraction of the molecules possess the energy necessary to react on collision (Figure 14.7).

An increase of 10°C from room temperature causes the rate of the average reaction approximately to double.

Note that the Maxwell–Boltzmann diagram showing the effect of temperature consists of *two* curves and *one* activation energy.

Tip

You must make it clear in your explanations that the area under the curve to the right of the activation energy is the fraction of molecules that have enough energy for the collision to be successful.

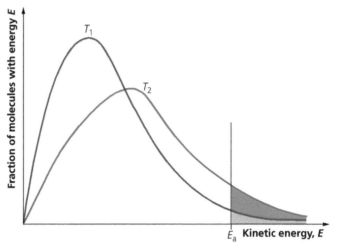

Figure 14.7 Maxwell–Boltzmann diagram showing the effect of temperature

The tinted area under each curve to the right of the activation energy is the fraction of molecules that have sufficient energy to react on collision. The red plus blue area under the higher temperature curve is larger than the blue area under the lower temperature curve. Therefore, at the higher temperature, a greater *proportion* of the collisions result in a reaction. This means that the reaction is faster at the higher temperature.

A second, and minor, effect of an increase in temperature is a slight increase in collision frequency. The additional rate caused by this is about 1% for a 10°C rise from room temperature. This effect is swamped by the increased rate due to the greater fraction of molecules with energy equal to or greater than the activation energy and the resulting increase in the fraction of successful collisions.

The effect of raising the temperature on the reaction between a piece of magnesium ribbon and dilute hydrochloric acid is shown in Figure 14.6. The red line shows the volume of hydrogen produced over time with $0.5\,mol\,dm^{-3}$ acid at a temperature 20°C higher than that of the blue line. The slope of this line is much steeper than the slopes of the other two lines.

Test yourself

2 State the effect of increasing the temperature on the rate of:

a) an exothermic reaction   b) an endothermic reaction

Catalysts

Catalysts are specific to reactions and they cause the reaction rate to increase.

Homogeneous catalysts

A **homogeneous catalyst** is one that is in the same phase as the reactants. An example is the Fe^{2+} ion catalyst in the oxidation of iodide ions, I^-, by persulfate ions, $S_2O_8^{2-}$:

$$S_2O_8^{2-}(aq) + 2I^-(aq) \xrightarrow{Fe^{2+}(aq)} 2SO_4^{2-}(aq) + I_2(s)$$

A homogeneous catalyst works by reacting with one of the reactants to form an intermediate compound:

$$S_2O_8^{2-}(aq) + 2Fe^{2+}(aq) \rightarrow 2SO_4^{2-}(aq) + 2Fe^{3+}(aq)$$

The intermediate compound then reacts with the other reagent to reform the catalyst:

$$2Fe^{3+}(aq) + 2I^-(aq) \rightarrow I_2(s) + 2Fe^{2+}(aq)$$

The route using the catalyst avoids collisions between two negative particles.

Heterogeneous catalysts

A **heterogeneous catalyst** is one that is in a different phase from the reactants. One example is iron when used in the Haber process (page 282):

$$N_2(g) + 3H_2(g) \xrightarrow{Fe(s)} 2NH_3(g)$$

A heterogeneous catalyst usually promotes a reaction through its active sites. These are places on the surface of the catalyst to which the reactants can bond. The sequence of reactions is:

gaseous reactants + active sites $\rightarrow$ adsorbed reactants

adsorbed reactants $\rightarrow$ adsorbed products

adsorbed products $\rightarrow$ gaseous products + free active sites

There are fewer active sites than there are reactant molecules, so an increase in pressure does not alter the rate of reaction because all the active sites are already occupied.

Another example is nickel when used in the addition of hydrogen to alkenes (page 185):

$$C_2H_4(g) + H_2(g) \xrightarrow{Ni(s)} C_2H_6(g)$$

> ### Key term
> A **catalyst** speeds up a reaction by providing an *alternative* path with a lower activation energy.

Note that the catalyst is written above the arrow in the equation.

> ### Test yourself
>
> 3 Which of the following is likely to have the *least* effect on the rate of the reaction:
>
> $$Mg(s) + 2H^+(aq) \rightarrow Mg^{2+}(aq) + H_2(g)$$
>
> - doubling the concentration of H^+ ions
> - raising the temperature by 10°C
> - doubling the pressure in the reaction vessel

Economic benefits of using catalysts

Industrial processes such as the Haber process for the manufacture of ammonia, one of the steps in the Contact process for the manufacture of sulfuric acid and the oxidation of ammonia in the manufacture of nitric acid all use heterogeneous catalysts. These have several economic benefits:

- They allow the reaction to proceed at a fast rate at a much lower temperature. This reduces the cost of energy since there will be less heat lost at the lower temperature.
- Because the reaction is faster, more product will be produced in a shorter time. This increases the efficiency and costs of the process.
- These three reactions are all exothermic. Therefore there will be a higher equilibrium yield at a lower temperature (see Chapter 15). This means that the percentage conversion is higher and there is less waste of reactants or a smaller proportion of the reactants will have to be recycled, thus reducing energy costs.

How catalysts work

The way that a catalyst speeds up a reaction can be explained using a Maxwell–Boltzmann diagram (Figure 14.8). The presence of a catalyst does not alter the average kinetic energy of the molecules, but the catalysed reaction route has a lower activation energy.

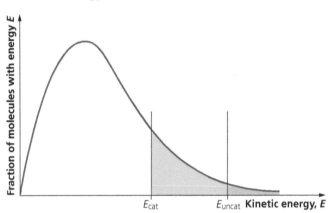

Figure 14.8 Maxwell–Boltzmann diagram for a reaction with and without a catalyst

The tinted area under the curve to the right of each activation energy is the fraction of molecules that have sufficient energy to react on collision. E_{cat} is less than E_{uncat}, so the green plus blue area under the curve to the right of E_{cat} is larger than the blue area to the right of E_{uncat}. This shows that a greater *proportion* of the collisions involving the catalyst result in a reaction. Therefore, the reaction is faster in the presence of the catalyst.

Enzyme catalysts

Enzymes are biological catalysts. They are specific to a particular biochemical reaction and can make the reaction go as much as 10^{10} times faster. Enzymes are large protein molecules that contain one or more **active sites**. The reactant, called the **substrate** in biochemistry, fits into the active site in a similar way to a key fitting into a lock. Only a key with the correct shape fits a lock — the same is the case with a substrate and an active site (Figure 14.9).

Summary of factors affecting the rate of reaction

- In homogeneous gas–phase reactions, an increase in pressure causes an increased *frequency* of collision and hence an increase in the rate of reaction.
- For reactions in solution, an increase in the concentration of a reactant increases the *frequency* of collisions and so increases the rate of reaction.

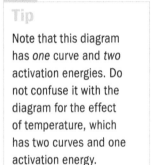

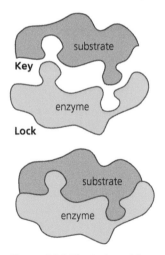

Figure 14.9 The lock-and-key hypothesis of enzyme action

- In heterogeneous reactions, an increase in surface area of the solid reactant increases the number of collisions in a given time between the solid and the gaseous or dissolved reactant, and hence increases the rate of reaction.
- A rise in temperature increases the average kinetic energy of the molecules. This results in more of the colliding molecules having energy equal to or greater than the activation energy, E_a. Therefore, a greater *proportion* of the collisions are successful and hence the rate increases.
- A catalyst speeds up a reaction by providing an alternative path with a lower activation energy. Addition of a catalyst causes more molecules to have energy equal to or greater than E_{cat} than have energy equal to or greater than E_{uncat}. Therefore, the *proportion of successful collisions* increases and hence the rate increases.
- Enzymes are biological catalysts.

The rate also increases slightly because of the increase in the frequency of collisions.

Reaction profile diagrams

A **reaction profile diagram** shows the energy levels of the reactants and products of the reaction and of the transition state that the reactants go through. The activation energy, E_a, and the enthalpy change, ΔH_r, are also shown on the diagram.

Consider the reaction:

$$CH_3I + OH^- \rightarrow CH_3OH + I^-$$

As the OH^- ion approaches the carbon atom from the side opposite from the iodine, it is subjected to an increasing force of repulsion. This is caused by the outside of both the oxygen and the carbon atoms being a sphere of negative charge (the outer electrons). If the OH^- ion does not have sufficient energy, it bounces off. However, if the OH^- ion possesses the activation energy, the oxygen approaches close enough to the carbon atom for a covalent bond to start to form. As this bond forms, the C–I bond begins to break. The transition state is the point of highest energy, when the O–C bond has partially formed and the C–I bond has partially broken (Figure 14.10).

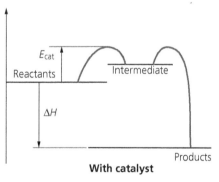

Figure 14.10

The energy changes during the course of an exothermic reaction are shown in the reaction profile diagrams in Figure 14.11. Note that the activation energy for the catalysed reaction is smaller than that for the uncatalysed reaction.

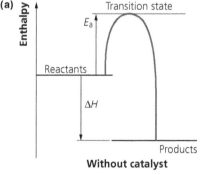

Figure 14.11 Reaction profiles for (a) an uncatalysed and (b) a catalysed exothermic reaction

Figure 14.11(a) is similar to an enthalpy level diagram (page 236). The difference is that an enthalpy level diagram does not show the transition state nor an intermediate.

A catalysed reaction takes place using a different route from the uncatalysed reaction. An intermediate forms between the reactant and the catalyst, so the reaction takes place in at least two steps.

Note that the reaction profile diagram for the catalysed reaction has two humps and that a catalyst has *no* effect on the value of ΔH_r.

Summary tasks

You must be able to:

- define rate of reaction and activation energy
- use experimental data to calculate the rate of reaction
- draw Maxwell–Boltzmann distribution curves at different temperatures
- explain how pressure, concentration, temperature and catalyst affect the rate of a reaction
- discuss the economic advantages of the use of catalysts in industrial processes
- draw reaction profile diagrams

Make sure you can describe experimental methods for following a reaction:

- producing a gas
- forming a precipitate
- producing or using up a strong acid or base
- where the number or type of ions change

Questions

1 Explain, using the collision theory, the reaction between two gases A and B.

2 Draw a diagram that represents the Maxwell–Boltzmann distribution of molecular energies for a gas at two temperatures, T_c and T_h, where T_c is lower than T_h.

Indicate a suitable value for the activation energy of the reaction and use your diagram to explain the effect of lowering the temperature on the rate of reaction.

3 Hydrogen and iodine react to form hydrogen iodide:

$$H_2(g) + I_2(g) \rightarrow 2HI(g) \quad \Delta H_r^\ominus = +51.8\,\text{kJ}\,\text{mol}^{-1}$$

State and explain the effect, if any, on the rate of reaction of:

a) halving the volume of the container at constant temperature

b) increasing the pressure by adding more hydrogen at constant volume and temperature

4 When petrol is burned in the engine of a car, the combustion is not complete and some carbon monoxide, CO, is produced. Nitrogen monoxide, NO, is another exhaust gas. These gases can be removed by a catalytic converter in the exhaust system.

a) Draw a Maxwell–Boltzmann distribution of molecular energies at a temperature, T. Indicate the activation energies of the reaction with and without catalyst, and use the diagram to explain how a catalyst speeds up this reaction.

b) Explain why petrol that contains lead should not be used in cars fitted with a catalytic converter.

Exam practice questions

1 a) Define the term **activation energy**. (2)

b) Which is a true statement?

A A fast reaction has a high activation energy, E_a.

B A fast reaction has a low activation energy, E_a.

C Exothermic reactions are fast.

D Endothermic reactions are slow. (1)

c) Consider the reaction:

$$Ca(HCO_3)_2(aq) \rightarrow CaCO_3(s) + H_2O(l) + CO_2(g)$$

Which would cause the greatest **decrease** in the rate of this reaction?

A a lower temperature and a lower pressure

B a lower temperature and an increase in pressure

C a lower concentration of the reactant and a lower temperature

D an increase in the concentration of the reactant and a lower temperature (1)

d) Consider the reaction between chalk and hydrochloric acid:

$$CaCO_3(s) + 2HCl(aq) \rightarrow CaCl_2(aq) + H_2O(l) + CO_2(g)$$

i) Explain why an increase in the concentration of the acid will cause the rate to increase. (1)

ii) Which would result in the shortest time to produce $10\,cm^3$ of gaseous carbon dioxide?

A large lumps of chalk, $1\,mol\,dm^{-3}$ acid and a temperature of 25°C

B small pieces of chalk, $1\,mol\,dm^{-3}$ acid and a temperature of 45°C

C small pieces of chalk, $1\,mol\,dm^{-3}$ acid and a temperature of 35°C

D large lumps of chalk, $1\,mol\,dm^{-3}$ acid and a temperature of 45°C (1)

(Total 6 marks)

2 An experiment was devised to investigate the effect of temperature on the rate of the reaction between magnesium and aqueous hydrochloric acid. $25\,cm^3$ of a $1.00\,mol\,dm^{-3}$ solution of hydrochloric acid was added to a beaker. A sample of magnesium of mass $0.06\,g$ was added and a stopwatch started. The watch was stopped when all the magnesium had reacted. It was assumed that the rate of the reaction is proportional to $1/t$, where t is the time taken for the magnesium to disappear.

$$Mg(s) + 2HCl(aq) \rightarrow MgCl_2(aq) + H_2(g)$$

a) Calculate the amounts (in moles) of magnesium and hydrochloric acid taken. (2)

b) Calculate the amount of acid used in the reaction. (1)

c) Calculate the percentage change in the amount of the acid during the experiment. (1)

d) i) Explain whether this means that $1/t$ is a fair measure of the rate? (2)

ii) If not, what change would you make to the volume or concentration of the acid to make it a fairer measure? (1)

(Total 7 marks)

3 Hydrogen peroxide decomposes into water and oxygen:

$$2H_2O_2(aq) \rightarrow 2H_2O(l) + O_2(g)$$

$$\Delta H_r^{\ominus} = -196\,kJ\,mol^{-1}$$

a) i) Draw labelled reaction profiles for the reaction with and without a platinum catalyst. (3)

ii) Explain the difference between heterogeneous and homogeneous catalysts. (2)

iii) Classify the type of catalyst used in part i) of this question. (1)

iv) Draw a diagram of an apparatus that could be used to measure the rate of this reaction, using either platinum or manganese(IV) oxide as a catalyst. State what measurements you would make and how you would estimate the rate of reaction from your data. (5)

b) State and explain the effect on the rate of reaction of:

i) increasing the temperature (3)

ii) increasing the concentration of hydrogen peroxide (3)

(Total 17 marks)

4 a) Consider the reaction $A \rightarrow B + C$. The initial rate of this reaction is:

    A proportional to 1/the time for the reaction to finish

    B proportional to the time for the reaction to finish

    C equal to the gradient at $t = 0$ of the graph of the concentration of A against time

    D equal to minus the gradient at $t = 0$ of the graph of the concentration of A against time (1)

b) Cyclopropane decomposes slowly at a temperature of 500°C into propene. The following results were obtained:

Concentration of cyclopropane/mol dm^{-3}	Time/min
0.080	0
0.062	5
0.048	10
0.038	15
0.023	25
0.014	35
0.0065	50

    i) Use the data to draw a graph of concentration of cyclopropane against time. (3)

    ii) Draw tangents at $t = 0$ and when half the cyclopropane has reacted, and hence calculate the rate of the reaction at $t = 0$ and when half the cyclopropane has reacted. (3)

c) 2-chloropropane is slowly hydrolysed by water:

$$CH_3CHBrCH_3 + H_2O \rightarrow$$
$$CH_3CH(OH)CH_3 + H^+ + Br^-$$

The rate of this reaction was followed by measuring the electrical conductivity at intervals of time. The concentration of product is proportional to the electrical conductivity. The following results were obtained.

Conductivity/ arbitrary units	3	5	7.5	8.7	9.4	10
Time/s	5	10	20	30	40	50

    i) Plot a graph of conductivity against time. (2)

    ii) Draw tangents at $t = 0$ and $t = 25$ and calculate the initial rate of reaction and the rate at $t = 25$ s. (3)

        (Total 12 marks)

15 Introduction to chemical equilibrium (Topic 10)

Liquid bromine in equilibrium with gaseous bromine

Some reactions go to completion, and others do not. The latter type of reaction is called a reversible reaction. When a mixture of hydrogen and oxygen in a 2:1 ratio is ignited with a spark, water is produced and no uncombined hydrogen or oxygen is left. This is an example of a complete or **irreversible** reaction.

$$2H_2(g) + O_2(g) \rightarrow 2H_2O(l)$$

Physical changes, such as evaporation, are reversible, for example:

$$Br_2(l) \rightleftharpoons Br_2(g)$$

When liquid bromine is mixed with air in a sealed container, a dynamic equilibrium between the liquid and gaseous bromine is reached. Gaseous bromine molecules condense into the liquid at exactly the same rate as bromine molecules evaporate from the surface of the liquid.

Many chemical reactions do not go to completion. If a mixture of hydrogen and iodine in a 1:1 molar ratio is heated to 300°C in a closed vessel, only about 90% of the hydrogen and iodine react.

$$H_2(g) + I_2(g) \rightleftharpoons 2HI(g)$$

At 300°C, no matter how long the mixture of hydrogen and iodine is allowed to react, 10% of the reactants will be left uncombined. If some hydrogen iodide is heated to 300°C, it partially decomposes and the composition of the resulting mixture is identical to that produced on starting with equimolar amounts of hydrogen and iodine. When there is no further change in the amounts of reactants and products, the system is said to be in equilibrium.

When the mixture of hydrogen and iodine is heated to 300°C, the two gases start to react and form hydrogen iodide. As time passes, the concentrations of hydrogen and iodine become lower, so the rate of the reaction decreases. As soon as the reaction starts, some of the hydrogen iodide formed begins to decompose to form hydrogen and iodine.

At first, this reaction is very slow, because the concentration of hydrogen iodide is very small. However, as time passes and more and more hydrogen and iodine react, the concentration of hydrogen iodide increases. This means that the rate of the reverse reaction also increases. Eventually, the rates of the forward reaction and the reverse reaction become equal. After this point, there is no further change in concentration. The system is now in equilibrium with the forward and reverse reactions taking place at the same rate. This is called a **dynamic equilibrium**.

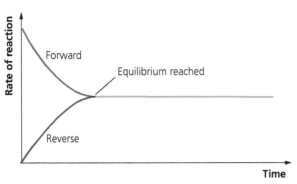

Figure 15.1 Graph showing how rates of reaction change until equilibrium is reached

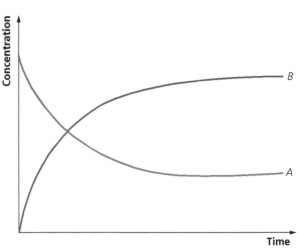

Figure 15.2 Graph showing the change in concentrations of A and B until equilibrium is reached

> **Tip**
>
> The rate of $H_2 + I_2 \rightarrow 2HI$ equals the rate of $2HI \rightarrow H_2 + I_2$.

> At equilibrium the concentration of B is greater than that of A, so the position is to the right.

> **Tip**
>
> Remember, the reactions do *not* stop when equilibrium is reached.

Dynamic equilibria are illustrated in Figures 15.1 and 15.2.

For the equilibrium reaction $A \rightleftharpoons B$, the graph showing how the concentrations of the reactants and products vary until equilibrium is reached is shown in Figure 15.2.

The fact that the reactions do not stop when equilibrium is reached can be proved by using radioactive tracers. Hydrogen iodide, containing a trace of the radioisotope ^{131}I, is mixed with hydrogen and iodine in *equilibrium* proportions at 300°C and left for several minutes. The amount of each substance does not change, but the radioisotope is found in both hydrogen iodide and iodine molecules. This shows that some hydrogen iodide must have decomposed into iodine and hydrogen. The ^{131}I is distributed between the hydrogen iodide and the iodine in the same ratio as in the overall equilibrium concentrations.

Test yourself

1 Explain the term **dynamic equilibrium** with reference to the equilibrium reaction when solid sodium chloride is suspended in a saturated solution of salt water.

$$NaCl(s) + aq \rightleftharpoons Na^+(aq) + Cl^-(aq)$$

Reversible changes

The reaction between hydrogen and iodine was studied by Guldberg and Waage in 1864. They mixed different amounts of hydrogen and iodine and allowed the mixtures to reach equilibrium at 480°C.

They then measured the concentration of the three substances at equilibrium and tried to find a mathematical relationship between these concentrations. Typical results for this are shown in Table 15.1.

Table 15.1 Reaction between hydrogen and iodine

Initial $[H_2]$	Initial $[I_2]$	$[H_2]$ at equilibrium	$[I_2]$ at equilibrium	$[HI]$ at equilibrium	$\dfrac{[HI]}{[H_2][I_2]}$	$\dfrac{[HI]^2}{[H_2][I_2]}$
0.040	0.040	0.0089	0.0089	0.062	783	49
0.080	0.040	0.0426	0.0026	0.0748	675	51
0.080	0.080	0.018	0.018	0.124	383	47
0.020	0.080	0.0005	0.0605	0.0389	1286	50

Square brackets around the symbol of a species mean the concentration, in $mol\,dm^{-3}$, of that substance.

The values in the final column are constant to within experimental error, so from these results, it appears that:

$$\frac{[HI]^2_{eq}}{[H_2]_{eq}[I_2]_{eq}} = \text{a constant}$$

The equilibrium constant, K_c

Law of mass action and K_c

The results given in Table 15.1, and those of other equilibrium reactions, enabled Guldberg and Waage to formulate the **law of mass action**. This states that when reactions reach equilibrium, the equilibrium concentrations of the products multiplied together and divided by the equilibrium concentrations of the reactants also multiplied together, with the concentration of each substance raised to the power appropriate to the reaction stoichiometry, are a constant at a given temperature.

For example, for the reaction:

$$N_2(g) + 3H_2(g) \rightleftharpoons 2NH_3(g)$$

$$\frac{[NH_3]^2_{eq}}{[N_2]_{eq}[H_2]^3_{eq}} = \text{a constant}$$

where $[NH_3]_{eq}$ is the concentration, in $mol\,dm^{-3}$, of ammonia at *equilibrium*.

The constant is called the **equilibrium constant** (measured in terms of concentrations) and has the symbol, K_c.

In general, for a reaction:

$$xA + yB \rightleftharpoons n_c + mD$$

where x, y, n and m are the stoichiometric amounts in the equation:

$$K_c = \frac{[C]^n_{eq}[D]^m_{eq}}{[A]^x_{eq}[B]^y_{eq}}$$

The right-hand side of this expression is called the 'quotient' and given the symbol Q.

The value of the equilibrium constant depends on
- the reaction as written
- the temperature

The value of K_c does *not* depend on the pressure or the presence of a catalyst.

> **Tip**
>
> Remember, that in an equilibrium constant expression, the products are on top and the reactants are on the bottom.

The chemical equation and the expression for K_c

This is defined in terms of the equilibrium concentrations of the reactants and products of the reversible reaction.

An equilibrium constant has no meaning unless it is linked to a chemical equation. Consider the equilibrium reaction of sulfur dioxide and oxygen reacting reversibly to form sulfur trioxide. This reaction can be represented by two equations and hence by two expressions for the equilibrium constant, K_c. The values given below are at 727°C (1000 K).

$$2SO_2(g) + O_2(g) \rightleftharpoons 2SO_3(g)$$

$$K_c = \frac{[SO_3]^2_{eq}}{[SO_2]^2_{eq}[O_2]_{eq}} = 2800 \, dm^3 \, mol^{-1}$$

or

$$SO_2(g) + \tfrac{1}{2}O_2(g) \rightleftharpoons SO_3(g)$$

$$K'_c = \frac{[SO_3]_{eq}}{[SO_2]_{eq} [O_2]^{\frac{1}{2}}_{eq}}$$

$$= \sqrt{K_c} = 52.9 \, dm^{\frac{3}{2}} \, mol^{-\frac{1}{2}}$$

The reaction can also be written in the other direction, giving a third expression for K:

$$2SO_3(g) \rightleftharpoons 2SO_2(g) + O_2(g)$$

$$K''_c = \frac{[SO_2]^2_{eq}[O_2]_{eq}}{[SO_3]^2_{eq}}$$

$$= 3.57 \times 10^{-4} \, mol \, dm^{-3}$$

Note that $\dfrac{1}{2800} = 3.57 \times 10^{-4}$

The three equilibrium constants are connected by the expression:

$$K_c = (K'_c)^2 = \frac{1}{K''_c}$$

The reactions above are all examples of homogeneous reactions.

Gases always mix, so reactions involving only gases are homogeneous. Reversible reactions in solution are also examples of homogeneous equilibria. In such reactions, the concentration terms of all the reactants and products appear in the expression for the equilibrium constant. For example, for the homogeneous reaction:

$$Fe^{3+}(aq) + I^-(aq) \rightleftharpoons Fe^{2+}(aq) + \tfrac{1}{2}I_2(aq)$$

$$K_c = \frac{[Fe^{2+}(aq)]_{eq}[I_2(aq)]^{\frac{1}{2}}}{[Fe^{3+}(aq)]_{eq}[I^-(aq)]_{eq}}$$

A heterogeneous reaction is one where the reactants and products are *not* all in the same phase. For example:

$$CaCO_3(s) \rightleftharpoons CaO(s) + CO_2(g)$$

For heterogeneous reactions it is assumed that the concentration of a pure solid is constant. This is because it is incompressible. Therefore [solid] is omitted from the expression for the equilibrium constant. Thus:

$$K_c = [CO_2]$$

[H$_2$O] in equilibrium expressions

- When water is in the gaseous state, [H$_2$O] must appear in equilibrium constant expressions.
- When water is a reactant but *not* the solvent, the term [H$_2$O] must always appear in the expression for the equilibrium constant.
- When water is the solvent, even if it is also a reactant or product, [H$_2$O] does *not* appear in the expression for the equilibrium constant. This is because its concentration remains constant.

Worked example 1

Write the expression for the equilibrium constant, K_c, for the reaction:

$$CH_3COOCH_3(l) + H_2O(l) \rightleftharpoons CH_3COOH(l) + CH_3OH(l)$$

Answer

$$K_c = \frac{[CH_3COOH]_{eq}[CH_3OH]_{eq}}{[CH_3COOCH_3]_{eq}[H_2O]_{eq}}$$

Water is a reactant but not the solvent, so [H$_2$O]$_{eq}$ appears in the equilibrium expression.

Worked example 2

Write the expression for the equilibrium constant, K_c, for the reaction:

$$Cr_2O_7^{2-}(aq) + H_2O(l) \rightleftharpoons 2CrO_4^{2-}(aq) + 2H^+(aq)$$

Answer

$$K_c = \frac{[CrO^4{}_{2-}]^2_{eq}[H_3{}^+O]^2_{eq}}{[Cr_2O^{2-}{}_7]_{eq}}$$

Water is a reactant *and* the solvent, so [H$_2$O]$_{eq}$ is omitted from the equilibrium expression.

Test yourself

2 Write the expression for K_c for:

a) $Sn^{4+}(aq) + 2Br^-(aq) \rightleftharpoons Sn^{2+}(aq) + Br_2(aq)$

b) $Fe_2O_3(s) + 3CO(g) \rightleftharpoons 2Fe(s) + 3CO_2(g)$

c) $HOCl(aq) + H^+(aq) + Fe^{2+} \rightleftharpoons \frac{1}{2}Cl_2(aq) + H_2O(l) + Fe^{3+}(aq)$

Factors affecting the position of equilibrium

It is important to realise that the equilibrium constant only equals the quotient, Q, when the system is at equilibrium.

- $Q = K$: the system *is* in equilibrium and there will be no further change in concentration of the reactants and products.
- $Q > K$ (or $K < Q$): the system is *not* in equilibrium and will react to make Q smaller. Products will be converted into reactants (the position of equilibrium will shift to the left) thus reducing the value of the numerator in the expression for Q and increasing the value of the denominator.

The numerator is the term on the top of the fraction.

- $Q < K$ (or $K > Q$): the system is *not* in equilibrium and will react to make Q larger. Reactants will be converted into products thus increasing the value of the numerator and decreasing the value of the denominator (the position of equilibrium will shift to the right).

Position of equilibrium

At equilibrium, the ratio of product to reactant concentrations defines the **position of equilibrium**. Using the example of equal moles of hydrogen and iodine in equilibrium with hydrogen iodide, the position of equilibrium at 300°C can be calculated:

$$K_c = \frac{[HI]_{eq}^2}{[H_2]_{eq}[I_2]_{eq}} = 49$$

$[H_2]_{eq} = [I_2]_{eq}$, and taking the square root of both sides:

$$\frac{[HI]_{eq}}{[H_2]_{eq}} = \frac{[HI]_{eq}}{[I_2]_{eq}} = 7$$

So:

ratio of $[HI]_{eq}$ to $[H_2]_{eq}$ or $[HI]_{eq}$ to $[I_2]_{eq} = 7{:}1$

where [HI] means the concentration of [HI] in $mol\,dm^{-3}$.

When the position of equilibrium is expressed as the percentage of a reactant that is converted into product, it is called the equilibrium yield.

The actual yield in a process may be less than the equilibrium yield. This occurs in an open system, such as when reactant gases are passed through a catalyst bed. The system may not reach equilibrium because the gases are not in contact with the catalyst for long enough.

Le Châtelier's principle

In 1884, Le Châtelier put forward an idea that can be used to predict (but not to explain) the way in which the position of equilibrium alters as the physical and chemical conditions are changed.

> **When the conditions of a system in equilibrium are altered, the position of equilibrium alters in such a way as to try to restore the original conditions.**

Effect of temperature

The direction of the change in equilibrium position depends upon whether the reaction is exothermic or endothermic. The direction of change can be predicted using Le Châtelier's principle.

If a system at equilibrium is heated, the temperature rises and the system reacts to remove the heat energy and bring the temperature down. This means that heat energy must be converted into chemical energy. Therefore, the position of equilibrium shifts in the endothermic direction, causing:

- a decrease in the equilibrium yield for an exothermic reaction
- an increase in equilibrium yield for an endothermic reaction

Square brackets mean concentration.

Key term

The **equilibrium yield** of a reversible reaction is the percentage or fraction of reactant that is converted into product.

An increase in temperature shifts the equilibrium in the endothermic direction.

A decrease in temperature moves the equilibrium in the exothermic direction, so that chemical energy is converted to heat energy. The reason for this is that the equilibrium constant alters as the temperature of a reaction is altered.

For an **exothermic** reaction, if the temperature is increased the value of K gets smaller.

This means that the quotient is now larger than K and the position of equilibrium will move to the left, making the quotient smaller until it equals the new (smaller) value of K.

For an **endothermic** reaction, if the temperature is increased the value of K gets larger.

This means that the quotient is now smaller than K and the position of equilibrium will move to the right, making the quotient larger until it equals the new (larger) value of K.

Tip

For exothermic reactions: T up, K down.

For endothermic reactions: T up, K up.

Worked example 1

Predict the effect on the position of equilibrium of increasing the temperature in the following equilibrium system:

$$N_2O_4(g) \rightleftharpoons 2NO_2(g) \qquad \Delta H = +58\,kJ\,mol^{-1}$$
colourless   brown

Answer

The reaction is endothermic left to right. An increase in temperature will increase the value of K and so the quotient is now less than the new K value. The position of equilibrium will move to the right (in the endothermic direction) until the quotient once more equals K. This causes more of the dinitrogen tetroxide to decompose and the gaseous mixture darkens.

A mixture of N_2O_4 and NO_2 in glass flasks; the flask on the left is at a lower temperature

Hazard: Nitrogen dioxide is an irritant gas.

Dinitrogen tetroxide is a colourless gas; nitrogen dioxide is a brown gas. When dinitrogen tetroxide is heated, the gas darkens as increasing amounts of brown NO_2 are formed from N_2O_4.

Worked example 2

Predict the effect on the position of equilibrium of increasing the temperature in the following equilibrium system:

$$N_2(g) + 3H_2(g) \rightleftharpoons 2NH_3 \qquad \Delta H_r^\ominus = -92.4\,kJ\,mol^{-1}$$

Answer

The reaction is exothermic from left to right. An increase in temperature will decrease the value of K, causing the quotient to be greater than the new value of K. So the position of equilibrium moves to the left (the endothermic direction). This reduces the equilibrium yield of ammonia.

Tip

Reversible reactions go both ways and therefore simply stating that the reaction is exothermic is not sufficient. You must state that it is exothermic *left to right*.

The chloride complex of cobalt(II) ions, $CoCl_4^{2-}$, is blue and is in equilibrium with pink hydrated cobalt(II) ions, $Co(H_2O)_6^{2+}$, according to the equation:

$$\underset{\text{blue}}{CoCl_4^{2-}} + 6H_2O \rightleftharpoons \underset{\text{pink}}{Co(H_2O)_6^{2+}} + 4Cl^-$$

When a blue solution of mainly $CoCl_4^{2-}$ ions is cooled by being put in a beaker of ice, the colour changes to pink. Deduce whether the reaction as written is exothermic or endothermic.

Answer

On cooling the equilibrium shifts to the right. This means that the value of K_c is now larger at the lower temperature and so the reaction must be exothermic as written.

An increase in temperature speeds up the endothermic reaction in the equilibrium more than the exothermic reaction. This is because the activation energy for the reaction in the endothermic direction is greater than that for the reaction in the exothermic direction (Figure 15.3) and reactions with high activation energies are more sensitive to temperature changes than reactions with lower activation energies.

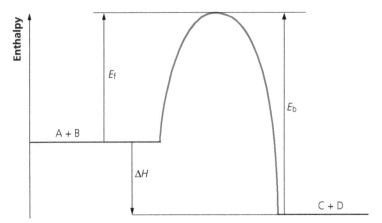

E_f is the activation energy for the reaction $A + B \rightarrow C + D$
E_b is the activation energy for the reaction $C + D \rightarrow CA + B$

Figure 15.3 Energy profile for the exothermic equilibrium reaction:
$A + B \rightleftharpoons C + D$

3 Nickel is purified by passing carbon monoxide gas over the heated metal. A gaseous nickel compound, $[Ni(CO)_4]$, is formed, according to the equilibrium:

$$Ni(s) + 4CO(g) \rightleftharpoons [Ni(CO)_4](g) \quad \Delta H_r^\circ = -161\,kJ\,mol^{-1}$$

The temperature is then altered and the equilibrium shifts in the reverse direction to produce pure nickel metal. Explain whether the temperature has to be increased or decreased to produce this effect.

Effect of concentration

A change in concentration has no effect on the value of the equilibrium constant. The effect of concentration applies to systems in which the reactants are dissolved in a solvent, usually water. If the concentration of one of the substances in the equilibrium reaction is increased, Le Châtelier's principle predicts that the position will shift to remove some of that substance. Consider the reaction used as a test for a bromide:

Concentration is measured by the number of moles of solute per dm³ of solution.

$$AgBr(s) + 2NH_3(aq) \rightleftharpoons [Ag(NH_3)_2]^+(aq) + Br^-(aq)$$

The position of equilibrium is normally to the left, so very little silver bromide dissolves in dilute aqueous ammonia. However, if concentrated ammonia is added, $[NH_3]$ increases. This drives the position of equilibrium to the right, causing the precipitate of silver bromide to disappear as it reacts to form $[Ag(NH_3)_2]^+$ ions.

If the concentration of one of the species in the equilibrium is decreased, the position of equilibrium shifts to produce more of that species.

Worked example 1

Dichromate(VI) ions, $Cr_2O_7^{2-}$, are orange and chromate(VI) ions, CrO_4^{2-}, are yellow. In aqueous solution, they are in equilibrium:

$$Cr_2O_7^{2-}(aq) + H_2O(l) \rightleftharpoons 2CrO_4^{2-}(aq) + 2H^+(aq)$$

orange   yellow

Predict and explain the colour change in the system when sodium hydroxide solution is added to a solution of potassium dichromate(VI).

Answer

The alkaline sodium hydroxide reacts with the $H^+(aq)$ ions in the equilibrium mixture, lowering the concentration of $H^+(aq)$ ions. This causes the equilibrium to shift to the right. The solution changes colour from orange to yellow, as chromate(VI) ions are formed from dichromate(VI) ions.

Worked example 2

When mixed, hydrated iron(III) ions are in equilibrium with thiocyanate ions:

$$Fe^{3+}(aq) + CNS^-(aq) \rightleftharpoons Fe(CNS)^{2+}(aq)$$

brown   colourless   blood red

$$K_c = \frac{[FeCNS^{2+}]}{[Fe^{3+}][CNS^-]} \text{ a large number}$$

Predict and explain the colour change when a few drops of the blood red equilibrium mixture are diluted by adding excess water.

Answer

The colour will change from blood red to a pale red-brown colour. This is because a decrease in the concentration of all the species will cause the quotient, Q, to get larger as the bottom line will decrease by more than the top line. The position will move to the left so that Q once again becomes equal to the unchanged value of K_c.

4 Copper hydroxide is in equilibrium with ammonia according to the equation below:

$$Cu(OH)_2(s) + 4NH_3(aq) \rightleftharpoons [Cu(NH_3)_4]^{2+}(aq) + 2OH^-(aq)$$
pale blue   deep purple

With dilute ammonia the position of equilibrium lies to the left. Describe the colour change when concentrated ammonia is then added.

Effect of pressure

The effect of pressure only applies to equilibrium reactions involving gases. Pressure is caused by the bombardment of the gas molecules on the walls of the container. At a given temperature, the pressure depends only on the number of gas molecules in a given volume.

The pressure of an equilibrium system at a given temperature can be increased by:

- reducing the volume
- adding more gas into the same volume

Both methods result in more moles per cm^3.

The direction of change of the equilibrium position caused by a change in pressure depends upon the number of gas molecules (or moles of gas) on each side of the equation. If the pressure is increased, Le Châtelier's principle predicts that the system will react in order to try to bring the pressure down again. This can only happen if the equilibrium shifts to the side with *fewer* gas molecules.

> An increase in pressure on the reaction mixture (at constant temperature) will cause the position of equilibrium to shift towards the side of the equation with fewer gas molecules (fewer moles of gas).

Consider an equilibrium:

gaseous reactants $\rightleftharpoons$ gaseous products

An increase in pressure has *no* effect on the value of the equilibrium constant. It will alter the value of the quotient if there is a different number of gas molecules on each side of the equation.

A decrease in pressure will cause the equilibrium to shift towards the side of the equation with more gas molecules.

Worked example 1

Predict the effect on the position of equilibrium of increasing the pressure in the following equilibrium system:

$$N_2(g) + 3H_2(g) \rightleftharpoons 2NH_3(g) \quad \Delta H_r^\ominus = -92.4\,kJ \quad K_c = \frac{[NH_3]^2}{[N_2][H_2]^3}$$

Answer

The value of K_c is only altered by a change in temperature.

There are four gas molecules on the left-hand side of the equation and only two on the right. An increase in pressure on the system at equilibrium will increase the bottom of the quotient more than the top. This means that the quotient gets smaller and is no longer equal to the unchanged value of K. The reaction moves to the right increasing the value of the quotient until it once again equals the unchanged value of K. The result is that the position of equilibrium shifts to the side with fewer gas molecules, which is to the right. High pressures will increase the proportion of nitrogen and hydrogen that is converted into ammonia.

Worked example 2

Predict the effect on the position of equilibrium of increasing the pressure in the following equilibrium system:

$$H_2(g) + I_2(g) \rightleftharpoons 2HI(g) \qquad \Delta H_r^{\ominus} = +51.8\,kJ$$

Answer

There are 2 moles of gas on each side of the equation. Therefore, an increase in pressure will have *no* effect on the quotient or on the position of equilibrium.

Worked example 3

Methane can be trapped in water as the solid methane hydrate, $[CH_4(H_2O)_6]$. The reaction between methane gas and water to form methane hydrate is exothermic:

$$CH_4(g) + 6H_2O(l) \rightleftharpoons [CH_4(H_2O)_6](s) \qquad \Delta H \text{ is negative}$$

Huge quantities of methane hydrate are found at the bottom of the sea off the Canadian coast, where the pressure is very high.

a) Predict what would happen if the pressure on solid methane hydrate were reduced to 1 atm.

b) Predict what would happen to the methane hydrate if it were heated.

c) Predict what would happen if methane hydrate crystals were brought to the surface of the sea, from the great depths off the Canadian coast.

Answer

a) There is 1 mol of gas on the left-hand side of the equation and none on the right. By Le Châtelier's principle, a decrease in pressure will cause the equilibrium to shift to the side with more gas molecules. This means that the methane hydrate will decompose and methane gas will be produced.

b) The reaction as written is exothermic. An increase in temperature will cause the equilibrium position to shift in the endothermic direction, which is to the left. Therefore, the methane hydrate will decompose.

c) Raising the solid methane hydrate from the cold ocean floor means a decrease in pressure and an increase in temperature. As can be seen from the answers to parts a) and b), this would result in the methane hydrate decomposing into methane gas and water.

Test yourself

5 Predict whether the position of equilibrium moves to the left, to the right or is unaltered when the pressure on each of the following systems is increased:

a) $2O_3(g) \rightleftharpoons 3O_2(g)$

b) $C(s) + H_2O(g) \rightleftharpoons CO(g) + H_2(g)$

Effect of a catalyst

A catalyst works by providing an alternative route that has a lower activation energy than that of the uncatalysed reaction. Therefore, the rate of reaction with a catalyst is much faster than the rate without the catalyst (page 265).

A catalyst has *no* effect on either the value of K or on the position of equilibrium of a reversible reaction. It speeds up the forward and back reactions equally, so equilibrium is reached sooner than without the catalyst.

Catalysts are important in industrial processes, many of which are extremely slow at room temperature. Finding a suitable catalyst is therefore very necessary. This is particularly so if the reaction is reversible and exothermic, which would result in a low yield at a high temperature.

The Haber process for the manufacture of ammonia is based on the equilibrium:

$$N_2(g) + 3H_2(g) \rightleftharpoons 2NH_3(g) \quad \Delta H_r^\ominus = -92.4\,kJ\,mol^{-1}$$

The reaction is very slow at room temperature because of the $N\equiv N$ bond energy of $945\,kJ\,mol^{-1}$. However, if it is heated, in the absence of a catalyst, to a temperature at which the rate is economic, the yield is extremely small.

For exothermic reactions such as this:

- a high temperature results in a *low* equilibrium yield, reached *quickly* because the reaction is fast. The low yield makes the process uneconomic.
- a lower temperature results in a *higher* equilibrium yield reached more *slowly* because the reaction rate is slow. The slow rate makes the process uneconomic.
- a catalyst is used to allow the reaction to take place rapidly at a lower temperature, so that an acceptable yield is produced at a reasonable rate. This is often called a 'compromise temperature' as it balances an economic yield with an economic rate.

Summary tasks

Make sure that you can:

- define what is meant by equilibrium in terms of concentrations and of rate
- write the expression for K_c given the equation

Check that you can predict and explain the effect on the position of equilibrium of:

- a change in pressure for gaseous reactions
- a change in temperature for both exothermic and endothermic reactions
- a change of concentration of a reactant or product
- the addition of a catalyst

Check that you can explain why the conditions for a given manufacture are chosen.

Questions

1 Explain the term **dynamic equilibrium** with reference to the equilibrium reaction:

$$2SO_2(g) + O_2(g) \rightleftharpoons 2SO_3(g)$$

2 Nitrogen and hydrogen react reversibly to form ammonia:

$$N_2(g) + 3H_2(g) \rightleftharpoons 2NH_3(g)$$

Under certain conditions, 1 mol of nitrogen and 3 mol of hydrogen were mixed and 20% of the gases reacted. Draw three graphs, on the same axes, showing the number of moles against time, for each of nitrogen, hydrogen and ammonia. Label your graphs.

3 Alcohols react reversibly with organic acids to produce an ester plus water. Predict the effect of increasing the temperature on the position of equilibrium of the esterification reaction between ethanol and ethanoic acid:

$$C_2H_5OH(l) + CH_3COOH(l) \rightleftharpoons$$
$$CH_3COOC_2H_5(l) + H_2O(l)$$
$$\Delta H_r^{\ominus} = 0\,kJ\,mol^{-1}$$

4 Gaseous carbon dioxide dissolves in water and forms a solution of carbonic acid, H_2CO_3:

$$CO_2(g) + H_2O(l) \rightleftharpoons H_2CO_3(aq) \quad \Delta H_r^{\ominus} = ?$$

Carbon dioxide is more soluble in cold water than in hot water. Explain whether ΔH for this reaction is exothermic or endothermic.

5 Hydrogen gas is manufactured by passing methane and steam over a heated nickel catalyst:

$$CH_4(g) + H_2O(g) \rightleftharpoons CO(g) + 3H_2(g)$$
$$\Delta H_r = +206\,kJ\,mol^{-1}$$

Explain why a temperature of 750°C and a catalyst are used.

6 The second stage in the manufacture of sulfuric acid is the oxidation of sulfur dioxide in air:

$$SO_2(g) + \tfrac{1}{2}O_2(g) \rightleftharpoons SO_3(g)$$
$$\Delta H_r = -98\,kJ\,mol^{-1}$$

Explain why the conditions used are a temperature of 420°C and a vanadium(V) oxide catalyst.

7 Predict whether the position of equilibrium moves to the left, to the right or is unaltered when the pressure on each of the following systems is increased:
   a) $4NH_3(g) + 5O_2(g) \rightleftharpoons 4NO(g) + 6H_2O(g)$
   b) $SO_2(g) + \tfrac{1}{2}O_2(g) \rightleftharpoons SO_3(g)$

8 At 15°C, red-brown iodine monochloride (melting temperature 27°C) reacts with chlorine to form the orange solid iodine trichloride (melting temperature 101°C), according to the equation:
$$ICl(s) + Cl_2(g) \rightleftharpoons ICl_3(s)$$
   a) On heating a mixture at equilibrium, the equilibrium position shifts to the left. What is the sign of ΔH for this reaction? Justify your answer.
   b) What would be the effect of increasing the pressure on an equilibrium mixture?
   c) What would you observe if a sample of iodine trichloride was heated to 50°C?

9 Lead chloride, $PbCl_2$, is an insoluble solid. When some dilute hydrochloric acid is added, the following equilibrium occurs:

$$PbCl_2(s) + 2Cl^-(aq) \rightleftharpoons PbCl_4^{2-}(aq)$$

The position of equilibrium is to the left, so most of the lead chloride is present as a solid. Predict what would happen if concentrated hydrochloric acid were added to solid lead chloride.

10 Write the expression for the equilibrium constant, K_c, for:
   a) $Mg(NO_3)_2(s) \rightleftharpoons MgO(s) + 2NO_2(g) + \tfrac{1}{2}O_2(g)$
   b) $4NH_3(g) + 5O_2(g) \rightleftharpoons 4NO(g) + 6H_2O(g)$
   c) $C_4H_6(g) + 2HBr(g) \rightleftharpoons C_4H_8Br_2(g)$

Exam practice questions

1 a) Consider the equilibrium reaction:

$$C(s) + 2H_2O(g) \rightleftharpoons CO_2(g) + 2H_2(g)$$
$$\Delta H = +90\,kJ\,mol^{-1}$$

    i) What is the correct expression for K_c?

      A $K_c = \dfrac{[CO_2][H_2]^2}{[C][H_2O]^2}$

      B $K_c = \dfrac{[CO_2][H_2]}{[C][H_2O]}$

      C $K_c = \dfrac{[CO_2][H_2]^2}{[H_2O]^2}$

      D $K_c = \dfrac{[CO_2][H_2]}{[H_2O]}$ (1)

    ii) Explain the effect on the position of equilibrium of increasing the temperature.   (2)

    iii) Explain the effect on the position of equilibrium of increasing the pressure.   (2)

b) Consider the equilibrium reaction:

$$3Fe(s) + 4H_2O(g) \rightleftharpoons Fe_3O_4(s) + 4H_2(g)$$
$$\Delta H = -149\,kJ\,mol^{-1}$$

Which will move the position of the equilibrium to the right?

A an increase in pressure
B a decrease in pressure
C an increase in temperature
D a decrease in temperature   (1)

c) In aqueous solution, orange dichromate(VI) ions are in equilibrium with yellow chromate(VI) ions:

$$Cr_2O_7^{2-}(aq) + H_2O(l) \rightleftharpoons$$
$$2CrO_4^{2-}(aq) + 2H^+(aq)$$

The equilibrium position lies to the left, so a solution of potassium dichromate(VI) is orange. Lead(II) chromate(VI) is an insoluble yellow solid. When a few drops of lead(II) nitrate are added to an aqueous solution of potassium dichromate(VI), there is:

A a yellow precipitate
B an orange precipitate
C a white precipitate in a yellow solution
D no precipitate because lead ions do not react with dichromate(VI) ions   (1)

d) In the presence of an iron catalyst, nitrogen and hydrogen react to form ammonia:

$$N_2(g) + 3H_2(g) \rightleftharpoons 2NH_3(g)$$
$$\Delta H = -92\,kJ\,mol^{-1}$$

An increase in temperature will:

A slow down the forward exothermic reaction and increase the rate of the reverse endothermic reaction, thus moving the position of equilibrium to the left
B have no effect as the catalyst controls the reaction
C make less ammonia more quickly
D make more ammonia more quickly   (1)

          (Total 8 marks)

2 Phosphorus(III) chloride reacts reversibly with chlorine to form phosphorus(V) chloride

$$PCl_3(g) + Cl_2(g) \rightleftharpoons PCl_5(g)$$
$$\Delta H = -124\,kJ\,mol^{-1}$$

a) State and explain the effect on the position of this equilibrium of decreasing:
    i) the temperature   (3)
    ii) the pressure   (3)

b) i) Draw a dot-and-cross diagram of a molecule of gaseous PCl_3 showing outer electrons only.   (2)
    ii) State the shape of this molecule and give an estimate of the Cl−P−Cl bond angle.   (2)

c) When equal amounts of phosphorus(III) chloride and chlorine are mixed at a temperature T, 75% of both gases react. Sketch a concentration/time graph showing equilibrium being set up.   (3)

d) Gaseous chlorine is slightly soluble in water. State and explain how the solubility of chlorine would change if the pressure of chlorine were increased.   (2)

          (Total 15 marks)

16 Exam technique and laboratory chemistry

This chapter is designed to help with answering questions in exams, especially those that are based on practical work — for example, enthalpy experiments and titrations.

Exam technique

Mark allocation

In all A level papers the marks for each part of the question are given in brackets. This is a much better guide as to how much to write than the number of dotted lines provided for the answer. If there are 2 marks, two statements must be made. For example, if the question asks for the conditions for a particular reaction and there are 2 marks available, there must be two different conditions given, such as solvent, temperature or catalyst.

Alternative answers

Do *not* give alternative answers. If one of them is wrong, the examiner will not award any marks for this part of the question. If both answers are correct, you *would* score the mark. However, there is no point in risking one answer being wrong. Beware also of contradictions, such as giving the reagent as concentrated sulfuric acid and then writing H_2SO_4(aq) in an equation.

Writing your answers

In Edexcel A level chemistry exams the answers are written in the spaces on the question paper. If part of your answer is written elsewhere on the page, alert the examiner by writing, for example, 'see below' or 'continued on page 5'. Exam papers will be marked online, so question papers and answers will be electronically scanned. For this reason, it is essential *not to write outside the borders* marked on the page, unless you indicate that you have done so.

For the multiple-choice questions, you must put a cross in the box corresponding to your chosen answer. If you change your mind, put a horizontal line through the cross. Then, mark your new choice with a cross. The multiple-choice questions contain four possible answers, labelled A, B, C and D. Only one of these is the correct answer to the question. Be aware that some questions are expressed as negatives — for example, 'Which of the following species is **not** polar?'

Correction fluid and coloured pens

Do not use either of these. Mistakes should be crossed out neatly before writing the new answer. Red or other coloured inks will not show up as being different from black or blue ink when the paper is scanned ready for online marking. If you cross something out and then wish you had not done so, add the words 'please ignore crossing out'. The examiner will then read and mark the crossed-out material.

Command words

It is important that you respond correctly to key words or phrases in the question.

- **Define** — definitions of important terms such as relative atomic mass or standard enthalpy of formation are frequently asked for. You *must* know these definitions. They are displayed as *key terms* in this book.
- **Name** — give the full name of the substance, *not* its formula.
- **Identify** — give either the name or the formula.
- **Write the formula** — a molecular formula, such as C_2H_5Cl, will suffice, as long as it is unambiguous. It is no use writing C_2H_4O for the formula of ethanal, or C_3H_7Br for the formula for 2-bromopropane. This also applies to equations. For example, the equation $C_2H_4 + Br_2 \rightarrow C_2H_4Br_2$ would not score a mark, because the formula $C_2H_4Br_2$ is ambiguous.
- **Draw or write the structural formula** — this must clearly show the position of the functional group. All double bonds should be shown. For example, an acceptable structural formula of but-1-ene is $H_2C=CHCH_2CH_3$.
- **Draw the displayed formula or the full structural formula** — all the atoms and all the bonds in the molecule *must* be shown. For example, the displayed formula of ethanoic acid is:

- **State** — give the answer without any explanation. For example, if asked to state in which direction the position of equilibrium moves, the answer is simply 'to the left' or 'to the right'.
- **State, giving your reasons** — this is a difficult type of question. First, look at the mark allocation. Then state the answer (usually 1 mark unless the answer is one of only two possibilities — a so-called 50/50 question) and follow this with an explanation containing enough chemical points to score the remaining marks.
- **Explain or justify your answer** — look at the mark allocation and then give the same number of pieces of chemical explanation, or even one extra. For example, in answer to the question 'Explain why but-2-ene has two geometric isomers (2)', the first point is that there is restricted rotation about the double bond and the second point is that there are two different groups on each double-bonded carbon atom.
- **Deduce** — the data supplied in the question, or an answer from a previous part of the question, are used to work out the answer. The data could be numerical or they could be the results of qualitative tests on an unknown substance. Alternatively, knowledge from another part of the specification may be needed to answer a question about a related topic or similar substance.
- **Predict** — you are not expected to know the answer. Knowledge and understanding of similar compounds have to be used to work out (deduce) the answer. For example, the shape of SF_6 is covered in the specification, so you should be able to deduce the shape of the PCl_6^- ion. Alternatively, the question might ask you to suggest the identity of an organic compound because there are not sufficient data to decide between two possible isomers.

- **Suggest** *or* **Apply your knowledge of…to answer this question** — you are not expected to have learnt the answer to the question, but you are expected to use your knowledge from a linked topic that is in the specification and apply it to the question. For example, 'Apply your knowledge of the mechanism of the electrophilic addition of HCl to alkenes to suggest the mechanism of the addition of iodine monochloride, ICl, to ethene'.
- **Compare** *or* **explain the difference between** — valid points must be made about *both* substances. For example, if the question asks for an explanation for the difference in the boiling temperatures of hydrogen fluoride and hydrogen chloride, the different types and strengths of intermolecular forces in *both* substances must be described, together with an explanation of what causes these differences.
- **Calculate** — it is advisable to show all working. For example, if the question asks for an empirical formula to be derived from % mass data, it must be clear to the examiner that you have first divided by the relative atomic mass and then by the smallest answer. Work should always be set out so that if you make a mistake and the wrong answer is calculated, the examiner can identify the mistake and award marks for the consequential steps in the calculation. Always give your final answer to the number of significant figures justified by the number of significant figures in the data. Never round to one or two significant figures in the intermediate steps of a calculation. It is best to leave *all* the numbers on your calculator and then round up at the end of the calculation.
- **Identify the reagent** — give the *full* name or formula. Answers such as 'acidified dichromate' or 'OH⁻ ions' may not score full marks. The name of a reagent is the name on the bottle.
- **State the conditions** — do not automatically write down 'heat under reflux'. The answer might be 'at room temperature' or you might be expected to know the necessary solvent (e.g. ethanol as a solvent for the elimination of HBr from bromoalkanes) or a specific catalyst (e.g. platinum or nickel in the addition of hydrogen to alkenes). If a concentrated acid is needed in a reaction, this must be stated.

Equations

- Equations must always be balanced. Word equations never score any marks.
- Ionic equations and half-equations must also balance for charge.
- State symbols must be included:
  - if the question asks for them
  - in all thermochemical equations
  - if a precipitate or a gas is produced
- The use of the symbols [O] and [H] in organic oxidation and reduction reactions, respectively, is acceptable. Equations using these symbols must still be properly balanced.
- Organic formulae used in equations must be written in such a way that their structures are unambiguous.

Stability

'Alkanes are stable' has no meaning. 'Stability' must only be used when comparing two states or two sets of compounds. Alkanes may be unreactive, but a mixture of methane and air is thermodynamically unstable. This means that methane and oxygen are unstable compared with their combustion products, carbon dioxide and water.

Graphs

Normally, there is a mark for labelling the axes. When sketching a graph, make sure that any numbers are on a linear scale. The graph should start at the right place, have the correct shape and end at the right place. An example is the Maxwell–Boltzmann distribution, which starts at the origin, rises in a curve to a maximum and tails off as an asymptote to the x-axis.

Diagrams of apparatus

Make sure that a flask and condenser are not drawn as one continuous piece of glassware. The apparatus must work. Be particularly careful when drawing a condenser. There must be an outlet to the air somewhere in the apparatus. In distillation, the top should be closed and the outlet should be at the end of the condenser. For heating under reflux, the top of the condenser must be open. It is always safer to draw an electrical heater, in case one of the reagents is flammable.

Doom and gloom

Avoid apocalyptic environmental predictions. For example, the ozone layer is only damaged by CFCs, not by other chlorine compounds; discarded plastic does not decimate all wildlife; inorganic fertilisers do not wipe out all aquatic life.

Read the question

In one paper I was marking, the students had been asked to draw an isomer of 2-bromopropane. About half failed to read the question properly and drew the structure of 2-bromopropane, not its isomer.

Quality of written communication (QWC)

The most important thing is to convey the meaning clearly, accurately and in a logical order. Minor spelling errors do not matter, unless they cause ambiguity or imply a different group in a molecule. You could spell phenolphthalein in a variety of ways without being penalised, but phenylphthalein will not earn a mark because 'phenyl' is a specific group and is different from phenol.

Laboratory tests

Tests for gases

The tests used to identify the common laboratory gases have to be learnt. It is also important to be able to draw conclusions from the identification of these gases. For example, if dilute sulfuric acid is added to a solid and a gas is produced that turns limewater milky, the conclusions are that:

- the gas is carbon dioxide
- the unknown solid is a carbonate or a hydrogencarbonate

Hydrogen
Test: ignite the gas

Observation: burns with a squeaky pop

Equation: $H_2 + \frac{1}{2}O_2 \rightarrow H_2O$

Hydrogen is produced by:

- the reaction between an acid and a reactive metal
- the reaction between water and either a group 1 metal, or calcium, strontium or barium

Oxygen

Test: place a glowing wooden splint in the gas

Observation: splint catches fire

Oxygen is produced by:

- heating a group 1 nitrate
- heating other nitrates, but NO_2 is also present
- the catalytic decomposition of hydrogen peroxide, H_2O_2

Carbon dioxide

Test: pass gas into limewater

Observation: limewater goes cloudy/milky

Equation: $CO_2(g) + Ca(OH)_2(aq) \rightarrow CaCO_3(s) + H_2O(l)$

Carbon dioxide is produced by:

- the reaction between an acid and a carbonate or hydrogencarbonate
- heating a carbonate (apart from sodium, potassium or barium carbonates)
- heating a group 1 hydrogencarbonate

Ammonia

Test: place damp red litmus paper in the gas

Observation: litmus paper goes blue

Ammonia is produced by:

- heating aqueous sodium hydroxide with an ammonium salt
- adding aqueous sodium hydroxide and aluminium powder to a nitrate

Nitrogen dioxide

Test: observe colour

Observation: gas is brown

Nitrogen dioxide is produced by:

- heating a group 2 nitrate or lithium nitrate

Chlorine

Test: place damp litmus paper in the gas

Observation: litmus paper is rapidly bleached

Chlorine is produced by:

- electrolysis of a solution of a chloride
- adding dilute hydrochloric acid to a solution containing chlorate(I) ions

> **Tip**
>
> The only hydrogen-carbonates that exist as solids are those of group 1 metals.

Hydrogen chloride

Test 1: place damp blue litmus paper in the gas

Observation: steamy fumes that turn damp litmus paper red

Test 2: place the stopper from a bottle of concentrated ammonia in the gas

Observation: white smoke (ammonium chloride) is formed

Equation: $HCl(g) + NH_3(g) \rightarrow NH_4Cl(s)$

Hydrogen chloride is produced by:

- the reaction between concentrated sulfuric acid and a chloride
- the reaction between phosphorus pentachloride and either an alcohol or a carboxylic acid

Sulfur dioxide

Test: place filter paper soaked in potassium dichromate(VI) solution in the gas

Observation: colour changes from orange to green

Equation: $3SO_2 + Cr_2O_7^{2-} + 2H^+ \rightarrow 3SO_4^{2-} + 2Cr^{3+} + H_2O$

Sulfur dioxide is produced by:

- warming an acid with a solid sulfite
- burning sulfur
- reducing concentrated sulfuric acid

Flame tests

To carry out a flame test, a *clean* platinum or nichrome test wire is dipped into concentrated hydrochloric acid, then into the solid to be tested and finally into the hottest part of a Bunsen flame.

The concentrated hydrochloric acid converts some of the unknown solid into a chloride. Chlorides are more volatile than other salts, so some of the unknown goes into the gas phase when heated in the hot flame. An electron is promoted to a higher energy level by the heat. It then falls back to the ground state and emits light of a colour specific to the metal present in the compound (see page 101). The colours obtained in flame tests are given in Table 16.1.

Table 16.1 Flame colours

Flame colour	Ion present in solid
Crimson	Li^+
Yellow	Na^+
Lilac	K^+
Yellow-red	Ca^{2+}
Red	Sr^{2+}
Pale green	Ba^{2+}

Tip

You must know the formulae of the ammonium ion, NH_4^+, and common polyatomic anions, such as carbonate, CO_3^{2-}, hydrogencarbonate, HCO_3^-, sulfate, SO_4^{2-}, sulfite, SO_3^{2-}, nitrate NO_3^- and chlorate(I), ClO^-.

Tip

The flame test is the only test for a group 1 metal in a compound.

Magnesium compounds do not colour a flame.

Tip

Flame tests cannot be used on mixtures containing two of these ions because the colour produced by one of the ions will mask the colour produced by the other metal ion.

Precipitation reactions

It is important to know which ionic compounds are soluble in water and which are insoluble.

Soluble ionic compounds include:

- all group 1 salts
- all ammonium salts
- all nitrates
- all chlorides, apart from silver chloride and lead(II) chloride. (The solubility of bromides and iodides is similar to that of chlorides.)
- all sulfates, apart from barium sulfate, strontium sulfate and lead(II) sulfate. Calcium sulfate and silver sulfate are slightly soluble.

Insoluble ionic compounds include:

- all carbonates, apart from group 1 carbonates and ammonium carbonate
- all hydroxides, apart from group 1 hydroxides, barium hydroxide and ammonium hydroxide. Calcium and strontium hydroxides are slightly soluble.

The results of some precipitation reactions are shown in Table 16.2.

Table 16.2 Precipitation reactions

Solutions containing these ions are mixed	Result
Ba^{2+} and SO_4^{2-} (sulfate ions could be from solutions of group 1 sulfates, ammonium sulfate or from sulfuric acid)	• White precipitate of barium sulfate • On adding dilute hydrochloric acid, the precipitate remains
Ba^{2+} and SO_3^{2-}	• White precipitate of barium sulfite • On adding dilute hydrochloric acid, the precipitate dissolves with no fizzing
Ag^+ and Cl^- (silver ions are normally from a solution of silver nitrate)	• Chalky-white precipitate of silver chloride • Precipitate dissolves in dilute aqueous ammonia
Ag^+ and Br^-	• Cream precipitate of silver bromide • Precipitate is insoluble in dilute ammonia, but soluble in concentrated ammonia
Ag^+ and I^-	• Pale yellow precipitate of silver iodide • Precipitate is insoluble in both dilute and concentrated ammonia
CO_3^{2-} and any cation, other than a group 1 metal or ammonium (carbonate ions could be from solutions of group 1 carbonates or ammonium carbonate)	• White precipitate of the insoluble metal carbonate • On adding acid, the precipitate fizzes as it gives off carbon dioxide and disappears

See pages 112–13.

The ionic equations for these precipitation reactions will always be of the form:

cation(aq) + anion(aq) → formula of precipitate(s)

For example, the ionic equation for the formation of barium sulfate by mixing solutions of barium chloride and potassium sulfate is:

$$Ba^{2+}(aq) + SO_4^{2-}(aq) \rightarrow BaSO_4(s)$$

Tests for anions

Sulfate

To a solution of the suspected sulfate, add dilute hydrochloric acid followed by aqueous barium chloride. A white precipitate, which remains when excess hydrochloric acid is added, proves the presence of sulfate ions.

Sulfite

To the suspected sulfite, add dilute sulfuric acid and warm. If it is a sulfite, sulfur dioxide gas will be given off. This is tested for by placing a piece of filter paper soaked in potassium dichromate(VI) in the gas. A colour change from orange to green on the paper confirms the presence of sulfite ions in the original solid.

This test can be carried out on either an unknown solid or a solution of the unknown.

Carbonate

Add dilute sulfuric acid to the suspected carbonate in solid form. If it is a carbonate, carbon dioxide will be given off. This is tested for by passing the gas into limewater, which goes milky.

Alternatively, heat the solid. Carbonates, other than sodium, potassium and barium carbonate, give off carbon dioxide.

Tip

Both these tests work with hydrogencarbonates as well, so the initial conclusion should be that carbonate or hydrogencarbonate is present. However, the only hydrogencarbonates that exist as solids are group 1 compounds. If the unknown is found to be a group 1 compound, the test for hydrogencarbonate must be carried out. If the result is negative, the original compound is a carbonate.

Hydrogencarbonate

There are three ways to distinguish between a group 1 carbonate and a hydrogencarbonate:

- add some of the unknown solid to almost boiling water. Hydrogencarbonates decompose with the production of carbon dioxide — fizzing occurs. Carbon dioxide can be tested for by passing it into limewater, which goes milky.
- add a solution of the unknown to a solution of calcium chloride. Hydrogencarbonates do not give a precipitate because calcium hydrogencarbonate is soluble; carbonates give a white precipitate of calcium carbonate.
- test a solution with pH paper. Carbonates have a high (alkaline) pH whereas hydrogencarbonates are almost neutral. On warming, if the solution is a hydrogencarbonate, the pH rises rapidly as the hydrogencarbonate decomposes to give a carbonate and carbon dioxide.

Chloride

To a solution of the suspected chloride, add dilute nitric acid until the solution is just acidic (test with litmus paper). Then, add silver nitrate solution. A chalky-white precipitate, which dissolves when excess dilute ammonia is added, proves the presence of chloride ions in the original solution.

Bromide

To a solution of the suspected bromide, add dilute nitric acid until the solution is just acidic (test with litmus paper). Then, add silver nitrate solution. A cream precipitate, which is insoluble in dilute ammonia but dissolves in concentrated ammonia, proves the presence of bromide ions in the original solution.

An alternative test is to add chlorine water to a solution of the unknown. Bromide ions are oxidised to bromine, which turns the colourless solution brown.

Iodide

To a solution of the suspected iodide, add dilute nitric acid until the solution is just acidic (test with litmus paper). Then, add silver nitrate solution. A pale yellow precipitate, which remains when concentrated ammonia is added, proves the presence of iodide ions in the original solution.

An alternative test is to add chlorine water to a solution of the unknown and then add a few drops of an organic solvent such as hexane. Iodide ions are oxidised to iodine, so the colourless hexane layer turns violet. The presence of iodine from the oxidation of iodide ions can also be detected by adding starch, which turns blue-black.

> The result would be the same if bromine water had been added. Bromine is a stronger oxidising agent than iodine and therefore oxidises iodide ions to iodine.

Nitrate

To the unknown solid, add aluminium powder or Devarda's alloy and sodium hydroxide solution and then warm. Nitrate ions are reduced to ammonia, which can be detected by the gas evolved turning damp red litmus paper blue.

An alternative is the 'brown-ring' test. Mix together solutions of the unknown and iron(II) sulfate. Then carefully pour some concentrated sulfuric acid down the side of the test tube. A brown ring forms where the concentrated acid and aqueous layers meet.

> Before doing this test you need to show that the compound is not an ammonium salt, as ammonium salts give ammonia when heated with alkali.

Test yourself

1 A solid X gave an apple green flame colour. When solutions of silver nitrate and X in acid were mixed, a white precipitate was observed. Identify X.

Tests for cations

Ammonium

Warm the unknown solid or solution with aqueous sodium hydroxide. Ammonium salts give off ammonia gas, which can be detected by placing damp red litmus paper in the gas. Ammonia turns the paper blue.

Group 1 and group 2 cations

Group 1 and group 2 cations are detected by the flame test (pages 100–01).

Magnesium compounds do not colour a flame, but are colourless in solution and give a white precipitate of magnesium carbonate when ammonium carbonate solution is added.

p-block and d-block cations

The detection of the ions of p-block and d-block elements is tested in the second year of A level.

Tests for organic functional groups

Test for a C=C bond

Add bromine water to the test compound. Compounds containing a C=C bond (unsaturated compounds) turn the bromine water from orange to colourless.

$$>C=C< + Br_2 + H_2O \rightarrow >C(OH)-C(Br)< + HBr$$

Test for a C—OH group

Add solid phosphorus pentachloride to the anhydrous compound. If the compound contains a C—OH group (carboxylic acids and alcohols), steamy fumes of hydrogen chloride will be produced. This can be detected by putting damp blue litmus in the gas. Hydrogen chloride turns the litmus red.

$$ROH + PCl_5 \rightarrow RCl + POCl_3 + HCl$$

> **Tip**
>
> Do not state that this is a test for alcohols. If a compound gives a positive result for a C—OH group, you then have to determine whether it is a carboxylic acid or an alcohol. To distinguish between the two, add some of the test compound to sodium hydrogencarbonate solution. An acid will produce fizzing as carbon dioxide is given off; with an alcohol there is no reaction.

Test for a C—halogen group

Warm the unknown with aqueous sodium hydroxide for several minutes, being careful not to boil off a volatile organic compound. Allow the solution to cool. Add nitric acid until the solution is just acidic to litmus. Then add silver nitrate solution.

$$R-hal + OH^- \rightarrow R-OH + hal^-$$

then

$$hal^-(aq) + Ag^+(aq) \rightarrow Aghal(s)$$

- Organic chlorides give a white precipitate of silver chloride, which is soluble in dilute ammonia.
- Organic bromides give a cream precipitate of silver bromide, which is insoluble in dilute ammonia but dissolves in concentrated ammonia.
- Organic iodides give a pale yellow precipitate of silver iodide, which is insoluble in both dilute and concentrated ammonia.

> A little ethanol is sometimes added to help dissolve the halogenoalkane and bring it into contact with the hydroxide ions.

> The organic halogen compound is hydrolysed by the sodium hydroxide to give halide ions in solution, which then react with the silver ions to form a precipitate.

> **Tip**
>
> Remember that an organic unknown may contain two functional groups.

> **Test yourself**
>
> 2 A neutral organic liquid $C_4H_{10}O$:
> - gave steamy fumes with phosphorus(v) chloride
> - produced a green solution and a ketone when warmed with acidified potassium dichromate(vi)
>
> Write the structural formula of the organic liquid.

Organic techniques

Heating under reflux

> **Tip**
>
> You are expected to know techniques used in organic preparations. You must be able to draw diagrams of the necessary apparatus and know when to use each method.

Organic substances are volatile and the rates of many organic reactions are slow. Heating is used to speed up reactions, but if this is done in an open vessel, such as a beaker, the organic reactant and the product may boil off. To prevent this happening, a reflux condenser is used. The organic vapours that boil off as the reaction mixture is heated are condensed and flow back into the reaction vessel. As most organic substances are flammable, it is safer to heat the mixture using an electric heater or a water bath rather than a Bunsen burner.

The essential points of the apparatus (Figure 16.1) are:

- a round-bottomed flask
- a reflux condenser with the water entering at the bottom and leaving at the top
- the top of the reflux condenser being open
- the flask being heated using an electric heater, a water or oil bath or a sand tray

Reactions where heating under reflux is necessary include:

- oxidising a primary alcohol to a carboxylic acid
- oxidising a secondary alcohol to a ketone
- converting a halogenoalkane to an alcohol
- converting an alcohol to a bromoalkane by reacting it with potassium bromide and 50% sulfuric acid

Distillation

Most organic reactions do not go to completion and there are often side reactions. This means that the desired product is present in a mixture. Organic substances are volatile, so they can be separated from non-volatile inorganic species, such as acids or alkalis, by distillation.

If there is a large enough difference in the boiling temperatures of organic substances present in a mixture, then distillation can be used to separate them.

The essential points about the apparatus (Figure 16.2) are:

- a round-bottomed or pear-shaped flask containing the mixture
- a still-head fitted with a thermometer, the bulb of which must be positioned level with the outlet of the still-head
- a condenser with the water going in at the bottom and leaving at the top
- an open receiving vessel, such as a beaker, or an adaptor open to the air joined to a flask
- the flask being heated using an electric heater, a water or oil bath or sand tray

The mixture is carefully heated and the vapour that comes over at ±2°C of the boiling temperature (obtained from a data book) of the particular substance is condensed and collected.

Steam distillation

A volatile organic substance can be separated from an aqueous mixture containing insoluble matter by steam distillation. The simplest method is to heat the mixture in a distillation apparatus and collect the organic product and water as they distil off. The organic product is then isolated using a separating funnel and dried with an anhydrous inorganic compound.

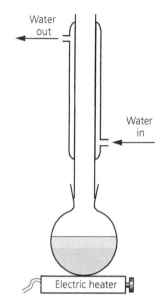

Figure 16.1 Apparatus for heating under reflux

Tip

Make sure that you draw a Liebig condenser correctly, with water flowing around the central tube. Do not draw the flask and condenser as a single unit — there must be a join between them.

Tip

Make sure that the top of the still-head is closed and that the Liebig condenser is drawn with a water jacket.

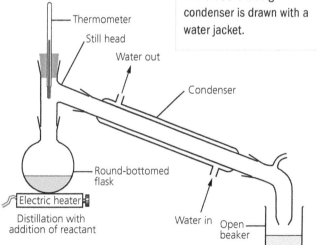

Figure 16.2 Apparatus for simple distillation

Tip

You must be able to draw the two types of apparatus shown in Figures 16.1 and 16.2.

Drying

A damp organic liquid can be dried by adding anhydrous sodium sulfate or anhydrous calcium chloride. The initial mixture will be cloudy but as the water is removed the liquid goes clear. The organic liquid can then be filtered off.

Solvent extraction

Clove oil can be extracted from cloves by crushing them in a pestle and mortar and then adding a suitable solvent such as hexane. The mixture is shaken and the oil dissolved in hexane is filtered off. It is then placed in a distillation apparatus and the hexane distilled off.

Boiling temperature determination

The purity of a liquid can be tested by measuring its boiling temperature. The liquid is placed in a distillation apparatus and heated. If the substance is pure it will boil at a constant temperature which should be that obtained from a data book. If it is impure, it will boil over a significant range of several degrees. Liquids that boil below 60°C should be heated by a water bath. Otherwise an electric heater should be used. This prevents the organic liquid catching fire if there is a leak in the apparatus.

Safety issues

Questions are often asked about the safety precautions that should be taken in a particular experiment. Safety precautions and the reasons behind them include the following:

Tip

It is assumed that laboratory coats and eye protection are always worn when carrying out practical work. Therefore, credit is not given for stating either of these as a specific safety precaution.

- Distillation and heating under reflux must be carried out in a fume cupboard if the vapour of one of the reactants or products is harmful, poisonous (toxic) or irritant. This applies to halogens, hydrogen halides, halogenoalkanes and ammonia.
- If a mixture is being heated under reflux or distilled, there must be some outlet to the air. If there is not, pressure will build up in the apparatus, which will then fly apart, spraying hot, flammable, and often corrosive, liquid around.
- Gloves must be worn when corrosive substances are used. Such substances must always be handled with care. This applies to concentrated acids and alkalis.
- The flask should never be heated with a naked Bunsen flame. This is because almost all organic substances are flammable and if the liquid being heated were to spill over or the flask to crack, a fire would result.

Yield

Tip

You must be able to calculate theoretical yield and percentage yield (pages 148 and 218-19).

Yields are less than 100% because of:

- competing reactions
- handling losses during purification, such as some product left dissolved after recrystallisation
- incomplete reaction

Test yourself

3 1.22 g of ethanol was heated under reflux with excess acidified potassium dichromate(VI). After separation and purification 1.56 g of ethanoic acid was made. Calculate the percentage yield.

Enthalpy change measurements

Enthalpy of combustion

The method for determining the enthalpy of combustion of a liquid, such as ethanol, is described on pages 244–45. Ways to increase the accuracy of the experiment include the following:

- The copper calorimeter should be first weighed empty and then when containing water. Alternatively, water could be added to the calorimeter using a pipette, *not* a measuring cylinder. If the volume of water is measured, the mass is calculated using the density of water, which is $1\,g\,cm^{-3}$.
- A screen should be placed around the calorimeter to maximise the transfer of heat from the hot combustion gases to the beaker of water.
- To ensure an even temperature throughout, the water in the calorimeter must be stirred continually.
- The temperature of the water should be measured for several minutes before lighting the fuel and for several minutes after putting out the burner flame.
- The temperature–time measurements are used to plot a graph from which the theoretical temperature rise is estimated by extrapolation. This reduces the error caused by heat loss from the beaker to the surroundings.
- The burner and its contents should be weighed before and immediately after the experiment, using a balance that reads to an accuracy of $0.01\,g$ or better.

The calculation is carried out in three steps.

Step 1: heat transferred by the combustion of the fuel $= m \times c \times \Delta T$

Step 2: amount of fuel burnt $= \dfrac{\text{mass before} - \text{mass after}}{\text{molar mass of fuel}}$

Step 3: enthalpy of combustion, $\Delta H_c = -\dfrac{\text{heat transferred}}{\text{moles of fuel burnt}}$

All combustions are exothermic, so the value of ΔH_c is negative.

Displacement reactions and enthalpies of solution

In both displacement reactions and experiments to determine the enthalpy of solution, a solid is added to a liquid and the temperature change is measured.

The method for determining ΔH_r of reactions, such as the displacement of copper from copper sulfate solution by a more reactive metal, is described on page 242. The same method is used to find the enthalpy of solution of a solid.

Temperature–time graphs are necessary because the reactions are not instantaneous.

Errors can be reduced by:

- using powdered solid rather than lumps — this speeds up the rate of reaction, so there is less time for heat losses
- making sure that, for displacement reactions, enough metal is taken to ensure that the solution of the salt of the less reactive metal is the limiting reagent. For enthalpy of solution experiments, the water must be in large excess to ensure that all the solid dissolves

> **Tip**
>
> The mass, m, is the mass of water in the beaker, *not* the mass of fuel burnt. The specific heat capacity of water, c, is $4.18\,J\,g^{-1}\,°C^{-1}$, so the unit of the heat produced is joules, *not* kilojoules.

A limiting reagent reacts completely, leaving an excess of the other reagent.

- measuring the temperature for several minutes before the start of the reaction and for several minutes after the reaction has finished. The measurements are used to plot a graph, which is extrapolated to find the theoretical temperature rise
- continually stirring the contents of the expanded polystyrene cup
- placing a lid on the cup to prevent heat loss through evaporation
- measuring the volume of the solution using a pipette rather than a measuring cylinder, so that the amount (moles) of solute can be accurately determined. This is not necessary for enthalpy of solution determinations

The calculation is carried out in three steps:

Step 1: heat produced by the reaction $= m \times c \times \Delta T$

> **Tip**
>
> The mass, m, is the mass of solution in the cup, *not* the mass of solute reacted. The specific heat of the solution is assumed to be the same as that of water ($4.18\,J\,g^{-1}\,°C^{-1}$), so the unit of the heat produced is joules, *not* kilojoules.

> **Tip**
>
> The unit of volume measured by a pipette is cm^3. This must be converted into dm^3 by dividing by 1000.

Step 2: amount of solute reacted $=$ concentration ($mol\,dm^{-3}$) $\times$ volume (dm^3)

(For enthalpy of solution determinations, amount of solute $=$ mass/molar mass.)

Step 3: $\Delta H_r = \dfrac{\text{heat produced or lost}}{\text{moles of solute reacted}}$

If there is a temperature rise, ΔH is negative; if the temperature falls, ΔH is positive.

Instantaneous reactions

Neutralisation and precipitation reactions are instantaneous reactions. The method used for following both types of reaction is the same and is described on page 243.

Errors can be reduced by:

- using pipettes, rather than measuring cylinders, to measure out the volumes of the two liquids
- making sure that one of the reactants is in excess. The value of ΔH can then be worked out using the amount in moles of the limiting reagent
- for neutralisation reactions only, weighing the expanded polystyrene cup empty and after the reaction. This is a more accurate way of obtaining the mass of solution than using a pipette and assuming that the solution has a density of $1\,g\,cm^{-3}$
- measuring the temperature of both liquids before mixing and averaging the two values
- stirring immediately on mixing the two solutions
- reading the maximum temperature reached

> This not only gives an accurate value for the amounts (moles) of each reactant, but also gives an accurate value for the volume of the solution.

> **Tip**
>
> There is no need to plot a temperature–time graph because the reaction is instantaneous, so there is no time for heat to be lost.

The calculation is carried out in three steps.

Step 1: heat produced by the reaction $= m \times c \times \Delta T$

Step 2: amount of solute reacted = concentration ($mol\,dm^{-3}$) × volume (dm^3)

Step 3: $\Delta H_r = \dfrac{\text{heat produced or lost}}{\text{moles of solute reacted}}$

If there is a temperature rise, ΔH is negative; if the temperature falls, ΔH is positive.

Test yourself

4 When 5.30 g of sodium nitrate, $NaNO_3$, was dissolved in 50 g of water the temperature fell from 15.7°C to 9.6°C. Calculate the standard enthalpy of solution of sodium nitrate. (Specific heat capacity of water = $4.18\,J\,g^{-1}\,°C^{-1}$)

Titration techniques

Preparation of a standard solution

In any titration, the concentration of one of the solutions must be accurately known. The method for preparing $250\,cm^3$ of such a solution — a **standard solution** — is as follows:

- Calculate the mass of solid needed to make a solution of the required concentration.
- Place a weighing bottle on a top-pan balance. Press the tare button, so that the scale reads zero.
- Add the solid to the weighing bottle until the required mass is reached. To make $250\,cm^3$ of a solution of concentration $0.100\,mol\,dm^{-3}$, $\frac{1}{4} \times 0.100\,mol$ has to be weighed out. This is because $250\,cm^3$ is a quarter of $1\,dm^3$.
- Tip the contents of the weighing bottle into a beaker. Wash any remaining solid from the bottle into the beaker.
- Add about $50\,cm^3$ of distilled water to the beaker containing the solid. Using a glass rod, stir until all the solid has dissolved. In order to dissolve the solid completely, it may be necessary to heat the beaker.
- Pour the solution through a funnel into a standard $250\,cm^3$ flask. Wash the stirring rod and the beaker, making sure that all the washings go through the funnel into the flask.

- Add more distilled water to the solution until the bottom of the meniscus is level with the mark on the standard flask.
- Put the stopper in the flask and mix thoroughly by inverting and shaking several times.

Primary standard solutions

To make a primary standard solution, the substance must:

- be able to be obtained pure
- not lose water of crystallisation to the air
- not absorb water or carbon dioxide from the air

A secondary standard solution, such as sodium hydroxide, is made up as accurately as possible and then standardised against a primary standard solution (such as ethanedioic acid).

Performing a titration

The pieces of apparatus required are:

- a burette
- a pipette (usually $25.0 \, cm^3$) and a pipette filler
- a conical flask

The chemicals required are:

- a standard solution
- the solution of unknown concentration
- a suitable indicator

The method for performing an accurate titration is as follows:

- Draw a small amount of one solution into the pipette using a pipette filler and rinse it with the solution. Discard the rinsings.
- Using a pipette filler, fill the pipette so that the bottom of the meniscus is on the mark.
- Allow the pipette to discharge into a washed conical flask. When the pipette has emptied, touch the surface of the liquid in the flask with the tip of the pipette.

- Making sure that the tap is shut, rinse out a burette with a few cm^3 of the other solution and discard the rinsings.
- Using a funnel, fill the burette to above the zero mark and run liquid out until the meniscus is on the scale. Check that the burette below the tap is filled with liquid and that there are no air bubbles. Remove the funnel.
- Record the initial volume by looking at where the bottom of the meniscus is on the burette scale.
- Run the liquid slowly from the burette into the conical flask, continually mixing the solutions by swirling the liquid in the flask. Add the liquid dropwise as the end point is neared and stop when the indicator shows the end point colour. Read the burette to 0.05 cm^3.
- Repeat the titration until three concordant titres have been obtained.
- Ignore any non-concordant titres and average the concordant values, to give the average (mean) titre.

Tip

Burettes are calibrated in 0.1 cm^3 divisions, but you should estimate the volume to the nearest 0.05 cm^3.

Tip

All readings and the mean titre must be recorded to 2 decimal places or to ±0.05 cm^3.

Titration calculations

These are described in Chapter 9 on pages 155–58.

Concordant means that the difference between the highest and the lowest titre is not more than 0.2 cm^3.

Tip

At A level, the equation for the reaction is normally given in the question. Look at it carefully to find the mole ratio of the two reactants. If the equation is not given, then you must write it before starting the calculation.

Remember that the calculation is carried out in three steps.

Step 1: calculate the number of moles in the standard solution used in the titration.

Tip

Don't forget to convert the volume (pipette or burette) from cm^3 to dm^3.

$$\text{volume in dm}^3 = \frac{\text{volume in cm}^3}{1000}$$

Step 2: use the stoichiometry of the equation to calculate the number of moles (amount) in the other solution used in the titration.

Tip

If the mole ratio is 1:1, make sure that you state that the number of moles in the second solution equals the number of moles in the first solution. If the ratio is not 1:1, make sure that the ratio is the right way up in the conversion:

$$\text{moles of A} = \text{moles of B} \times \frac{\text{number of moles of A in equation}}{\text{number of moles of B in equation}}$$

Step 3: calculate the concentration of the second solution.

Tip

Make sure that you give your answer to the correct number of significant figures. If in doubt, give it to 3 s.f.

Worked example

A sample of 2.65 g of pure sodium carbonate, Na_2CO_3, was weighed out, dissolved in water and made up to 250 cm³ in a volumetric flask. Some of this solution was placed in a burette and used to titrate 25.0 cm³ portions of a solution of hydrochloric acid. The titres obtained are shown in the table.

Experiment	Titre/cm³
1	22.35
2	22.40
3	21.85
4	22.50

The equation for the reaction is:

$$2HCl + Na_2CO_3 \rightarrow 2NaCl + H_2O + CO_2$$

a) Calculate the concentration of the sodium carbonate solution.

b) Calculate the mean titre.

c) Calculate the amount (in moles) of sodium carbonate solution in the mean titre.

d) Calculate the amount (in moles) of hydrochloric acid that reacted.

e) Calculate the concentration of the hydrochloric acid solution.

Answer

a) molar mass of sodium carbonate $= (2 \times 23.0) + 12.0 + (3 \times 16.0) = 106.0 \, g \, mol^{-1}$

amount of sodium carbonate $= (2 \times 23.0) + 12.0 + (3 \times 16.0) = 106.0 \, g \, mol^{-1}$

$$concentration = \frac{mol}{volume} = \frac{0.0250 \, mol}{(250/1000) \, dm^3} = 0.100 \, mol \, dm^{-3}$$

b) The titre for experiment 3 is at least 0.5 cm³ less than any other titre, and so is not used in the calculation.

$$mean \, titre = \frac{22.35 + 22.40 + 22.50}{3} = 22.42 \, cm^3$$

c) amount of sodium carbonate $=$ concentration $\times$ volume

$$amount = 0.100 \, mol \, dm^{-3} \times \frac{22.42 \, dm^3}{1000} = 0.00224 \, mol$$

ratio $HCl:Na_2CO_3 = 2:1$

$$amount \, of \, HCl = \frac{2}{1} \times 0.00224 \, mol = 0.00448 \, mol$$

$$concentration \, of \, hydrochloric \, acid = \frac{mol}{volume}$$

$$= \frac{0.00448 \, mol}{(25.0/1000 \, dm^3)} = 0.179 \, mol \, dm^{-3}$$

Note that all volumes were converted from cm³ to dm³ by dividing by 1000.

5 25.0 cm³ portions of a saturated solution of strontium hydroxide, Sr(OH)$_2$, were titrated against a 0.100 mol dm^{-3} solution of hydrochloric acid. The mean titre was 32.85 cm³. Calculate the concentration of the strontium nitrate solution a) in mol dm^{-3} and b) in g dm^{-3}.

Evaluation of error

There is always a built-in error when using apparatus such as balances, thermometers, burettes and pipettes.

The pipette may be stamped with the volume 25.0 cm³, or the balance may read 1.23 g, but these quantities are all subject to some error. For example, the manufacturer of a balance may state that the mass of an object is accurate to ±0.01 g. Therefore, a reading of 1.23 g may mean a mass anywhere between 1.22 g and 1.24 g.

If a container is weighed empty and then reweighed containing some solid, *each* weighing would be subject to a possible error of ±0.01 g and so the mass of the solid could have an error of ±0.02 g.

Worked example 1

An empty crucible was weighed, using a balance with a possible error of ±0.01 g. It was reweighed containing some solid metal carbonate, MCO$_3$, and was then heated to constant weight. On heating, the metal carbonate decomposes according to the equation:

$$MCO_3 \rightarrow MO + CO_2$$

The readings were as follows:

- mass of empty crucible = 14.23 g
- mass of crucible + carbonate = 16.46 g
- mass of crucible + contents after heating to constant weight = 15.61 g

a) Calculate the mass of carbon dioxide given off.

b) Hence, calculate the amount in moles of carbon dioxide produced.

c) Calculate the mass of metal carbonate taken.

d) Using your answers to b) and c), calculate the molar mass of the metal carbonate and hence the molar mass of the metal, M.

e) Assuming all the measurements of mass had an uncertainty of ±0.01 g, calculate the uncertainty in the value of the molar mass of M.

Answer

a) mass of carbon dioxide = 16.46 − 15.61 = 0.85 g

b) amount = $\dfrac{\text{mass}}{\text{molar mass}}$ = $\dfrac{0.85\,\text{g}}{44.0\,\text{g mol}^{-1}}$ = 0.0193 mol

c) mass of MCO$_3$ = 16.46 − 14.23 = 2.23 g

d) amount (moles) of MCO_3 = amount (moles) of CO_2 = 0.0193 mol

$$\text{molar mass of } MCO_3 = \frac{\text{mass}}{\text{moles}} = \frac{2.23\,g}{0.0193\,mol} = 116\,g\,mol^{-1}$$

molar mass of M = $116 - [12.0 + (3 \times 16.0)] = 56.0\,g\,mol^{-1}$

e) mass of $CO_2 = 0.85 \pm 0.02\,g$

The amount (moles) of CO_2 lies between $\dfrac{0.83}{44.0} = 0.0189\,mol$ and $\dfrac{0.87}{44.0}$ = 0.0198 mol.

Since the ratio of MCO_3 to CO_2 is 1:1, the amount (moles) of MCO_3 also lies between 0.0189 mol and 0.0198 mol.

mass of $MCO_3 = 2.23 \pm 0.02\,g$

$$\text{maximum molar mass of } MCO_3 = \frac{\text{biggest mass}}{\text{smallest mass}} = \frac{2.25}{0.0189} = 119\,g\,mol^{-1}$$

maximum molar mass of M = $119 - 60.0 = 59\,g\,mol^{-1}$

$$\text{minimum molar mass of } MCO_3 = \frac{\text{smallest mass}}{\text{biggest mass}} = \frac{2.21}{0.0198} = 112\,g\,mol^{-1}$$

minimum molar mass of M = $112 - 60.0 = 52\,g\,mol^{-1}$

The uncertainty of the molar mass of M is that it is between 52 and $59\,g\,mol^{-1}$.

The element, M, could be Cr, Mn, Fe, Co or Ni, as their molar masses lie in the range 52–59 $g\,mol^{-1}$.

Worked example 2

A thermometer is labelled as having an accuracy of ±0.2°C.

In an enthalpy of neutralisation reaction, the temperature before the reaction was 17.4°C and after the reaction was 24.5°C. The mass of liquid used was 100 g. The specific heat capacity of the liquid is 4.18 $J\,g^{-1}\,°C^{-1}$.

Calculate the percentage error caused by the thermometer and hence the error in the evaluation of the heat produced.

Answer

temperature rise = $(24.5 - 17.4) \pm 0.4 = 7.1 \pm 0.4°C$

percentage error caused by the thermometer = $(\pm 0.4/7.1) \times 100 = \pm 5.63\%$

heat produced = $100\,g \times 4.18\,J\,g^{-1}\,°C^{-1} \times 7.1°C = 2968\,J$

error in value of heat produced = $\pm 5.63\%$ of $2968\,J = \pm 167\,J$

Summary tasks

Make sure that you know:

- the tests for gases, anions and ammonium compounds
- flame tests
- the tests for alkanes, alcohols and halogenoalkanes

Check that you can describe:

- heating under reflux and distillation
- the preparation of a primary standard solution
- titration techniques and identify sources of error
- how heat changes of combustion are measured
- how heat changes in solution are measured

Questions

1 Describe how a flame test should be carried out on a sample of a solid.

2 Substance A is a white inorganic solid.
 • The flame test on A produced a lilac flame.
 • When 4 drops of dilute hydrochloric acid were added to a solution of substance A, followed by 4 drops of barium chloride solution, a white precipitate was formed.
 Identify substance A.

3 Substance B is thought to be either a chloride or a bromide. Describe how the identity of the anion could be established.

4 Two neutral organic liquids C and D were tested as follows:
 • Both gave off steamy fumes when phosphorus(v) chloride was added.
 • When warmed with acidified potassium dichromate(vi), C turned it from orange to green, but with D the solution remained orange.
 What can you deduce about C and D?

5 2-bromopropane reacts when heated with an ethanolic solution of potassium hydroxide to give propene. Draw a fully labelled diagram of the apparatus you would use to prepare and collect this alkene.

6 Propan-1-ol (boiling temperature 97°C) can be oxidised by heating with acidified potassium dichromate(vi) to either propanoic acid (boiling temperature 141°C) or propanal (boiling temperature 49°C). Draw a fully labelled diagram of the apparatus for preparing and collecting propanal. Give any special conditions.

Exam practice questions

1 a) Natural oils, such as rapeseed oil, can be isolated by solvent extraction. The seeds are crushed and shaken with an organic solvent such as hexane. The solution is filtered and then distilled, collecting the hexane that boils off at 68–70°C.

Draw a diagram of the apparatus that would be used for distilling off the hexane. (3)

b) Rapeseed oil contains between 30% and 50% erucic acid, which is the *Z*-isomer of the monounsaturated omega 9 acid of formula $C_8H_{17}CH=CHC_{11}H_{22}COOH$.

i) What is meant by the term omega 9? (1)

ii) Explain why erucic acid is classified as a *Z*-isomer. (2)

iii) Erucic acid can be reacted with hydrogen over a nickel catalyst, forming a saturated acid.

3.36 g of rapeseed oil reacted with 124 cm^3 of hydrogen. Calculate the percentage by mass of erucic acid in the sample of rapeseed oil. (Molar volume under the conditions of the experiment = 24 dm^3 mol^{-1}) (4)

iv) What assumption did you make in your calculation that could make it very inaccurate? (1)

(Total 11 marks)

2 The stems of rhubarb are used as a fruit but the leaves contain ethanedioic acid, $H_2C_2O_4$, which is poisonous. A student decided to find out the percentage by mass of ethanedioic acid in some rhubarb leaves. The method used was as follows:

- 26.00 g of shredded leaves were boiled in a beaker with water to extract the ethanedioic acid.
- After cooling the contents were filtered into a volumetric flask and the contents of the beaker thoroughly washed into the flask, which was then made up to 250 cm^3.

- 25.00 cm^3 portions of this solution were then titrated against a 0.0200 mol dm^{-3} solution of sodium hydroxide, using phenolphthalein as indicator. The readings are shown below.

Titration	Initial volume/cm^3	Final volume/cm^3	Titre/cm^3
1	1.20	16.45	
2	17.30	32.00	
3	2.25	17.05	

$$H_2C_2O_4 + 2NaOH \rightarrow Na_2C_2O_4 + 2H_2O$$

a) i) What colour change would be observed during the titration? (1)

ii) Complete the table above. (2)

iii) Which values should be used to calculate the mean titre? Explain your answer. (1)

iv) Calculate the mean titre and use it to calculate the amount in moles of ethanedioic acid in 250 cm^3 of solution. (4)

v) Use your answer to iv) to calculate the percentage by mass of ethanedioic acid in rhubarb leaves. (2)

b) State and explain what would be the effect on the percentage if:

i) some of the solution had remained in the beaker

ii) the student had blown out the last drop from the pipette. (2)

c) i) Assuming that the error in a burette reading is ±0.05 cm^3, calculate the possible percentage error in the mean titre. (2)

ii) Another student took 10.00 g of shredded leaves. Explain whether the result from this would be as reliable. (2)

(Total 16 marks)

Index

Page numbers in **bold** indicate definitions of important terms.

A

heterogeneous catalyst 265
    industrial processes 265–66
heterogeneous reactions **263**, 267, 274
heterolytic fission 187, 188–89, 215
homogeneous catalysts 265
homogeneous reactions **263**, 274
homologous series **169**
homolytic fission **180**
hot and cold packs 237
human body, elements in 2
hydrated copper(II) ion 48
hydrated magnesium ion 48
hydration 73
hydrocarbons **170**
    naming 170–72
hydrogenation, vegetable oils 185
hydrogen-bonded molecular
        substances 71–72
hydrogen bonds 64–66
hydrogencarbonates 116, 292
hydrogen halides 111–12
    reaction with ethene 188–90
hydrolysis 176, 200, 201, 215
hydronium ion 48

I

ideal gas equation for molar mass 122
ideal gas law 136
identity of substance, molar
        calculations 138–39
indicators 156, 300
infrared absorption 225–28
infrared spectroscopy 228–31
inorganic compounds, analysis of 115–16
instantaneous induced dipole–induced
        dipole forces 63–64
instantaneous reactions, measurement
        techniques 298–99
intermolecular forces 63–66
iodination 210
iodine 104, 105
ion **5**
ion-electron bonds 62–63
ionic bonding 39–43
ionic compounds, formulae 124–28
ionic equations 131–33
ionic half-equations 84–87
ionic radii/radius 31, 38, 40, 68
    group 2 elements 93
    halogens 104
    and ion–ion bond strength 62

and polarising power of the cation 98
    trends 41
ionic solids 67–68
    solubility 73
ion–ion bonds 62
ionisation energies 16–20
    group 2 elements 93–94
    metals 38
ion shapes 50–56
ion–water molecule bonds 63
isomerism 173–76
isomers **173**
    geometric 174–76
isotopes 10, **11**, 12

K

ketone 169, 212, 215, 223–24
kinetically stable system 262
kinetic energy 234
kinetics 257–68
    collision theory 260–62
    experimental methods 258–60
    rate of reaction 257–58
    reaction profile diagrams 267–68
    reaction rate, factors affecting 262–67

L

laboratory tests *see* tests
law of conservation of energy 234, 237
law of mass action 273
Le Châtelier's principle 276–81
Lewis, G. N. 44
limiting reagent **151–52**
    worked examples 152–53
linear molecules 52, 56, 58
liquids
    boiling 67
    enthalpy of combustion 244–46
London forces 63–64, 69, 70, 71, 73
    alcohols 209
    alkanes 177
    halogenoalkane 199
    halogens 104
    hydrogen halides 111
lone pair of electrons 46, 48–56
    hydrogen bond 63, 64, 65
Lyman series 20, 21

M

malleability, metals 38
margarine, manufacture of 186
Markovnikoff's rule 189, 190

Marsden, Ernest 9, 10
mass 5–6
mass-to-mass calculations 144–45
mass number 10, **11**, 12
mass spectrometers/spectroscopy 12–16,
        223–25
mass to volume of gas calculations 146–47
'matter' 1
Maxwell–Boltzmann distribution of
        molecular energies 261–62
melting a solid 67
melting temperatures 29
    alkenes 184, 193
    answering questions on 72–73
    diamond 46, 68, 70
    ionic compounds 42–43
    ionic solids 67–68
    metals 37–38
    polymeric substances 72
    simple molecular substances 70–71
Mendeléev, Dmitri 2, 10, 26
metallic bonding 37–39
metallic radius/radii 37, **38**
metalloids 4
metals 3–4
    chemical properties 3–4, 38–39
    physical properties 37–38
    reactions 94–96
methane 44, 53, 77, 167, 178, 227
    C–H bond enthalpy 249
    free-radical substitution 180–81
methane hydrate deposits 182–83, 281
methylisocyanate (MIC) 194
methyl orange 156, 300
Millikan, Robert A. 9
molar mass (*M*) 119, 121
    of a volatile liquid 137
    calculating 122–23, 134–37
    ionic compounds 127
molar volume **146**
molecular formula 119, 168, 217–18
    from empirical formula 121–22
molecular ion, fragmentation
        of 223–24
molecular mass
    and atom economy 149
    from mass spectra 14
    and mole calculations 134
    molecular formula derivation 121
mole ratios 7–8

The periodic table

Group

Key:

Relative atomic mass
Atomic symbol
name
Atomic (proton) number

Period	1	2												3	4	5	6	7	0
1	1.0 **H** hydrogen 1																		4.0 **He** helium 2
2	6.9 **Li** lithium 3	9.0 **Be** beryllium 4												10.8 **B** boron 5	12.0 **C** carbon 6	14.0 **N** nitrogen 7	16.0 **O** oxygen 8	19.0 **F** fluorine 9	20.2 **Ne** neon 10
3	23.0 **Na** sodium 11	24.3 **Mg** magnesium 12												27.0 **Al** aluminium 13	28.1 **Si** silicon 14	31.0 **P** phosphorus 15	32.1 **S** sulfur 16	35.5 **Cl** chlorine 17	39.9 **Ar** argon 18
4	39.1 **K** potassium 19	40.1 **Ca** calcium 20	45.0 **Sc** scandium 21	47.9 **Ti** titanium 22	50.9 **V** vanadium 23	52.0 **Cr** chromium 24	54.9 **Mn** manganese 25	55.8 **Fe** iron 26	58.9 **Co** cobalt 27	58.7 **Ni** nickel 28	63.5 **Cu** copper 29	65.4 **Zn** zinc 30		69.7 **Ga** gallium 31	72.6 **Ge** germanium 32	74.9 **As** arsenic 33	79.0 **Se** selenium 34	79.9 **Br** bromine 35	83.8 **Kr** krypton 36
5	85.5 **Rb** rubidium 37	87.6 **Sr** strontium 38	88.9 **Y** yttrium 39	91.2 **Zr** zirconium 40	92.9 **Nb** niobium 41	95.9 **Mo** molybdenum 42	[98] **Tc** technetium 43	101.1 **Ru** ruthenium 44	102.9 **Rh** rhodium 45	106.4 **Pd** palladium 46	107.9 **Ag** silver 47	112.4 **Cd** cadmium 48		114.8 **In** indium 49	118.7 **Sn** tin 50	121.8 **Sb** antimony 51	127.6 **Te** tellurium 52	126.9 **I** iodine 53	131.3 **Xe** xenon 54
6	132.9 **Cs** caesium 55	137.3 **Ba** barium 56	138.9 **La** lanthanum 57	178.5 **Hf** hafnium 72	180.9 **Ta** tantalum 73	183.8 **W** tungsten 74	186.2 **Re** rhenium 75	190.2 **Os** osmium 76	192.2 **Ir** iridium 77	195.1 **Pt** platinum 78	197.0 **Au** gold 79	200.6 **Hg** mercury 80		204.4 **Tl** thallium 81	207.2 **Pb** lead 82	209.0 **Bi** bismuth 83	[209] **Po** polonium 84	[210] **At** astatine 85	[222] **Rn** radon 86
7	[223] **Fr** francium 87	[226] **Ra** radium 88	[227] **Ac** actinium 89	[261] **Rf** rutherfordium 104	[262] **Db** dubnium 105	[266] **Sg** seaborgium 106	[264] **Bh** bohrium 107	[277] **Hs** hassium 108	[268] **Mt** meitnerium 109	[271] **Ds** darmstadtium 110	[272] **Rg** roentgenium 111								

Elements with atomic numbers 112–116 have been reported but not fully authenticated

Lanthanides (Period 6):

140.1 **Ce** cerium 58	140.9 **Pr** praseodymium 59	144.2 **Nd** neodymium 60	144.9 **Pm** promethium 61	150.4 **Sm** samarium 62	152.0 **Eu** europium 63	157.2 **Gd** gadolinium 64	158.9 **Tb** terbium 65	162.5 **Dy** dysprosium 66	164.9 **Ho** holmium 67	167.3 **Er** erbium 68	168.9 **Tm** thulium 69	173.0 **Yb** ytterbium 70	175.0 **Lu** lutetium 71

Actinides (Period 7):

232 **Th** thorium 90	[231] **Pa** protactinium 91	238.1 **U** uranium 92	[237] **Np** neptunium 93	[242] **Pu** plutonium 94	[243] **Am** americium 95	[247] **Cm** curium 96	[245] **Bk** berkelium 97	[251] **Cf** californium 98	[254] **Es** einsteinium 99	[253] **Fm** fermium 100	[256] **Md** mendelevium 101	[254] **No** nobelium 102	[257] **Lr** lawrencium 103